DESIGNERS CASEBOOK
Number 5

DESIGNERS CASEBOOK
Number 5

PREPARED BY THE EDITORS OF

Electronics

Fifth in a continuing series of selected Designer's Casebook sections of Electronics magazine. This edition includes Electronics issues from June 19, 1980 through November 3, 1981. Also included are feature articles and items from Engineer's Notebook of particular interest to the circuit designer.

ISBN 0-07-606808-0

McGraw-Hill Publications Co.
1221 Avenue of the Americas
New York, New York 10020

CONTENTS

SIGNAL SOURCES

AUDIO AND ANALOG

Pulse modulator provides switched-mode amplification

by P. H. Pazov
Polytechnic of Central London, England

Using pulse-width modulation to provide switched-mode amplification, this circuit affords the same advantages in the analog world as does its switching power supply counterpart—simplicity, efficiency, and low power consumption when a complementary-MOS logic family is employed. Noise rejection and distortion characteristics also are better than can be achieved with a conventional analog arrangement.

As shown in the general function diagram (a), a feedback current, I_{mod}, is derived from the audio input signal for the purpose of varying the pulse width of a free-running oscillator, which itself is formed by a digital integrated-circuit integrator and a hysteresis/power stage. C_2 and R_4 develop a dc feedback signal from comparison of V_{out} with the audio input, from which an error current is created. The ratio of R_4/R_5 sets the amplification factor. C_2 and C_3 act to integrate V_{out}, so that any long-term imbalance appears as an error and can be corrected.

The active digital elements thus switch in the linear mode, ensuring that the output pulse width is proportional to the amplitude of the input signal. The output, as taken at the junction of L and C_o, represents the instantaneous change in the oscillator's pulse width. With such an arrangement, the amplifier's efficiency is better than 90% at any signal level, as would be expected with any linear switched circuit.

The practical implementation is shown in (b). One 4049 inverter is used for all switching functions. C_2 and R_4 set the total bandwidth at about 20 kilohertz, with C_3 determining the lower cutoff frequency of 100 hertz. The circuit has an amplification factor of 15. It will drive a load as low as 2 ohms at a noise level that appears low enough for headphone-monitoring applications. With a supply voltage of 6 volts, the current consumption will be a mere 5.6 milliamperes.

As mentioned, the circuit's noise performance is very good. This is partly due to the fact that, as the modulation current increases toward the maximum charging current required to attain the maximum pulse width in the oscillator, a form of frequency modulation occurs, giving rise to an S-shaped transfer curve that is characteristic of an fm discriminator. This characteristic results in a lower noise and distortion factor than can be achieved using a purely linear approach.

As with all high-frequency circuits, a good earth ground and no ground loops are essential to proper operation. Otherwise, all sorts of oscillations appear and add to the noise level. □

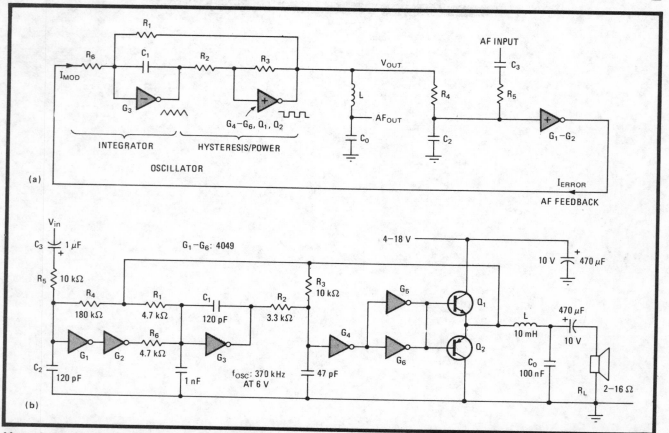

Linear logic. This digitally switched network (a) amplifies audio signals linearly by modulating the pulse width of an RC oscillator. The practical circuit (b) is uncomplicated. Excellent noise-rejection performance is achieved by the modulator's S-shaped transfer curve.

Antilog amplifiers improve biomedical signal's S/N ratio

by T. G. Barnett and D. L. Wingate
London Hospital Medical College, Department of Physiology, England

Low-voltage, biphasic signals recorded by instruments monitoring biomedical variables such as heart rate are often accompanied by high noise levels due to inadequate sensing, movement artefact, paging systems and power-line interference. Using paired antilogarithmic amplifiers, however, to provide the nonlinear amplification required, the level of the biphasic signals can be raised well above the amplitude of the interfering signals. The signal-to-noise ratio can thus be improved from 2:1 at the input to 10:1 at the output.

Such a scheme is superior to the use of paired logarithmic amps, which cannot handle biphasic signals at the zero-crossing points (log 0 = ∞), and provides more sensitivity than conventional diode clippers, which introduce noise and cannot pass signals that drop below the circuit's 0.7 clipping threshold.

Input signals are amplified by A_1 and are separated into their positive and negative components by precision half-wave rectifier A_2 and inverter A_3. The corresponding outputs are then introduced into the AD759N and AD759P log/antilog amplifiers, which are wired to yield $e_o = E_{ref}10^{-e_{in1}}/K$ for $-2 \leq e_{in1}/K \leq 2$, where E_{ref} is an internal reference voltage of approximately 0.1 volt and K is a multiplying constant that has been set at 1 as a consequence of utilizing input e_{in1}. The output voltages generated by A_4 and A_5 are of negative and positive polarity, respectively.

These components are then summed by A_6, whose output yields a bipolar, antilogged signal that can be introduced to appropriate trigger circuits. If desired, the original signal can be reconstructed by passing it through paired logarithmic amplifiers. □

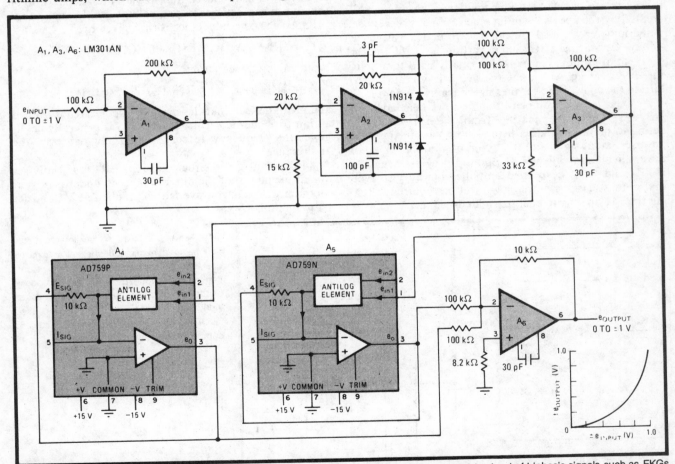

Biomedical booster. Paired AD759 antilog amps provide bipolar, nonlinear amplification, thus raising level of biphasic signals such as EKGs with respect to noise and so increasing S/N ratio. Circuit is superior to those using log amps, which cannot provide accurate output at zero crossings of signals, and is more sensitive than diode clippers, provides greater noise rejection than filters, and introduces no phase shift.

Bilateral speaker networks form switchless intercom

by Frank Kasparec
St. Poelten, Austria

Only one transducer—a dynamic loudspeaker—is required at each station of this intercom to permit transfer of audio information in both directions simultaneously. Having no need for push-to-talk switches, the circuit is less costly and less bulky than conventional transceiver units. Undesired acoustic distortion normally encountered in this type of transmission system is eliminated by using a simple phase-compensation network.

As described for the receiver portion of the unit, audio signals at the input are converted into their acoustical equivalent, S_1, by the speaker after passing through the RC network made up of C_1 and resistors R_3 to R_7, which is required to offset the frequency-dependent phase shift created by the speaker's inductance. When properly set, potentiometer R_6 also cancels the feedback (talkback) voltage appearing at the noninverting input of the 741 differential amplifier, which is normally used to amplify the electrical equivalent of the acoustic vibrations, S_2, hitting the cone of the speaker in the transmit mode.

As expected, the compensation network responds similarly to voltages emanating from the speaker's coil, acting to minimize phase distortion at V_{out}. In this case, however, input signals to the differential amplifier are in the millivolt range. The 741 op amp provides a gain of R_9/R_8 and thus the needed amplification at V_{out}. Note that in most cases a power stage will be required following the 741 op amp to energize a loudspeaker.

The design of the phase-shift network, although easy, must be done with care if acoustic feedback is to be reduced to a minimum. The phase differences as seen by the differential amplifier must be canceled, and thus $(R_1 + R_2)/Z_1 = Z_{C1}/(R_3 + R_4/2)$, where $Z_1 = jX_{L1}$, Z_{C1} is the reactance of capacitor C_1, and L_1 is the speaker's inductance. It is also assumed that R_2 is approximately equal to R_1, and R_3 and R_4 are much smaller than R_5–R_7. For the general purpose speaker, R_1 will be about 4 or 8 ohms. The above equation reduces to $(R_1 + R_2)(R_3 + R_4/2) = L_1/C_1$. At the same time, for direct current balance at the output of the op amp, $R_2/R_1 = (R_7 + R_6/2)/(R_5 + R_6/2)$.

To determine the element values in the phase-compensation network, and to estimate the frequency response of the unit, it is necessary to measure both the loudspeaker's dc resistance and its inductance. The best way to find the dc resistance is to use a digital ohmmeter. To determine coil inductance, it is necessary to apply an audio signal (preferably at $f = 1$ kHz) to the loudspeaker, as shown in the inset, and to measure A, the ratio of the root-mean-square output voltage to the rms input voltage. The coil inductance is then given by:

$$L_1 = [R_1^2 - A^2(R_1 + R_2)^2/4\pi^2f^2(A^2 - 1)]^{1/2}$$

Rearranging the equation:

$$A = [R_1^2 + 4\pi^2f^2L^2/(R_1 + R_2)^2 + 4\pi^2f^2L^2]^{1/2}$$

and it can be seen that the speaker response tends toward a high-pass characteristic. Because L_1 is generally negligible, the frequency response is largely flat over the audio range.

Adjustment of the circuit is simple. R_4 is initially set to null the output of the differential amp under no-signal conditions. A square wave is then applied at V_{in} and R_6 set to minimize V_{out}. ☐

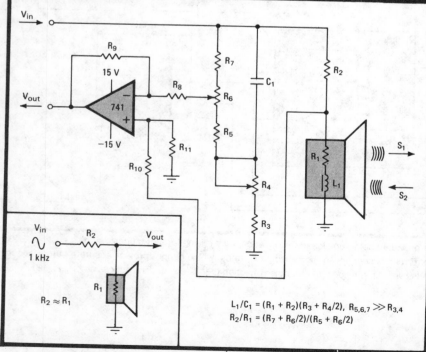
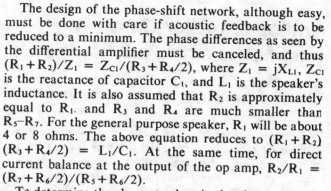
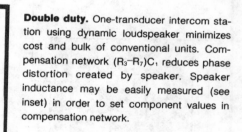

Double duty. One-transducer intercom station using dynamic loudspeaker minimizes cost and bulk of conventional units. Compensation network $(R_3-R_7)C_1$ reduces phase distortion created by speaker. Speaker inductance may be easily measured (see inset) in order to set component values in compensation network.

$L_1/C_1 = (R_1 + R_2)(R_3 + R_4/2)$, $R_{5,6,7} \gg R_{3,4}$
$R_2/R_1 = (R_7 + R_6/2)/(R_5 + R_6/2)$

TTL line drivers link fiber optics

by Vernon P. O'Neil and Imre Gorgenyi
Motorola Inc., Discrete Semiconductor Division, Phoenix, Ariz.

Designers who need to convert an existing twisted-pair communications interface into an optical-fiber link can minimize their efforts by simply combining their fiber-optic detector-preamplifiers with TTL line receivers like the industry-standard MC75107 devices. Such an arrangement has other advantages besides simplicity, namely, providing the builder with access to two receivers, complete with strobing inputs, in a single 75107. And although no similar optical line receivers are yet offered as a standard product, this interface will yield good performance at low cost. Building fiber-optic transmitters using TTL line drivers is equally simple.

The union of the 75107 with Motorola's MFOD404F optical detector is shown in (a) of the figure. The detector is packaged in a nose-cone type of fixture that can be directly mounted in standard AMP-connector bushings, making the connection to the optical-fiber cables extremely simple.

The resulting optical receiver will handle data rates of up to 10 megabits per second at a sensitivity as low as 1 microwatt. For even greater data rates, an MFOD405F can be used to extend the data-rate capacity to 50 Mb/s at a sensitivity of 6 μW.

Because the receiver is ac-coupled to the detector, it is necessary to restrict the duty cycle of incoming signals to the range of 40% to 60%. Coupling components between the detector and the 75107 are selected to ensure that the reference level developed at the input of the receiver tracks the average voltage of the input data stream. In this way the circuit self-adjusts to a wide range of input optical power levels.

At the other end of the system (b), a compatible ac-coupled optical transmitter can be constructed from an ordinary 75452 line driver. A 0-to-2-Mb/s fiber-optic transmitter suitable for handling bipolar-pulse (dc-coupled) encoded data (c) is almost as simple. □

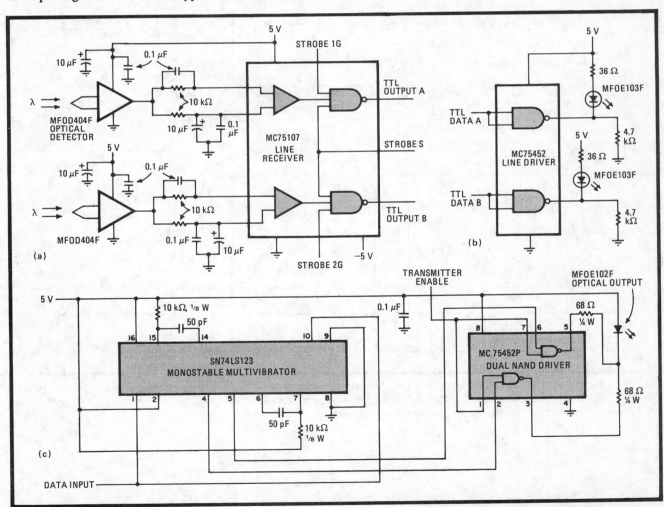

Light line. Standard line receivers such as the 75107 serve well in interface for fiber-optic systems (a). Off-the-shelf TTL line drivers at the transmitting end (b) makes possible low-cost systems. A 0-to-2-Mb/s bipolar-pulse—encoded transmitter (c) is almost as simple to build.

5

Dc-coupled trigger updates quickly

by Andrzej M. Cisek
Electronics for Medicine, Honeywell Inc., Pleasantville, N. Y.

Two operational amplifiers and a few components build this broadband trigger, which is absolutely immune to the problems created by dc offset and base-line wandering. A self-adapting stage for maintaining a constant level of hysteresis, as well as dc coupling at the input, permits a low-cost yet superior performance over a wide range of input signals that makes the circuit very attractive for biomedical applications.

Input signals are applied to the LM307 amplifier, A_1, through charge-storage network $D_1 D_2 R_1 R_2 C$ (a). Diodes D_1 and D_2 quickly charge capacitor C to the peak of the input voltage (less one diode drop) and minimize C's discharge until the signal falls more than two diode drops below the peak voltage.

The output of A_1 is then compared with the original signal at A_2. The amount of hysteresis is set by constant-current source Q_1 and Q_2, two p-channel field-effect transistors wired as diodes in A_2's positive feedback loop, and R_3. Q_1 and Q_2 ensure that the level of hysteresis is maintained virtually constant for any dc offset at the input. Resistor R_1 provides a zero level for input signals whose amplitude is smaller than one diode drop, and R_2 protects the input-signal source.

Such an arrangement has a reliable triggering level and responds fast, its speed being limited only by time constant $(R_{D1,2} + R_2)C$. This time constant can be easily adjusted to meet the requirements of practically any application.

As for the circuit's use in medical electronics, consider the two cases illustrated in (b) and (c), where a cardiac signal representing heart rate is superimposed on the respiratory (breath) signal. Depending on the trigger level, either heart rate (b) or respiration rate (c) may be counted. □

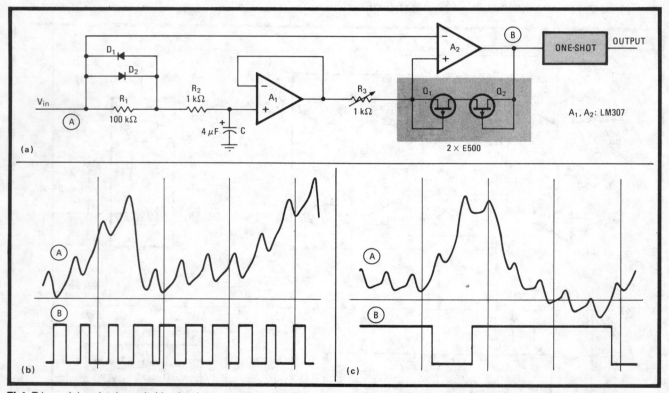

Flat. Trigger (a) maintains switching level over a wide band of frequencies and input-signal amplitudes. Operation is independent of input dc offset and problems created by baseline shift. Directly coupled arrangement at input contributes to circuit's high-speed response. In biomedical application, trigger switches on superimposed signals produced by heart rate (b) and respiration rate (c).

Optical agc minimizes video measurement errors

by D. Sporea and N. Miron
National Center of Physics, Magurele, Rumania

In an optical system, pulse width and peak amplitude are two information-bearing parameters that must be measured accurately for intensity-distribution and frequency-domain analysis—parameters that are difficult to determine when variations occur in the intensity of the signal's laser light source. This difficulty may be virtually eliminated by using the unmodulated laser signal to provide automatic gain control of the amplifier that processes the optical signal from a video camera. Such a scheme rejects the black level of the optical input signal, minimizes drift of low-level detector thresholds, and reduces noise caused by light scattering through optical components for near-zero level signals.

Signals are applied in a balanced fashion to the μA733 video amplifier, as shown. R_1C_1, R_2C_2, and the excellent common-mode characteristics of the operational amplifier reject most optical noise and bias the black level below the amplifier's active region.

The gain is controlled by a phototransistor operating in its linear region and two field-effect transistors whose drain-to-source resistance varies directly as a function of the reference laser signal. If the laser power increases, amplifier gain will be proportionally lowered, and vice versa, so that the output amplitude for a given video signal will be relatively independent of changes in the reference level. The signal is then amplified by the μA715 operational amplifier and presented to the μA710 high-speed comparator, where the switching threshold is set by the user.

In operation, the circuit provides excellent agc characteristics. Typically, the peak voltage (V_p) at the output of the 715 (see inset) will vary only 0.35 decibel for a given video signal and a change in laser input power of more than 10 dB. The roll-off response of filters R_1C_1 and R_2C_2 is such that the detector's threshold voltage, V_t, varies to a similar degree. Consequently, the ratio of V_p/V_b is virtually unchanged, a condition required for accurate measurements of width versus intensity. □

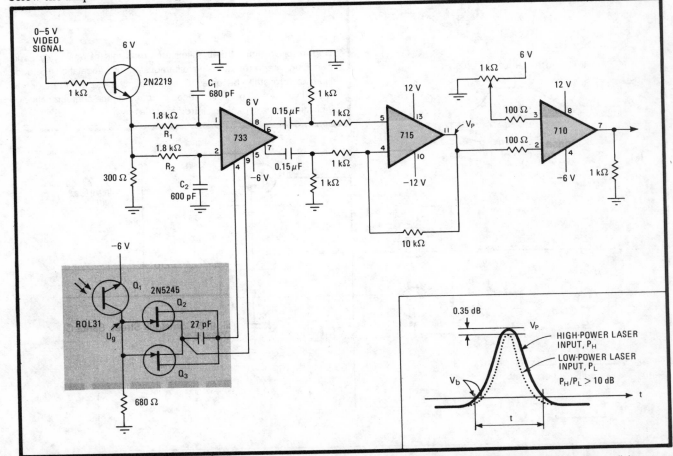

Lightbeam leveler. Phototransistor sets gain of input amplifier, ensuring that variations in output power of unmodulated laser light source have little effect on pulse-width measurements of optical input signal, which is derived from video camera. Change in output amplitude is only 0.35 dB for laser-power variations of more than 10 dB. Detector's threshold voltage varies to a similar degree.

Differential amp cancels integrator's crosstalk

by Elzbieta Nowicka
Atomic Energy of Canada Ltd., Ottawa

The performance of a high-speed integrator can be improved considerably by utilizing the excellent common-mode rejection characteristics of an operational amplifier to reduce crosstalk caused by the switching of waveforms during the circuit's integrate-and-hold sequence. More specifically, operating the amp in its differential mode enables the integrator to virtually cancel the switching offsets that are generated by the almost ideal switch—the complementary-MOS analog gate, which is inexpensive and has low on-resistance but rela-

tively high feedthrough. The supporting circuitry required (two extra gates) is minimal.

The technique generally used to start and terminate the three-step integration sequence is shown in (a), where S_1 and S_2 represent two electronic switches. These switches must be selected carefully, the main requirement being that the on-resistance of these devices be as low as possible, especially when the R_1C_1 time constant is small.

The C-MOS CD4066 transmission gate, with its nominal on-resistance of only 80 ohms for a supply voltage of 15 volts, would normally serve well in these applications, except that its crosstalk (the unwanted feedthrough of the gating signal) is high—typically, 50 millivolts for a 10-v square wave having $t_r = t_f = 20$ nanoseconds and a gate-output load of 1 kilohm. By introducing a pair of switches at each of both inputs of the LM218 op amp (b), however, the integrator will provide virtual elimination of the crosstalk by means of differential cancelation of gate feedthrough signals 1 and 2. There will be little error introduced by the differences between the on resistance of each individual gate in the 4066 package because of the balanced circuit arrangement. Typically, Δ_{on} will be less than 5 Ω for a 15-v supply.

Utilizing this scheme, the crosstalk will be reduced to less than 3 mV over a temperature range of 0° to 70°C. □

Negated. Op amp virtually eliminates crosstalk of analog gates in switching integrator by using differential-input cancelation method. Nominal crosstalk becomes 3 mV, sharply reduced from gate's typical value of 50 mV. Differences in on-resistance characteristics of individual gates in package introduce little error.

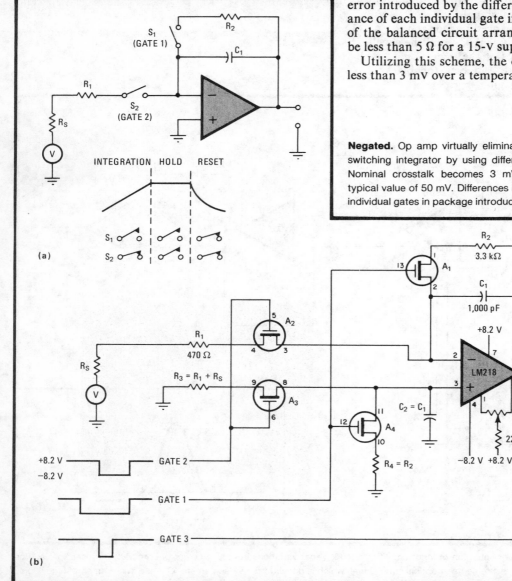

On-chip transistors extend audio amp's design flexibility

by Jim Williams
National Semiconductor Corp., Santa Clara, Calif.

The availability of extremely low-cost audio-amplifier integrated circuits with on-chip transistor arrays, such as National's LM389, gives designers a great deal of flexibility in designing audio circuits. They make it much easier to develop low-cost versions of circuits unrelated to basic audio amplification, such as dc-dc converters, touch switches, stabilized frequency standards, scope calibrators, low-distortion oscillators, and logarithmic amplifiers. The designs of the often-needed converter, a bistable touch switch, and a tuning-fork frequency standard are discussed here in the first part of this two-part presentation.

The LM389 contains a 250-milliwatt audio amplifier

and an array of three npn transistors, each of which is uncommitted. The amp has differential inputs and separate pins for setting its gain (from 20 to 200) via a resistor and runs off a single supply that may range from 4 to 15 volts. The three transistors have a minimum current-handling capability of 25 milliamperes and a minimum current gain of 100 for $V_{ce\,max} = 12$ v and for a wide range of collector currents. The chip is therefore ideal for general use.

One area in which the chip will be useful is in dc-dc switching conversion. The device in Fig. 1 is intended for use as a power supply in a digital system where it is necessary to supply ± 15 v to a low-power load. As can be seen from the oscilloscope photograph, the LM389 switches at 20 kilohertz. That rate is determined by the triangular-wave feedback signal, whose time constant is set by $R_1C_1C_2$, and its square-wave output is applied to transistors Q_1 and Q_3. The series diodes ensure clean turn-off for Q_1 and Q_3.

Q_1's inverted output drives one half of the transformer primary through Q_2, while Q_3 drives the other half. The diodes across Q_2 and Q_3 suppress spikes. Thus there is an

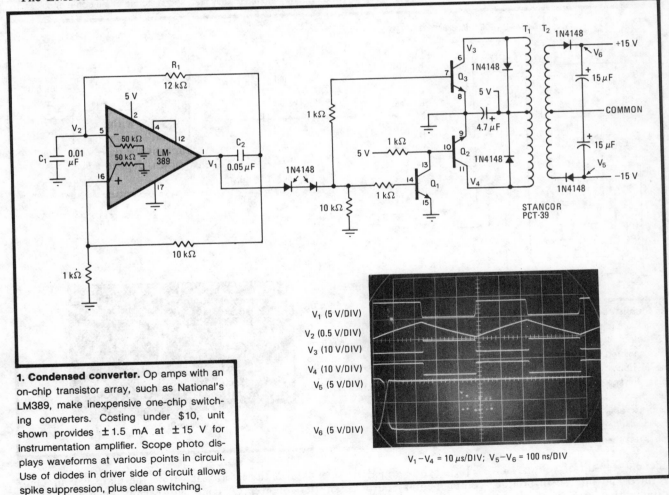

1. Condensed converter. Op amps with an on-chip transistor array, such as National's LM389, make inexpensive one-chip switching converters. Costing under $10, unit shown provides ± 1.5 mA at ± 15 V for instrumentation amplifier. Scope photo displays waveforms at various points in circuit. Use of diodes in driver side of circuit allows spike suppression, plus clean switching.

V_1 (5 V/DIV)
V_2 (0.5 V/DIV)
V_3 (10 V/DIV)
V_4 (10 V/DIV)
V_5 (5 V/DIV)
V_6 (5 V/DIV)

$V_1 - V_4 = 10\,\mu s$/DIV; $V_5 - V_6 = 100\,ns$/DIV

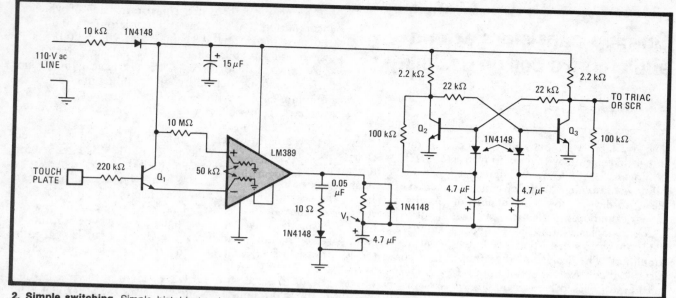

2. Simple switching. Simple bistable touch switch may be similarly constructed. Op amp works as comparator and trigger for flip-flop Q_2–Q_3, which changes state each time plate is contacted. Thus, SCR at output may be alternately fired and switched off on command.

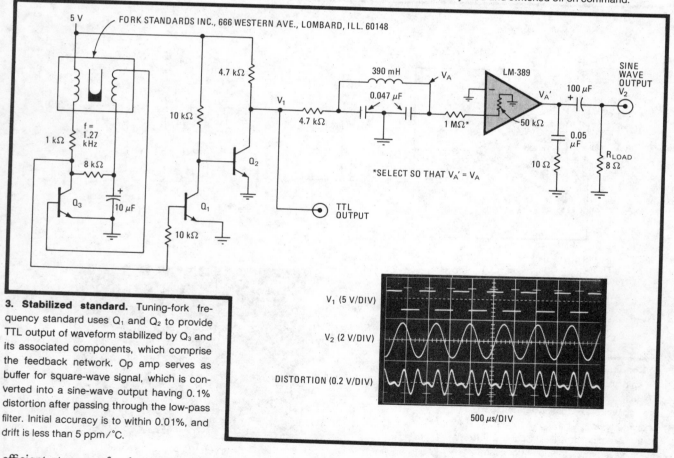

3. Stabilized standard. Tuning-fork frequency standard uses Q_1 and Q_2 to provide TTL output of waveform stabilized by Q_3 and its associated components, which comprise the feedback network. Op amp serves as buffer for square-wave signal, which is converted into a sine-wave output having 0.1% distortion after passing through the low-pass filter. Initial accuracy is to within 0.01%, and drift is less than 5 ppm/°C.

efficient step-up of voltage across T_2. This ac signal is rectified and filtered to produce complementary output voltages that may be used to power the desired linear components, in this case delivering ±1.5 mA, enough to power an operational or instrumentation amplifier.

The bistable touch switch (Fig. 2) allows a line-powered load to be controlled from a touch plate by means of a thyristor. Each time the plate is contacted, emitter-follower Q_1 conducts, permitting a fraction of the 60-hertz input signal to be applied to the inverting input of the amplifier. Consequently, the normally high output of the op amp follows the 60-Hz line input, causing V_1 to drop sharply.

This negative transition triggers a toggling flip-flop

formed by Q_2 and Q_3. In this manner, the output of the flip-flop changes state each time the touch plate is contacted, prompting the firing of the silicon controlled rectifier or triac that switches ac power to the load.

Figure 3 shows a tuning-fork frequency standard that is stabilized by appropriate feedback. Both sine-wave and TTL-compatible outputs are available. As the circuit needs only 5 V, it can run off a battery.

The tuning fork proper supplies a low-frequency output that is very stable (typically to within 5 ppm/°C) and has an initial accuracy of within 0.01%. Moreover, it will withstand vibration and shock that would fracture a quartz crystal. Here, Q_3 is set up in a feedback configuration that forces the fork to oscillate at its resonant frequency. Q_3's output is squared up by Q_1 and Q_2, which provide a TTL-compatible output. When passed through an LC filter and the op amp, which provides a low-impedance (8-ohm) output, the signal is converted into a sine wave having less than 1% distortion, as shown in the figure.

Several other useful circuits also can be built. The second part of this article will deal with the chip's use in a portable scope calibrator, a low-distortion oscillator, and as a logarithmic amplifier. □

On-chip transistors add versatility to op amp

by Jim Williams
National Semiconductor Corp., Santa Clara, Calif.

Low-cost audio-amplifier chips containing uncommitted transistor arrays are widely applicable, as discussed in part 1 of this article [*Electronics*, Jan. 27, 1981, p. 118]. Besides uses in nonaudio applications such as dc-dc converters, touch switches, and stabilized frequency standards, array amplifiers like National's LM 389 are especially suited for general service in portable oscilloscope calibrators, low-distortion oscillators, and logarithmic amplifiers.

For example, the circuit in Fig. 1 allows a quick check of an oscilloscope's time base and vertical calibration. It can be built into a small hand-held enclosure and may be powered by a 12.5-volt battery.

When suitably trimmed, the amplifier will oscillate at 1 kilohertz ± 5 hertz. Transistor Q_1 serves as a switch to provide fast, sharp edges to Q_2's base. This transistor drives Q_3, which functions as a zener diode so that a relatively constant 10-v square wave is applied across the resistive divider at the output. Q_3's breakdown potential is scaled by the 2-kilohm potentiometer to provide a 5-, a 1-, and a 0.1-v square wave at the appropriate output taps. Loading of the circuit by a 1-megohm oscilloscope impedance will not introduce any appreciable error.

In Fig. 2, the LM389 is called on to provide a low-distortion sine wave and a synchronous in-phase square wave. The circuit's 0.25-watt output capability enables it to drive such loads as a transducer bridge. In such an application, the in-phase square-wave output can be used to drive a set of synchronous demodulation switches.

The oscillator's low distortion (0.2%) is directly traceable to the use of a light bulb that provides smooth amplitude-limiting for the Wien-bridge network of the amplifier. The oscillation frequency is 1 kHz. The in-phase square-wave output is ensured by Q_1–Q_3 and the potentiometer R_1, with Q_2 and Q_3 speeding up the waveform's edges. Calibration for synchronism is simply performed by adjusting R_1 so that the edges of the square wave line up precisely with the zero-crossings of the sine-wave output.

As shown in Fig. 3, the LM389 is used in an unorthodox fashion to build a logarithmic amplifier that eliminates the complex and expensive means by which temperature compensation is usually achieved. Thus, the cost of the log amp is reduced by some 90% compared with that of conventional approaches.

Q_2–Q_3 operate in a heat-generating and -sensing feedback network, with Q_2 serving as the heater and Q_3 the temperature sensor. This combination keeps the temperature virtually constant, so that the LF353 op amp's transfer function, as determined solely by logging transistor Q_1 and the 1N4148 diode, will be independent of any variation in temperature.

When power is first applied, Q_2's emitter voltage rises to about 3.3 V and a current of 120 milliamperes flows. This current forces Q_2 to dissipate about 1.5 w, which raises the chip to operating temperature very rapidly because of its small size. At this time, the thermal servo Q_2–Q_3 takes over, because the LM389 senses the depen-

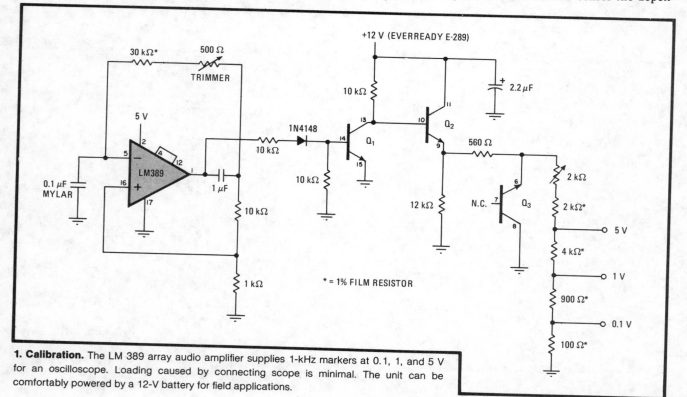

1. Calibration. The LM 389 array audio amplifier supplies 1-kHz markers at 0.1, 1, and 5 V for an oscilloscope. Loading caused by connecting scope is minimal. The unit can be comfortably powered by a 12-V battery for field applications.

dence of Q₃'s base-to-emitter voltage drop on temperature and drives Q₂ to a temperature (50°C) corresponding to the setting of the 10-kΩ-to-1-kΩ divider string. Since the LM340 never has a voltage of more than 3 V across it, the power dissipation never exceeds 0.3 w. Note that the zener diode at the base of Q₂ will prevent servo lock-up when the circuit is initialized.

To calibrate the temperature servo, the base of Q₂ must first be grounded. The collector potential of Q₃ must then be measured at a known room temperature. Calculate what Q₃'s potential should be at 50°C, assuming a temperature coefficient of −2.2 millivolts/°C. Next, trim the 1-kΩ resistor in the resistive divider so that the voltage at the LM389's inverting port approximates the calculated potential. Finally, unground Q₂'s base. The Q₂–Q₃ servo loop should then be functional. As

a check, note Q₃'s collector voltage stability (within 100 mV) and temperature change (0.05°C maximum) as cool air is applied to the LM389. ☐

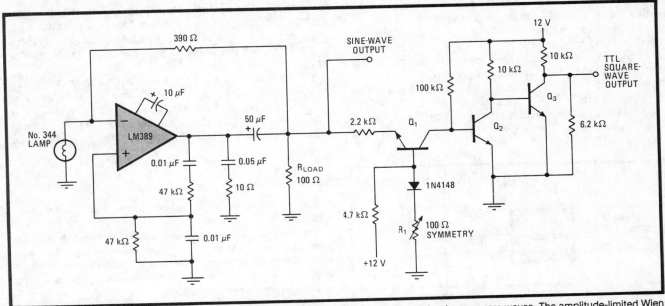

2. Sines and squares. This oscillator provides a 1-kHz sine-wave output and synchronous in-phase square waves. The amplitude-limited Wien bridge contributes to low distortion (0.2%). Single-knob calibration for synchronization is provided by potentiometer R₁.

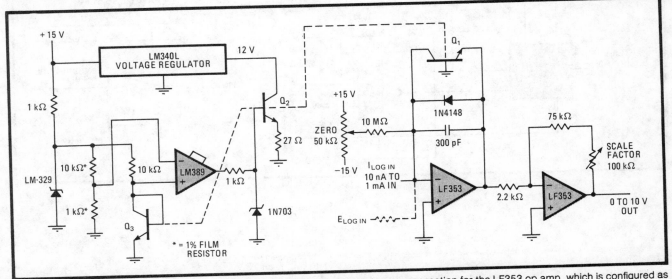

3. Holding heat. The LM389's servo loop, Q₂–Q₃, performs low-cost temperature compensation for the LF353 op amp, which is configured as a logarithmic amplifier. The chip temperature, initially determined by current through Q₂, is set with the 1-kΩ-to-10-kΩ resistive divider.

Integrator improves 555 pulse-width modulator

by Larry Korba
Ottawa, Ont., Canada

In one method of providing linear pulse-width modulation with the 555 timer, a current source charges a timing capacitor, creating a ramp signal that drives the modulation input of the 555. Unfortunately, the circuit offers only a limited dynamic range of pulse widths and is highly sensitive to temperature. A better way is to use a resettable integrator as the timing element.

Charging with a constant current source (a) at best yields a 2:1 dynamic range for a supply of 5 volts—the linear operating range for voltage-to-pulse-width conversion is approximately 2.1 to 4.1 v, and the timing capacitor is totally discharged every timing cycle. Furthermore, the circuit requires temperature compensation to eliminate any timing fluctuation due to the temperature sensitivity of Q_1, since the base-emitter voltage varies at the relatively high rate of -5 millivolts per °C. And, to add to the circuit's woes, I_{cbo} varies with temperature as well.

The resettable integrator (b) made up of A_2, Q_1, C, and R applies a trigger pulse to the 555, causing Q_1 to turn off. Integrator A_2 then ramps up until the voltage level at the modulation input of the timer equals that at pin 5. When that happens, Q_1 is turned on again, resetting the integrator and turning off the 555.

The voltage applied to the integrator, V_c, is set to 2.1 v. This makes the shortest linearly modulated pulse width equal to the trigger pulse width—2 microseconds. With the timing values shown, the maximum pulse width is 6 milliseconds, producing a dynamic range of more than 3,000:1 over the linear operating region.

The active components affecting the timing circuit are A_2, Q_1, A_1, and V_{cc}. Since the average temperature coefficient for the offset voltage of A_2 is a very low 5 microvolts/°C (affecting the timing by only 2.5 parts per million/°C), the circuit's almost negligible adverse temperature effects are largely due to the variation with temperature of the off current of Q_1, I_{dss}. I_{dss} doubles every 10°C; for the 2N4360, it is about 10 nanoamperes at room temperature.

It is important to note that for both circuits, the effects of V_{cc} and the 555 on timing stability are the same. As a bonus, however, the new circuit provides a linear ramp output that can be loaded fairly heavily without seriously affecting circuit timing. □

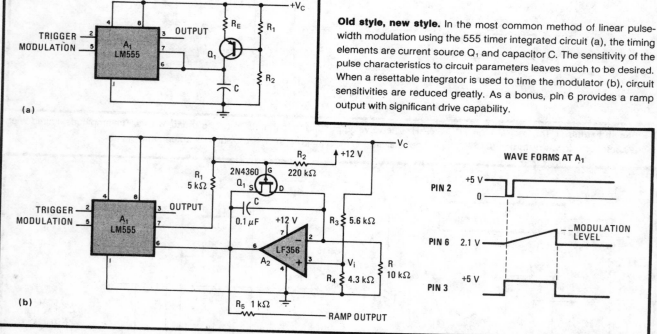

Old style, new style. In the most common method of linear pulse-width modulation using the 555 timer integrated circuit (a), the timing elements are current source Q_1 and capacitor C. The sensitivity of the pulse characteristics to circuit parameters leaves much to be desired. When a resettable integrator is used to time the modulator (b), circuit sensitivities are reduced greatly. As a bonus, pin 6 provides a ramp output with significant drive capability.

Bi-FET op amps simplify AGC threshold design

by John H. Davis
Warm Springs, Ga.

Operational amplifiers with the bandwidth and input impedance available using bipolar–field-effect-transistor (bi-FET) technology are well suited for integrating the threshold detection and automatic-gain-control amplification functions in audio limiters or receiver AGC circuits. Generally, such circuits are implemented with discrete components. But this often entails component selection and critical trimming adjustments, or both. An op amp approach makes an AGC design more predictable, stable, and easier to troubleshoot.

The circuit of Fig. 1 requires only one adjustment, to zero the output of the TL071 op amp under no-signal conditions. In this circuit, a control voltage is required over the range from zero (at full gain) to the negative value corresponding to the FET's cutoff voltage. A zener diode supplies the reference voltage. It is connected in a way that makes use of the common-mode rejection properties of the op amp; thus, R_3 nulls the static output, which thereafter is quite stable.

The threshold is the voltage appearing at the junction of R_1 and R_2, plus the forward drop of the detector diodes, and can be readily computed for any desired limiting level. For the detected peaks, the threshold detector has a voltage gain of:

$$A_{det} = (R_1 + R_2)/R_1$$

Not much gain is ordinarily required; too much imposes tighter tolerances on driver gain, diode properties, and

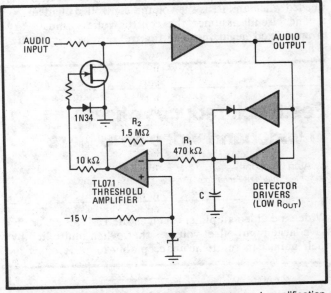

2. Simpler. Threshold detection, time constants, and amplification are consolidated in this single stage. For a receiver's i-f strip, an emitter follower is recommended, however. The control voltage here varies from a fixed negative value toward zero.

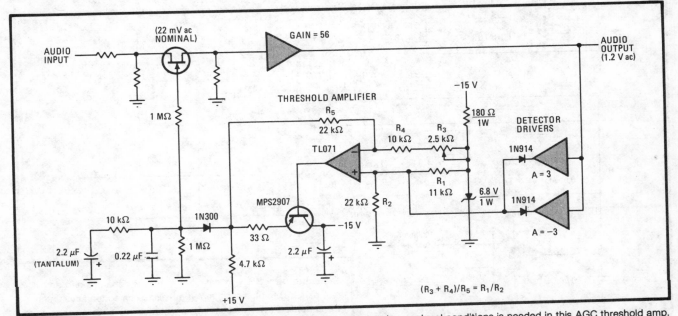

1. Easy play. Only one adjustment to zero the output of the TL071 op amp under no-signal conditions is needed in this AGC threshold amp. Good performance is achieved by using the amp's common-mode properties. The control voltage must vary from zero to a negative value.

trimmer adjustment. Driver gain can be adjusted, within output swing limits, to tailor limiting slopes.

The emitter follower improves the attack time of the time constant network. The dual set of time constants shown prevents short-duration peaks from depressing system gain longer than necessary.

Further simplification (Fig. 2) is possible if the driver amplifiers have low output impedance. Here the threshold detection, time constants, and amplification are consolidated in a single stage. This consolidation around one op amp means that little additional circuitry is needed when an FET is the voltage-controlled element.

The circuit assumes the control voltage must vary from a fixed negative value toward zero as gain reduc-

tion is needed. With no signal, the threshold op amp is referenced to the desired voltage by the zener diode. As long as no signal peaks are applied to time constant capacitor, C, the op amp acts as a voltage follower. Detected peaks charge C more negative than the reference, and the difference is amplified by a gain of $R_3 \div R_1$. This shifts the control voltage toward zero.

The release time constant is determined by C and R_1 and R_2. (Although only a single capacitor is shown, a dual arrangement as in Fig. 1 can be used.) The simplified circuit shown in Fig. 2 can also provide a fixed positive voltage that ranges toward zero for gain reduction if all the diodes and the reference-voltage polarity are reversed. □

Feedback reduces offset in wideband video amplifiers

by Alan Cocconi
California Institute of Technology, Pasadena, Calif.

Wideband video amplifiers such as the LM733 generally have large input offset voltages that, when multiplied by their gain, can result in unacceptably high dc offset at the output. This undesirable effect can be reduced by feedback by means of a low–input-offset integrator.

As shown in (a), summing resistors R_1 and R_2 are selected so that the input to the integrator is proportional to the video amplifier's input offset voltage. The integral feedback drives the video amp's input offset to zero, leaving only the low offset of the integrator (which can be trimmed to zero) to appear at the amplifier output.

A practical implementation of the approach is given in (b). The integrating operational amplifier, a CA3140, was chosen for its low input offset voltage. Here, the 1N4371 zener diode and the 2N2222 transistor, in an emitter-follower configuration, are required to ensure that the output can go down to 0 volt, since the 733 video amp suffers from the restriction of a minimum positive output voltage. □

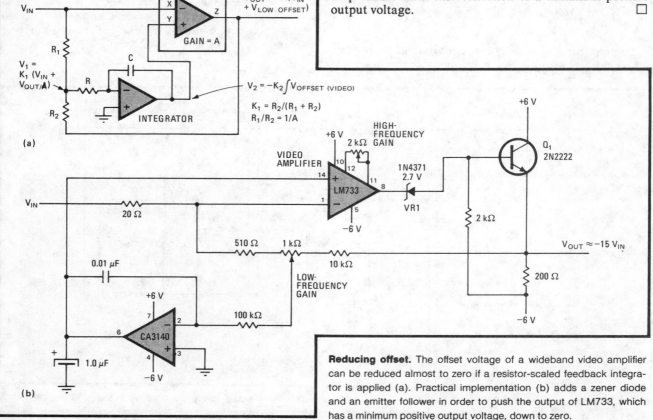

Reducing offset. The offset voltage of a wideband video amplifier can be reduced almost to zero if a resistor-scaled feedback integrator is applied (a). Practical implementation (b) adds a zener diode and an emitter follower in order to push the output of LM733, which has a minimum positive output voltage, down to zero.

Dual-function amp chip simplifies many circuits

by Jim Williams
National Semiconductor Corp., Santa Clara, Calif.

Various circuits that combine low cost, single- or dual-supply operation, and ease of use can easily be built with comparators and operational amplifiers like National Semiconductor's LM339 and LM324 because of their general applicability to a wide range of design problems. Now circuit complexity can be reduced even further with up-and-coming dual-function devices like the LM392, which put both a comparator and an op amp on one chip. Besides allowing a degree of flexibility in circuit function not readily implemented with separate chips, this device retains simplicity at low cost. The building of such circuits as a sample-and-hold circuit, a feed-forward low-pass filter, and a linearized platinum thermometer is

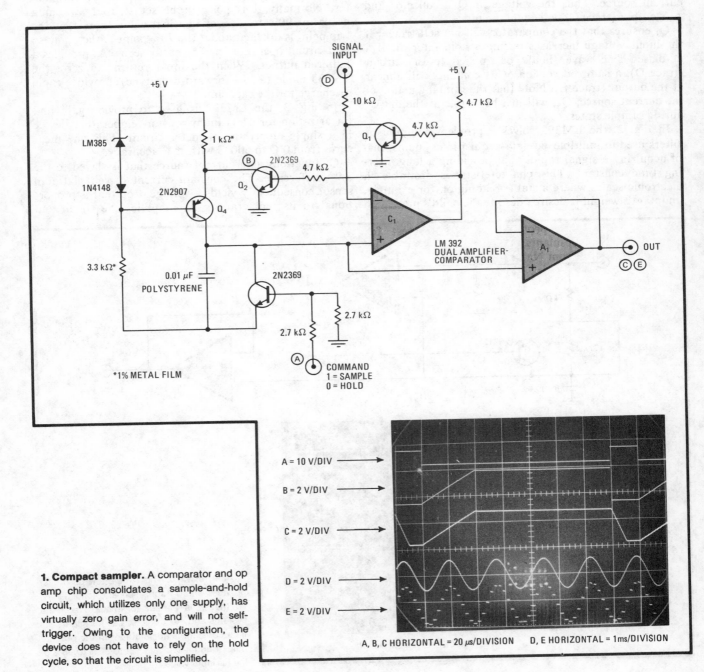

1. Compact sampler. A comparator and op amp chip consolidates a sample-and-hold circuit, which utilizes only one supply, has virtually zero gain error, and will not self-trigger. Owing to the configuration, the device does not have to rely on the hold cycle, so that the circuit is simplified.

A = 10 V/DIV
B = 2 V/DIV
C = 2 V/DIV
D = 2 V/DIV
E = 2 V/DIV

A, B, C HORIZONTAL = 20 μs/DIVISION   D, E HORIZONTAL = 1ms/DIVISION discussed here in the first of two articles.

The circuit in Fig. 1 is an unusual implementation of the sample-and-hold function. Although its input-to-output relationship is similar to standard configurations, its operating principle is different. Key advantages include no hold-step glitch, essentially zero gain error and operation from a single 5-volt supply.

When the sample-and-hold command pulse (trace A) is applied to transistor Q_3, it turns on, causing Q_4's collector to go to ground. Thus the output sits at ground. When the command pulse drops to logic 0, however, Q_4 drives a constant current into the 0.1-microfarad capacitor (trace B). At the instant the capacitor ramping voltage equals the signal input voltage, comparator C_1 switches, thereby causing transistor Q_2 to turn off the current source. Thus the voltage at Q_4's collector and A_1's output (trace C) will equal the input.

Q_1 ensures that the comparator will not self-trigger if the input voltage increases during a hold interval. If a dc-biased sine wave should be applied to the circuit (trace D), a sampled version of its contents will appear at the output (trace E). Note that the ramping action of the current source, Q_4, will just be visible at the output during sample states.

In Fig. 2, the LM392 solves a problem common to filters used in multiplexed data-acquisition systems, that of acquiring a signal rapidly but providing a long filtering time constant. This characteristic is desirable in electronic scales where a stable reading of, for example, an infant's weight is desired despite the child's motion on the scale's platform.

When an input step (trace A) is applied, C_1's negative input will immediately rise to a voltage determined by the setting of the 1-kilohm potentiometer. C_1's positive input, meanwhile, is biased through the 100 K −0.01 F time constant, and phase lags the input. Under these conditions, C_1's output will go low, turning on Q_1.

This action causes the capacitor (trace B) to charge rapidly up to the input value. When the voltage across the capacitor equals the voltage at C_1's positive input, C_1's output will go high, turning off Q_1. Now, the capacitor can only charge through the 100-kΩ resistor and the time constant must therefore be long.

The point at which the filter switches from the short to the long time constant is adjustable with the potentiometer. Normally, this pot will be set so that switching occurs at 90% to 98% of the final value (note that the trip point is taken at about the 70% point in the photo so that circuit operation may be easily seen). A_1 provides a buffered output. When the input returns to zero, the 1N933 diode (a low forward-drop type), provides rapid discharge for the capacitor.

In Fig. 3, the LM392 is used to provide gain and linearization for a platinum resistor-temperature device in a single-supply thermometer circuit. This one measures from 0°C to 500°C with ±1° accuracy.

Q_1 functions as a current source that is slaved to the 3.9-v reference. The constant-current–driven platinum sensor consequently yields a voltage drop that is proportional to its temperature. A_1 amplifies the signal and

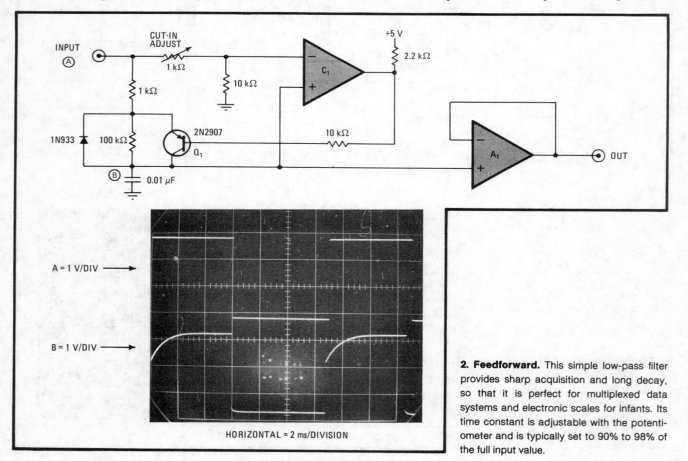

A = 1 V/DIV →

B = 1 V/DIV →

HORIZONTAL = 2 ms/DIVISION

2. Feedforward. This simple low-pass filter provides sharp acquisition and long decay, so that it is perfect for multiplexed data systems and electronic scales for infants. Its time constant is adjustable with the potentiometer and is typically set to 90% to 98% of the full input value.

provides the circuit output.

Normally, the slightly nonlinear response of the sensor would limit the circuit accuracy to about ±3°C. C_1 compensates for this error by generating a breakpoint change in A_1's gain at sensor outputs corresponding to temperatures exceeding 250°C. Then, the potential at the comparator's positive output exceeds the potential at the negative input and C_1's output goes high. This turns on Q_2, which shunts A_1's 6.19-kΩ feedback resistor and causes a change in gain that compensates for the sensor's slight loss of gain from 250° to 500°C. Current through the 220-kΩ resistor shifts the offset voltage of A_1 so no discernible glitch will occur at the breakpoint.

A precision decade box should be used to calibrate this circuit. Once inserted in place of the sensor, it is adjusted for a value of 1,000 ohms and a 0.10-v output by means of resistor R_1. Next, its resistance is set to 2,846 Ω (500°C) and its gain trim control adjusted for an output of 2.6 v. These adjustments are repeated until the zero and full-scale readings remain fixed at these points. □

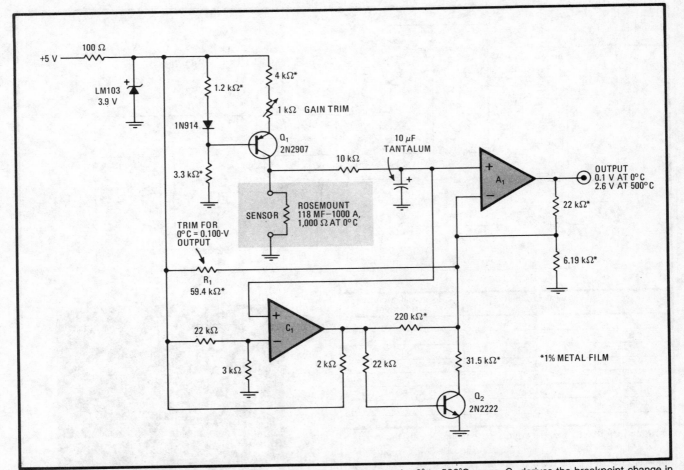

3. Tracking thermals. This platinum RTD thermometer has 99% accuracy over the 0°-to-500°C range. C_1 derives the breakpoint change in A_1's gain for sensor outputs exceeding 250°C, compensating for the sensor's nonlinearity. Current through the 220-kΩ resistor shifts A_1's offset voltage, in effect preventing glitches at the breakpoint. The instrument is calibrated only at two points with a decade resistor box.

Dual-function amplifier eases circuit design

by Jim Williams
National Semiconductor Corp., Santa Clara, Calif.

To simplify and cut the cost of the myriad of general-purpose and specialized circuits, chips like National's LM392 combine both amplifier and comparator functions on a single substrate. As has already been noted [*Electronics*, May 5, p. 142], it can be used to build a sample-and-hold circuit, a feed-forward low-pass filter and a linearized–platinum-resistor thermometer. This article will present designs for its use in the construction of a variable-ratio digital divider, an exponential voltage-to-frequency converter for electronic music, and a temperature controller for quartz-crystal stabilization.

Figure 1 shows a divider whose digital-pulse input can be divided by any number from 1 to 100 by means of a single-knob control. This function is ideal for bench-type work where the ability to set the division ratio rapidly is advantageous.

With no input signal, transistors Q_1 and Q_3 are off and

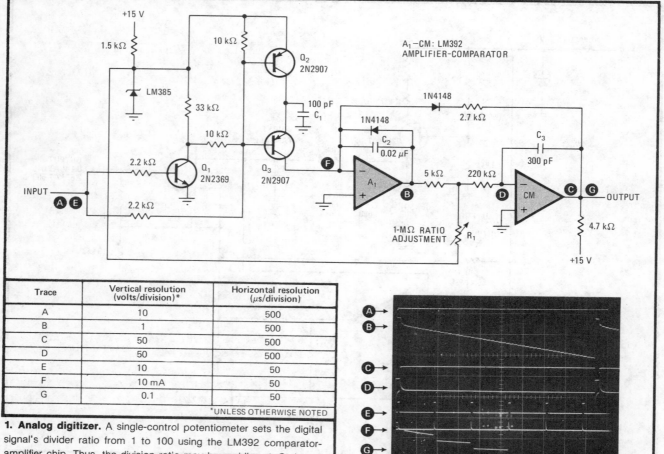

Trace	Vertical resolution (volts/division)*	Horizontal resolution (μs/division)
A	10	500
B	1	500
C	50	500
D	50	500
E	10	50
F	10 mA	50
G	0.1	50

*UNLESS OTHERWISE NOTED

1. Analog digitizer. A single-control potentiometer sets the digital signal's divider ratio from 1 to 100 using the LM392 comparator-amplifier chip. Thus, the division ratio may be rapidly set. Staircase signals are derived from a charge-balancing arrangement, which acts to maintain A_1's summing junction at a voltage null.

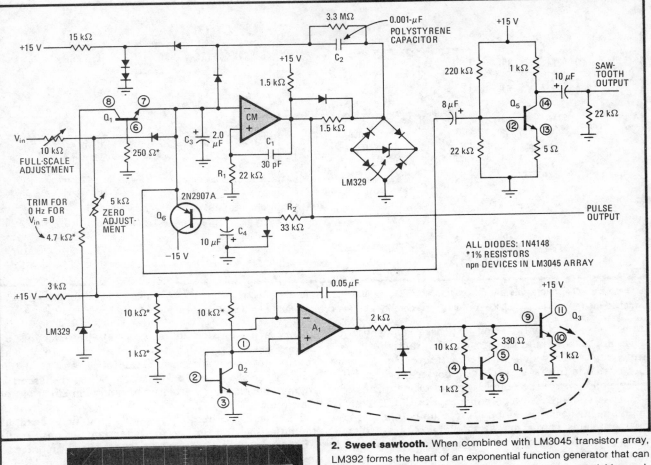

2. Sweet sawtooth. When combined with LM3045 transistor array, LM392 forms the heart of an exponential function generator that can easily be built. Waveform conformity to a pure exponential is excellent — ±0.25% over the 20-Hz-to-15-kHz range. Thermal drift is minimized with a simple servo loop. Provision is made for eliminating servo lock-up under virtually all conditions.

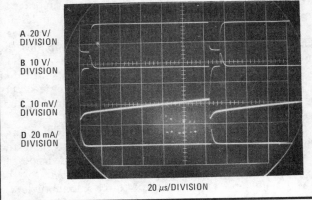

A 20 V/DIVISION
B 10 V/DIVISION
C 10 mV/DIVISION
D 20 mA/DIVISION

20 μs/DIVISION

Q_2 is on. Thus, the 100-picofarad capacitor (C_1) at the junction of Q_2 and Q_3 accumulates a charge equal to $Q_{cap} = C_1V_0$, where V_0 is the potential across the LM385 zener diode (1.2 volts), minus the saturated collector-to-emitter potential across Q_2.

When the input signal to the circuit goes high (see trace A, in the photograph), Q_2 goes off and Q_1 turns on Q_3. As a result, the charge across C_1 is displaced into A_1's summing junction. A_1 responds by jumping to the value required to maintain its summing junction at zero (trace B).

This sequence is repeated for every input pulse. During this time, A_1's output will generate the staircase waveshape shown as the 0.02-microfarad feedback capacitor (C_2) is pumped by the charge-dispensing action to the A_1 summing junction. When A_1's output is

just great enough to bias the noninverting input of the comparator (CM) below ground, the output (trace C) goes low and resets A_1 to zero. Positive feedback to the comparator (trace D) is applied through the 300-pF capacitor (C_3), ensuring adequate reset time for A_1.

Potentiometer R_1 sets the number of steps in the ramp required to trip the comparator. Thus the circuit's input-to-output division ratio may be conveniently set. Traces E through G expand the scope trace to show the dividing action in detail. When the input E goes high, charge is deposited into A_1's summing junction F, and the resultant waveform G takes a step.

Professional-grade electronic-music synthesizers require voltage-controlled frequency generators whose output frequency is exponentially related to the input voltage. The one shown in Fig. 2 provides conformity within 0.25% over the range from 20 hertz to 15 kHz using a single LM392 and an LM3045 transistor array. These specifications will be adequate for all but the most demanding of applications.

The exponential function is generated by Q_1, whose collector current varies exponentially with its base-emitter voltage in accordance with the well-known relationship between that voltage and current in a bipolar

21

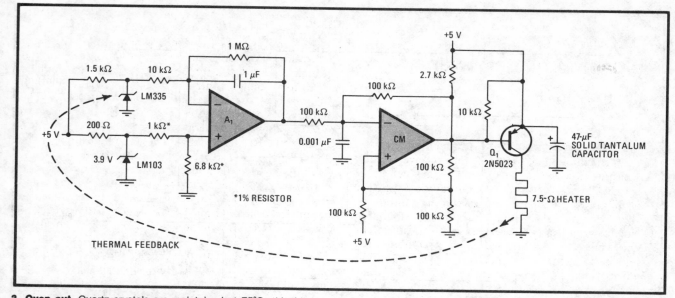

3. Oven cut. Quartz crystals are maintained at 75°C with this temperature controller, thus stabilizing output frequency of these sources. Switched-mode servo loop simplifies circuitry considerably. Long-term temperature accuracy is estimated at 10 parts per million.

transistor. An elaborate and expensive compensation scheme is usually required because the transistor's operating point varies widely with temperature. Here, Q_2 and Q_3, located in the array, serve as a heater-sensor pair for A_1, which controls the temperature of Q_2 by means of a simple servo loop. As a consequence, the LM3045 array maintains its constant temperature, eliminating thermal-drift problems in the operation of Q_1. Q_4 is a clamp, preventing the servo from locking up during circuit start-up.

In operation, Q_1's current output is fed into the summing junction of a charge-dispensing current-to-frequency converter. The comparator's output state is used to switch the 0.001-μF capacitor between a reference voltage and the comparator's inverting input, the reference being furnished by the LM329.

The comparator drives the capacitor C_1 and resistor R_1 combination, this network providing regenerative feedback to reinforce the direction of its output. Thus, positive feedback ceases when the voltage across the R_1C_1 combination decays, and any negative-going amplifier output will be followed by a single positive edge after the time constant R_1C_1 (see waveforms A and B in the photograph).

The integrating capacitor C_3 is never allowed to charge beyond 10 to 15 millivolts because it is constantly reset by charge dispensed from the switching of C_2 (trace C). If the amplifier's output goes negative, C_2 dumps a quantity of charge into C_3, forcing it to a lower potential (trace D). When a short pulse is transferred through to the comparator's noninverting input, C_2 is again able to charge and the cycle repeats. The rate at which this sequence occurs is directly related to the current into the comparator's summing junction from Q_1. Because this current is exponentially related to the circuit's input voltage, the overall current-to-frequency transfer function is exponentially related to the input voltage.

Any condition that allows C_3 to charge beyond 10 to

20 mv will cause circuit lock-up. Q_6 prevents this by pulling the inverting input of A_1 towards -15 v. The resistor and capacitor combination of R_2 and C_4 determines when the transistor comes on. When the circuit is running normally, Q_6 is biased off and is in effect out of the circuit.

The circuit is calibrated by simply grounding the input and adjusting first the zeroing potentiometer until oscillations just start and then the full-scale potentiometer so that the circuit's frequency output exactly doubles for each volt of input (1 v per octave for musical purposes). The comparator's output pulses while Q_5 amplifies the summing junction ramp for a sawtooth output.

The circuit in Fig. 3 will maintain the temperature of a quartz-crystal oven at 75°C. Five-volt single-supply operation permits the circuit to be powered directly from TTL-type rails.

A_1, operating at a gain of 100, determines the voltage difference between the temperature setpoint and the LM335 temperature sensor, which is located inside the oven. The temperature setpoint is established by the LM103 3.9-v reference and the 1-to-6.8-kilohm divider.

A_1's output biases the comparator, which functions as a pulse-width modulator and biases Q_1 to deliver switched-mode power to the heater. When power is applied, A_1's output goes high, causing the comparator's output to saturate low. Q_1 then comes on.

When the oven warms to the desired setpoint, A_1's output falls and the comparator begins to pulse-width–modulate the heater via the servo loop. In practice, the LM335 should be in good thermal contact with the heater to prevent oscillation in the servo loop. □

Fm receiver mixes high gain with low power

by Peter Whatley
Motorola Inc., Phoenix, Ariz.

Scanning receivers, ham transceivers, and other narrow-band frequency-modulated systems that receive voice or digital information need as much gain as they can get to pick up weak signals. Normally such gain is expensive. But the Motorola MC3359P chip, which has an oscillator-mixer, limiting amplifier, quadrature discriminator, operational amplifier, squelch, scan control, automatic frequency control, and mute switch neatly combines low cost, high gain, and as a bonus, low power consumption. It requires only a front-end tuner and a few other components to form a complete narrow-band scanning receiver (see figure).

A typical application of the MC3359P is as a narrow-band fm scanning receiver for voice communication. As shown, the input to pin 18 (typically 10.7 megahertz) is converted down by a mixer-oscillator combination to 455 kilohertz, and most of the amplification is done by the chip at this frequency. The mixer is doubly balanced to reduce the fm receiver's spurious responses. Its output at pin 3 has a 1.8-kilohm impedance to match an external

ceramic filter. For its part, the oscillator is a Colpitts design that can readily be controlled by a crystal.

After limiting, the fm signal is demodulated using a quadrature detector. The recovered audio is filtered through R_1 and C_1 to remove noise and is then coupled via C_2 to a volume control. The recovered audio is 800 millivolts peak to peak at the junction of R_2 and C_2. The unfiltered recovered audio at pin 10 is fed through R_4 to an internal inverting operational amplifier that, with R_5, C_4, C_5, and R_6, forms an active bandpass filter in the 6-kHz range. Therefore any noise or tone frequency, which may be present above the normal audio range, can be selected, amplified, and then detected by the C_6 and D_1 combination. This detected signal is, in turn, sent to the squelch control at pin 14. Squelch sensitivity may be adjusted by R_9, which provides a bias to the squelch input.

If pin 14 is raised to 0.7 volt by the detected noise, tone, or dc bias, the squelch detector will be activated. This causes pin 15 to act as an open circuit and pin 16 to be shorted to ground via pin 17. Pin 16 is thus connected to the input of the audio amplifier and mutes the audio signal during squelching. Pin 15 can be used for scan control and may be connected to a frequency synthesizer in the receiver's front end. An afc connection is also available at pin 11. In this crystal-controlled application, an afc is not required, so that pin 11 can be grounded or tied to pin 9. With this last connection, the recovered audio is doubled in amplitude. ☐

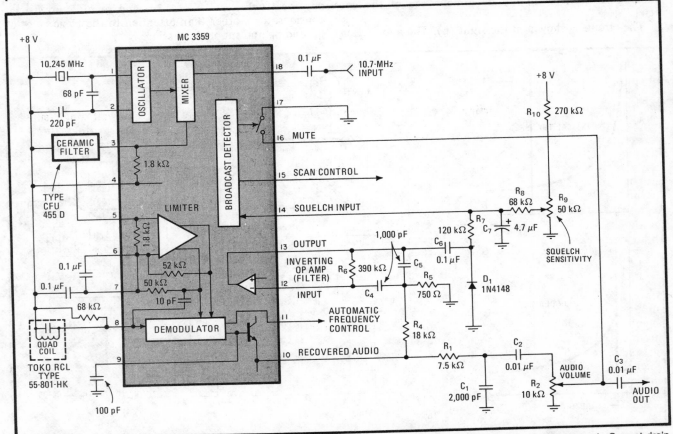

Narrow band. In the scanning-receiver circuit shown, the MC3359P provides an audio output voltage of 800 mV peak to peak. Current drain from a 6-V supply is 3 mA, and the sensitivity is 2 µV for −3 dB of input limiting. Only one crystal and some passive components are needed.

Agc prevents noise build-up in voice-operated mike

by Russell S. Thynes
Kirkland, Wash.

Hands-free operation of intercoms has several advantages over push-to-talk intercom systems. Constantly keyed "live" microphones, however, have the disadvantage of receiving undesirable environmental noise in the absence of speech. When such mikes are used in conjunction with intercoms having automatic gain control in the microphone mixing stages, this environmental noise will produce a swelling tide of sound each time normal communication is interrupted.

Shown here is an agc-VOX (voice-operated switch) scheme that allows constantly keyed microphones to be used in noisy environments without suffering from the effects of noise build-up.

Although the operation of the circuit is twofold, the function is primarily that of a gain-clamped agc circuit. Part (a) of the figure shows the transfer function of an agc with gain clamping and that of typical configuration. For input levels below those of normal speech, clamping the gain to a fixed value limits the area of the gain curve, reducing noise susceptibility—but without placing restrictions on the dynamic range of the agc itself.

The circuit is shown on the right (b). The agc section consists of operational amplifier A_1 and transistor Q_1, with diode D_1 and capacitor C_1 deriving the feedback control voltage. Q_1 is placed in a T configuration to achieve a wide control range and to ensure low levels of distortion. Distortion is further reduced by the gate-biasing resistors R_6 and R_7. As configured, this agc should provide 30 decibels of gain control with less than 0.5% distortion for most of the audio range.

A_3 is arranged as an adjustable noninverting amplifier, the gain of which can be varied from 20 to 40 dB. R_{12} (also in a T configuration) allows the user to set the VOX sensitivity to offset environmental noise conditions. A_4 simply compares the detected output of A_3 with a reference and switches to either a high or a low output limit depending on the VOX input level.

When input levels to the agc are below the VOX sensitivity setting, the output of A_4 will be at its lower limit, biasing Q_1 off and thus clamping the gain of A_1 to $(R_2+R_3)/R_1$.

When the VOX sensitivity level is exceeded, however, the comparator output swings to its upper limit and effectively disconnects the VOX from the agc feedback loop through blocking diode D_2. The gain is then expressed as:

$$-\frac{R_2+R_3}{R_1} \leq A_v \leq -\left(\frac{R_2+R_3}{R_1}-\frac{R_2R_3}{R_{on}R_1}\right)$$

where R_{on} is the practical on-resistance of the transistor.

This entire circuit can be configured using one quad op amp (such as an XR 4136) and requires no special considerations other than attention to the basic rules of grounding and supply bypassing. □

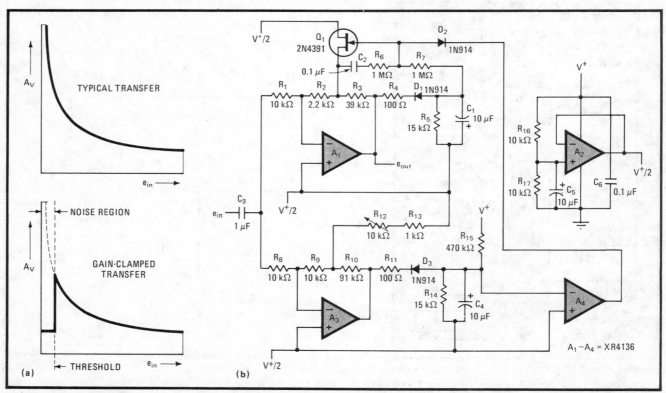

Hands off. If the gain is clamped to a minimum at input signal levels below the noise threshold, the surrounding noise is filtered out of the amplifier network (a), whereas speech kicks in the amplifier's automatic gain control. Both functions are performed by the circuit shown in (b).

Power-sharing bridge circuit improves amplifier efficiency

by Jim Edrington
Texas Instruments Inc., Austin, Texas

This linear bridge amplifier offers several advantages in driving motors and servo systems, including obtaining maximum efficiency with a single power supply and with dc coupling, which as a result reduces circuit complexity. Most notable, however, is that the four transistors in the amplifier will equally share load currents, as well as simplifying the drive requirements. These factors permit lower-cost transistors to be applied and allow their heat-sink requirements to be reduced.

Shown in (a) is one half of the bridge-type circuit, which illustrates the amplifier's operation. Positive input excursions from the driver turn on current sink Q_2, with a portion of Q_2's collector current passing through transistor Q_3. Q_3's current flow causes source transistor Q_1 to turn on.

Because the majority of the flow must pass through Q_1 and Q_2, the collector-to-emitter voltage of both transistors must be equal to ensure equal power dissipation. This voltage-matching requirement is achieved by clamping the gain of Q_1 to the voltage at the center of the load with a zener diode. Thus the virtual center of the load will be maintained at $V_{cc}/2$ and $V_{Q_1ce} = V_{Q_2ce}$, provided $R_1 = R_2$. The zener diode, D_1, must have a value of $V_z = (V_{cc}/2) - 1.4$ to meet the requirement for the reference potential.

Two of these circuits may be readily incorporated into a full-bridge arrangement, as shown in (b), that is suitable for driving electromechanical devices. Adding diodes D_2 through D_5 isolate one branch's functions from the other. With this configuration, each branch conducts for half of the input cycle thereby eliminating virtually all crossover difficulties.

The isolation diodes will alter the divider's center voltage by 0.7 volts, however, and so the value of the zener voltage must be slightly changed. In this case, it will be $V_z = (V_{cc}/2) - 1.4 + 0.7 = 11.3$ v. In most applications, selecting the nearest standard zener value will suffice. □

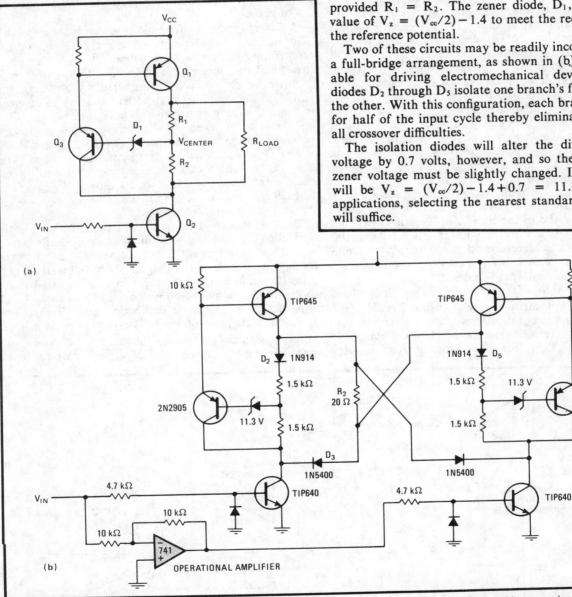

Divided driver. A rudimentary amplifier (a) may be designed so that Q_1 and Q_2 carry equal load on a positive excursion of an input signal, using a zener diode of suitable value for biasing a load center to cause $V_{Q_1ce} = V_{Q_2ce}$. Combining two such sections in a balanced bridge arrangement (b) builds a dc-coupled amplifier that is simple, can run from one supply, and can ensure that all amplifiers may handle a proportionate share of the power. This combination reduces electrical specifications of individual transistors, thereby reducing their cost.

Bi-FET op amps invade 741's general-purpose domain

by Jim Williams
National Semiconductor Corp., Santa Clara, Calif.

Thanks to their low-drift microampere supply currents and picoampere bias currents, recently introduced bipolar field-effect-transistor operational amplifiers like National's LF441 can be used in applications that general-purpose amplifiers like the 741 cannot address. A high-performance pH meter, logarithmic amplifiers, and a voltmeter-checker reference source may be inexpensively built with this bi-FET operational amplifier.

The low-bias input of the 441 provides an excellent nonloading port for a pH probe, which is used to measure the acidity or alkalinity of a solution (Fig. 1). This simple four-chip interface yields a linear 0-to-10-volt output corresponding directly to the value of the pH (0 to 10) being measured, a range that is more than adequate for many applications.

The output from buffer A_1 is applied to A_2, a tuned 60-hertz filter that removes power-line noise. A_2 also biases op amp A_3, which provides a compensation adjustment for the probe's temperature. A_4 allows the probe to be calibrated.

To calibrate the circuit, the probe is immersed in a solution having a pH of 7. The solution's temperature is normalized for the meter by R_1, a 10-turn 1,000-ohm potentiometer whose value may be set between 0 and 100 units. These values correspond directly to a solution temperature range of 0° to 100°C. Potentiometer R_2 is then adjusted for an output voltage of 7 V.

A conventional logarithmic amplifier (Fig. 2a) utilizes the well-known logarithmic relationship between the base-to-emitter voltage drop in a transistor and its collector current. Here, A_1 acts as a clamp, forcing the current through Q_1 to equal the input current, E_{in}/R_{in}.

Q_2 provides feedback to A_2, forcing Q_2's collector current to equal A_2's input current, which is established by the LM185 zener-diode reference.

Because Q_2's collector current is constant, its emitter-to-base voltage is fixed. The base-to-emitter drop of Q_1, however, varies with the input current. The circuit's output voltage is therefore a function of the difference in the V_{be} voltages of Q_1 and Q_2 and is proportional to the logarithm of the input current. In this manner, the V_{be} drift is cancelled. The coefficient of this term will vary with temperature, however, and cause a drift in the output voltage. The 1,000-Ω thermistor compensates for this drift, stabilizing A_1's gain.

The 441's 50-pA bias current allows accurate logging down into the nanoampere region. With the values shown in the circuit, the scale factor for the amplifier is 1 V/decade.

A second type of logarithmic amplifier is shown in (b). This unconventional design completely eliminates the temperature-compensation problems of (a) by temperature-stabilizing logging transistor Q_1. This temperature problem is economically eliminated by utilizing the LM389 audio-amplifier-and-transistor array as an oven to control the logging transistor's environment.

Transistor Q_2 in the LM389 serves as a heater, and Q_3 functions as the chip's temperature sensor. The LM389 senses Q_3's V_{be}, which is temperature-dependent, and drives Q_2 to feed back the chip's temperature to the set point established by the 1-to-10-kilohm divider. The LM329 reference ensures that the power supply is independent of temperature changes.

Q_1, the logging transistor, operates in this tightly controlled thermal environment. When the circuit is first turned on, Q_2's current flow becomes 50 milliamperes forcing the transistor to dissipate about 0.5 watt, which raises the chip to its operating temperature rapidly. At this point, the thermal-feedback circuit takes control and adjusts the chip's power dissipation accordingly. The LM340L voltage regulator has only 3 V across it, so it never dissipates more than about 0.3 W. The pnp-transistor clamp at the base of Q_2 prevents feedback

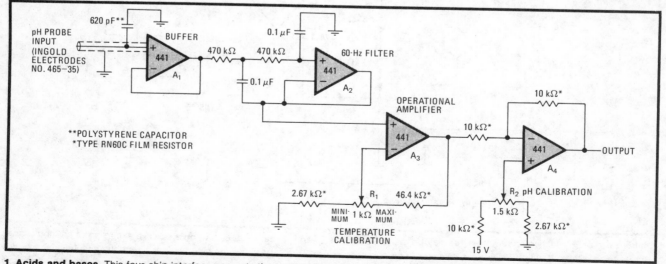

1. Acids and bases. This four-chip interface converts the output of a pH probe into direct readings of a solution's acidity and alkalinity. The circuit has a filter to reject the ac line noise that plagues instruments of this type. This unit can easily compensate for temperature variations.

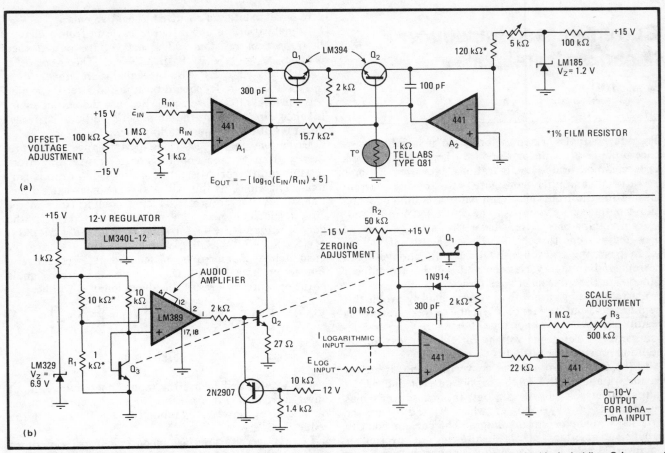

$$E_{OUT} = -[\log_{10}(E_{IN}/R_{IN}) + 5]$$

2. Low-power loggers. With amplifier A_1 clamping current through transistor Q_1 to input value E_{in}/R_{in} and with A_2 holding Q_2's current constant with LM185's reference, circuit (a) yields a logarithmic response by virtue of proportional differences between Q_1 and Q_2's well-known V_{be}-to-collector current relation. A more advanced version (b) uses an LM389 to eliminate temperature effects on output.

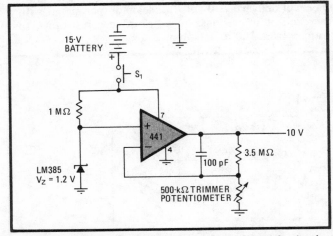

3. Long-term accuracy. Using a single LF441 and a 1.2-volt reference, this circuit for calibrating digital voltmeters with a 10-V signal draws only 250 microamperes. Using a 15-v power source, the circuit has an output accuracy within 0.1% over a year's time.

lock-up during circuit start-up.

To adjust this circuit, the base of Q_2 should be grounded, then the power applied to the circuit, and the collector voltage of Q_3 measured at room temperature. Next, Q_3's potential at 50°C is calculated, a drop of −2.2 millivolts/°C being assumed. The value of R_1 should be selected to yield a voltage close to the calculated potential at the LM389's negative input. After Q_2's base is removed from ground, the circuit will be operational.

A_1's low bias current allows values as low as 10 nanoamperes to be logged within 3%. Potentiometer R_2 provides zeroing for the amplifier. Potentiometer R_3 sets the overall gain of the circuit.

The low power consumption of the 441 is useful in a calibration checker for digital voltmeters that only draws 250 μA (Fig. 3). Here, the 441 is used as a noninverting amplifier. The LM385 is a low-power reference that provides 1.2 v to the input. This voltage is simply scaled by the feedback-resistor network to yield exactly 10 v at the circuit's output. The circuit will be accurate to within 0.1% for over a year, even with frequent use. ☐

Current-biased transducer linearizes its response

by Jerald Graeme
Burr-Brown Research Corp., Tucson, Ariz.

Transducers that work on the principle of variable resistance produce a nonlinear response when voltage-biased, as in common bridge configurations. However, a single operational amplifier configured to provide current biasing for the transducer eliminates this difficulty and allows output offset voltages to be controlled or removed.

As a voltage-biased transducer's resistance varies, so does the current through it. Thus, any signal voltage taken from the transducer will be a function of both current and voltage variations and will be a nonlinear function of the transducer's resistance.

Current biasing rather than voltage biasing avoids this nonlinearity, but reference current sources are not as readily available as voltage ones. Fortunately, an op amp can convert a reference voltage for this purpose and in addition provide other benefits.

In (a), a voltage-to-current converter circuit is adapted for voltage control of the supply current and of the output offset voltage. As laid out, the transducer's bias current is $I_X = (V_2 - V_1)/R_1$, where V_1 and V_2 are the externally applied control voltages. The current polarity can be set at either $+$ or $-$, allowing an inverted or noninverted voltage response to variations in transducer resistance.

The resulting current flow in the nominal transducer resistance, R, produces an offset voltage at the circuit's output with a counteracting voltage developed by V_1: $V_{oso} = (1 + (R_2/R_1))I_xR - (R_2/R_1)V_1$. Thus, through the proper selection of V_1, the output offset may be nulled to

zero or set to either a positive or negative polarity.

Signal variations about that level result from a change in transducer resistance. The net voltage output then becomes $e_o = [1 + (R_2/R_1)]I_x\Delta R + V_{oso}$. This response is linearly related to ΔR. Also the signal is amplified.

To set the gain, R_2 should be adjusted after R_1, which sets the level of I_X, is selected. Because the output signal is taken directly from the amplifier's output, the transducer is buffered against loading effects.

Deviations in the described performance result primarily from voltage and resistor tolerances and from resistor-ratio error. Mismatch of the $R_2:R_1$ ratio is particularly serious, as this will make I_X somewhat a function of ΔR, thereby reintroducing nonlinearities in the circuit. Such a mismatch will alter the term in the denominator of the I_X formula to read $((R + \Delta R)/R_2) \times ((R_2/R_1) - (R_2'/R_1'))$, where R_1' and R_2' are the mismatched counterparts of R_1 and R_2, respectively. Further errors will result from the dc input-error signals of the op amp. As a result, the deviation in e_o will be:

$$\Delta e_o = \left[1 + \frac{R_x}{R_2}\left(1 + \frac{R_2}{R_1}\right)\right]\left[\left(1 + \frac{R_2}{R_1}\right)v_{os}\right] + \left(1 + \frac{R_2}{R_1}\right)R_xI_{os} + R_2I_{B\cdot}$$

where V_{os}, I_{os}, and $I_{B\cdot}$ are the input offset voltage, input offset current, and the inverting input-bias current of the op amp, respectively. Making the R_2/R_x ratio large reduces this error.

In practice, it is either inconvenient or sometimes undesirable to supply two voltage references to the circuit. A single reference voltage may be applied, as shown in (b), which is the Thévenin equivalent of the circuit in (a). For the specific component values given, the amplifier will deliver a 1.0-volt full-scale output signal with a zero offset in response to a transducer resistance that ranges from 300 to 350 ohms. ☐

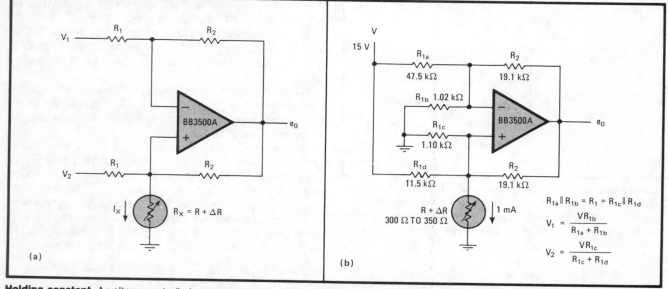

Holding constant. A voltage-controlled current source drives transducer (a) so that its output voltage is a function of its resistance change only, thereby reducing the circuit's nonlinear response. The output offset can also be virtually eliminated. The single-reference current source circuit (b), which is the Thévenin equivalent of (a), may be more attractive to implement in some cases.

Counter indicates when its probe is compensated

by Dale Carlton
Tektronix Inc., Beaverton, Ore.

Using a scope probe with a counter or other measuring instrument has a number of well-known benefits—namely, it ensures minimal source loading, physical ease of circuit connection, and minimum distortion of high-frequency signal components. Still, matching the probe to the counter's input impedance to secure wideband response can be troublesome, especially if the elements needed to perform the standard compensation procedure (a scope and a source of square waves) are not available and the input impedance of the scope and counter are not identical. Fortunately, the counter's own input-trigger circuit may be employed as a peak detector to indicate that proper probe compenstion has been achieved.

The equivalent input circuit of the typical $5\times$ and $10\times$ (attenuating) probe appears as in (a), where C_1 is the ac coupling capacitor and C_2 represents the probe's compensating capacitance, cable capacitance, and the input capacitance of the measuring instrument. R_1 is the dc coupling resistance. R_2 is the instrument's input resistance. For flat response, the product of R_1 and C_1 should be equal to the product of R_2 and C_2.

Compensation is achieved by applying to the probe/counter a 1-kilohertz square-wave signal having a rise time of less than 100 microseconds. The amplitude of the square wave should be as large as the counter's dynamic range will allow. The counter should be set to trigger on the low-frequency components of the square wave so that a reference level is established. Then the probe's compensating capacitor is adjusted so that the counter will trigger on the highest-frequency components of the signal.

Specifically, the counter should be set to the $1\times$ position. The counter's function control is then set to the frequency, period, or event position, so that the counter's display or input-trigger LED will indicate triggering when the square wave is applied.

To establish the reference level, the probe is adjusted so that triggering occurs in the waveform's so-called roll-off region. This is done by setting C_2 and the trigger level in turn so that triggering occurs at the peak of the acquired signal and at the minimum level required to ensure consistent operation. The point at which this occurs for a given trigger level is reached when an increase or decrease in C_2 does not stop triggering. If the acquired signal could be observed, it would appear as in the illustration in (b).

For compensation at the high frequencies, the response of the probe must be flattened (c). This is achieved by setting the trigger level to a position where triggering just stops or is erratic. C_2 is then adjusted to the point where triggering is again reliable, and probe compensation is complete.

Availability of a constant-amplitude sine-wave oscillator greatly simplifies the compensation procedure. Setting sine-wave frequency at 100 hertz and a convenient amplitude, the user need only set the counter's trigger level at the sine wave's peak voltage. The frequency is then increased to 10 kHz or higher and C_2 is

Match. Universal counter's display or trigger LED is used to indicate that probe/circuit's elements $R_1C_1C_2$ (a) are matched to input impedance (R_2) of measuring device. Procedure used is to first position triggering region on roll-off of input-signal curve (b) with C_2 and counter's trigger-level control. Probe will be compensated over a wide band after C_2 is peaked (c) to detect high-frequency components of square wave.

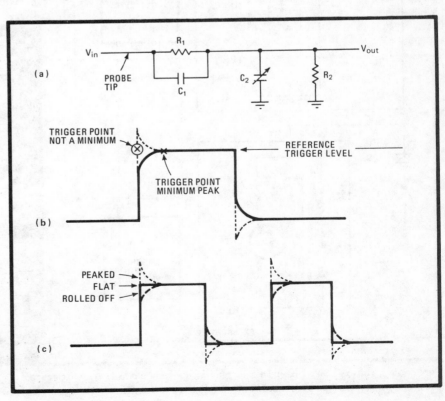

adjusted to just restore triggering. Typically, the flatness achieved by this method will be 2%. In equation form, $\%F = (AS)(100)/V_{in\ p\text{-}p}$, where A is the probe's attenuation factor, S is the settability or trigger-level resolution, and $V_{in\ p\text{-}p}$ is the peak-to-peak amplitude of the input signal.

Some counters have a tapered trigger-level knob and the maximum setability occurs at the 0-volt level. For best accuracy when using one of these counters, a waveform that is square near 0 V or an offset sine wave that has peaks near 0 V should be used.

It should be noted that many of the newer counters now available have a large input capacitance, and some conventional scope probes may not have sufficient compensating capacitance. Using such a probe in this situation reduces system sensitivity above 1 kHz and could cause additional time-interval measurement error. □

Transistor probe simplifies solid-state gaussmeter

by Shanker Lal Agrawal and Rama Swami
Banaras Hindu University, Department of Physics, Varanasi, India

As a result of the subatomic energy exchanges that take place in many semiconductors because of particle-wave interaction, the electrical characteristics of the unijunction-transistor oscillator can be significantly changed by an external magnetic field. This property makes the low-cost unijunction transistor ideal for use as a probe in a gaussmeter or other flux-measuring instrument. Although it is not as linear, is not as easily calibrated, and does not provide the readout precision of some of the more elegant designs,[1] this circuit is simpler, just as sensitive, and virtually as accurate.

As shown, the gaussmeter is based on the comparator technique, wherein the frequency of the relaxation oscillator-probe is matched against a reference whose nominal frequency is about 400 hertz. Both generate positive-going spikes, which are lengthened by the pulse-stretching 74121 one-shot multivibrators. The NAND gate serves as a digital comparator, turning off the light-emitting diode when frequency $f_1 = f_2$.

In operation, the frequency of the reference oscillator is adjusted by resistor R until f_2 equals the free-running

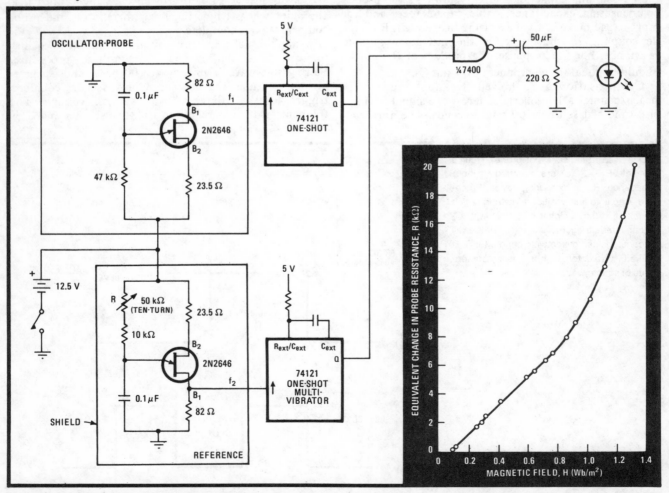

Flux finding. The low cost of the rudimentary unijunction transistor, which is sensitive to externally applied magnetic fields, makes it ideal for use in comparison-type gaussmeters. The circuit range is 0 to 1.5 Wb/m², with circuit response linear to 1.0 Wb/m².

(free-field) frequency of the probe. Placing the oscillator-probe within the field to be measured will cause its frequency to change; potentiometer R in the reference must then be adjusted until the difference between f_1 and f_2 is minimized. The change in resistance of R from its nominal position may then be related to the strength of the magnetic field with the aid of the unit's individual calibration curve, which is shown at the right side of the figure.

As for calibration, at least three standard magnets will be required over the range of 0 to 1.5 weber per square meter, which is the range of the instrument. The circuit response is not likely to be linear above 1.0 wb/m², and depending on the particular UJT used, the standard-marker points will vary considerably as a function of R. Still, the circuit will hold calibration and will serve well in most general-purpose applications. □

References
1. Henno Normet, "Hall-probe adapter converts DMM into gaussmeter," *Electronics*, Jan. 3, 1980, p. 179.

Five-chip meter measures impedances ratiometrically

by N. E. Hadzidakis
Athens, Greece

Measuring both inductance and capacitance usually requires either a manual bridge, which is difficult to use, or a digital bridge, which is expensive. Recently, inexpensive hand-held capacitance meters have appeared on the market, but they employ a time-to-charge technique that cannot be applied to the measurement of inductance. The circuit shown here, however, utilizes a ratiometric method that is suitable for both types of measure-

ment. Its only disadvantage is the requirement for one calibrated reference component per range. Still, it is inexpensive and easy to use.

Generally, the potentials across a reference and test inductor or capacitor, which are dependent on the frequency of the 8038 square-wave driving source, are applied to two ac-to-dc converters built around CA3130 operational amplifiers. The converters' output is then compared at the ICL7107 ratiometric converter. Because the value of the reference inductor or capacitor is a multiple of 10, the value of the test element can be read directly from the display.

In the case of measuring inductors, it can easily be shown that:

$$L_x = \frac{L_{ref}\,e}{2 + 1/e} + \frac{L^2_{ref}\,e^2(e+1)}{(2e+1) - R^2/4\pi^2 f^2}$$

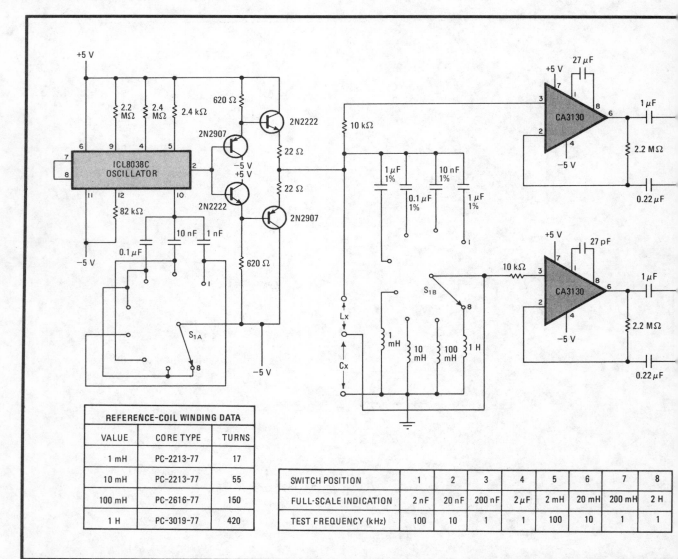

REFERENCE-COIL WINDING DATA		
VALUE	CORE TYPE	TURNS
1 mH	PC-2213-77	17
10 mH	PC-2213-77	55
100 mH	PC-2616-77	150
1 H	PC-3019-77	420

SWITCH POSITION	1	2	3	4	5	6	7	8
FULL-SCALE INDICATION	2 nF	20 nF	200 nF	2 µF	2 mH	20 mH	200 mH	2 H
TEST FREQUENCY (kHz)	100	10	1	1	100	10	1	1

Coils and capacitors. Ratiometric meter, easier to use than manual bridges and less expensive than digital types, measures inductances of reasonable Q over the 2-mH-to-2-H range and capacitances over the 2-nF-to-2-µF range to within 1%. Calibration, required for capacitance measurements, is easy and maintains long-term stability.

where R is the dc resistance of L_x, f is the test frequency, and e is the display indication divided by 1,000 and with the decimal point disregarded. Because f is varied appropriately with range and the Q of L_{ref} is greater than 100 at 1 kilohertz—coils are hand-wound on Amidon pot cores using the largest-diameter wire possible (see table)—the equation given above reduces to $L_x = L_{ref}e$ for almost all practical measurements. For example, the error in measuring a 1-millihenry inductor having a Q of only 0.1 at 1 kHz will be less than 1%.

The concept of measuring capacitance is similar. Potentiometers R_1, R_2, and R_3 are used to cancel out the effect of parasitic capacitance at the converter's input terminals so that the display will read zero with no test capacitor connected. When that is done, the display will read $1,000 C_x/C_{ref}$.

Construction is not critical. The only exception to that is the wiring to the input terminals, which should be kept reasonably short.

The calibration procedure for the circuit is straightforward. S_1 is set to 2 microfarads full scale and R_1 is adjusted for a zero display reading. Then S_1 is placed in the 20-nanofarad full-scale position and R_2 adjusted for a zero reading. Finally, the switch is set in the 2-nF full-scale position and R_3 adjusted for a zero display reading. In the prototype tested, no readjustment was necessary over a nine-month period of normal use, and accuracy was maintained to within 1%. □

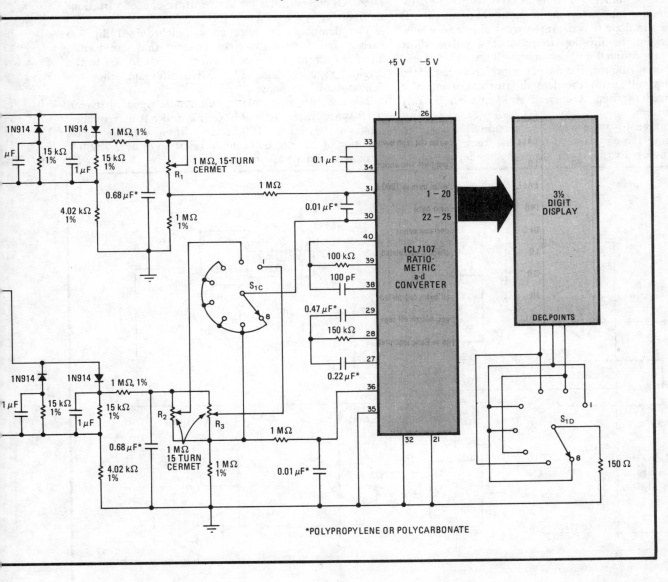

*POLYPROPYLENE OR POLYCARBONATE

Charge-balancing modulator aids analog-signal isolation

by Tadeusz Goszczynski and Jerzy Harasimowicz
Industrial Institute of Automation and Measurements, Warsaw, Poland

For engineers trying to solve ground loop problems in industrial instrumentation, here is a novel and inexpensive isolation circuit for analog signals. It employs a voltage–to–pulse-width modulator to convert analog signals into digital ones so that the job can be handled easily by low-cost opto-isolators. This is done by using a clock-synchronized charge-balancing scheme to economically achieve an accuracy of within 0.01%.

The charge-balancing modulator consists of an operational-amplifier integrator on the input that feeds the D input of a flip-flop. A constant-current sink and switch are driven by the flip-flop to produce a pulse whose width is proportional to the input voltage. This signal feeds the opto-isolator, the output of which is converted back into a voltage by the demodulator consisting of a synchronized flip-flop, a current sink, and an op-amp low-pass filter.

The voltage–to–pulse-width conversion is facilitated by switching the constant-current sink from the output of the flip-flop to the input summing mode of the op amp. Initially, the current switch is open, so that when the input voltage is applied, a negative-going ramp is produced at the integrator's output. When this voltage passes the flip-flop's input threshold voltage, it changes state synchronously with the next clock pulse, thereby closing the current switch. This action causes the reference current (which is always greater than the maximum input current) to be subtracted from the integrator's input current, producing a negative-going ramp at its output that eventually causes the flip-flop to toggle again. The time between toggles is proportional to the input voltage, and a transistor converts that time into a corresponding pulse width that drives the opto-isolator.

The current reference is actually a voltage-reference diode, D_1, and a resistor, R_1, that uses the fact that the integrator summing node is at virtual ground (0 volts) thus making the reference current equal to V_{REF}/R_1. Diode D_3 compensates for temperature-caused variations in diode D_2.

The demodulator relies on a synchronized flip-flop (driven from the same clock source) that can switch another current source on to charge capacitor C_1 to the original input voltage. The active filter smoothes the demodulator's response.

The analog-signal isolator can handle signals between ±10 v accurately to within 0.01% and has a frequency range of 0 (dc) to 100 hertz with a common-mode rejection of 100 decibels and an isolation of over 2,500 v dc between inputs and outputs. □

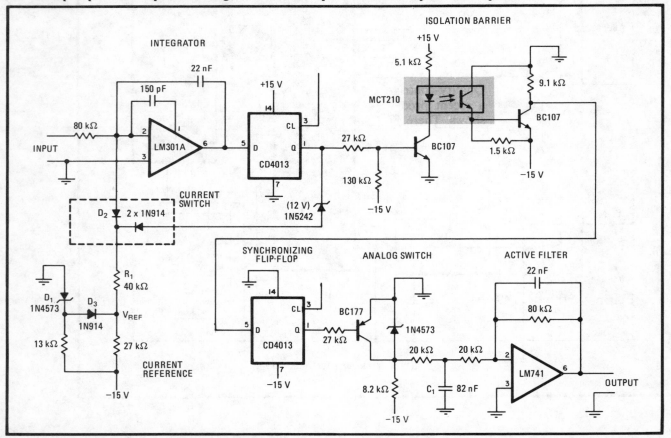

1. Analog-signal isolator. Input voltages are converted into proportional pulse widths that are fed to an inexpensive opto-isolator. The pulse is then converted back into a voltage that tracks the input voltage accurately to within 0.01%. The circuit uses a minimum of precision parts.

CONTROL

Thermocouple simplifies temperature controller

by V. J. H. Chiu
National Research Council, Division of Chemistry, Ottawa, Canada

Virtually all the designs for low-noise, high-temperature controllers of the type that use zero-crossing switches have thermistors in the sensing circuit—an impractical configuration in many cases because of the size requirements and availability of the thermistor itself. To overcome these inconveniences, this simple circuit substitutes an ordinary thermocouple for the thermistor, yet works as well as a thermistor-based one—for instance, it controls the environmental (furnace) temperature from room temperature to 1,100°C to within ±2%.

In general operation, the furnace is heated from the ac line through a triac, triac driver A_1, and the CA3079 zero-voltage switch A_2. The CA3079, in turn, switches on when the output differential from the thermocouple drops below a value corresponding to a given furnace temperature. Switching occurs because the amplified thermocouple voltage, V_T, at the output of A_3 falls below the user-preset reference potential, V_R, at the input to A_4. Note that in addition, the CA3079 must be biased so that potential V_{13} is initially less than the comparator's output, V_9, in order that the circuit containing R_L of the furnace will be completed and current will flow when the furnace is cold.

The thermocouple voltage is linearly proportional over its entire range to the temperature in the furnace; consequently, if potentiometer R_1 is linear, it can be directly calibrated in terms of temperature. For optimum switching, the voltage V_{13} should be set at half of the LM324's supply voltage.

As for cost, the prototype circuit was built for an outlay of less than $20. □

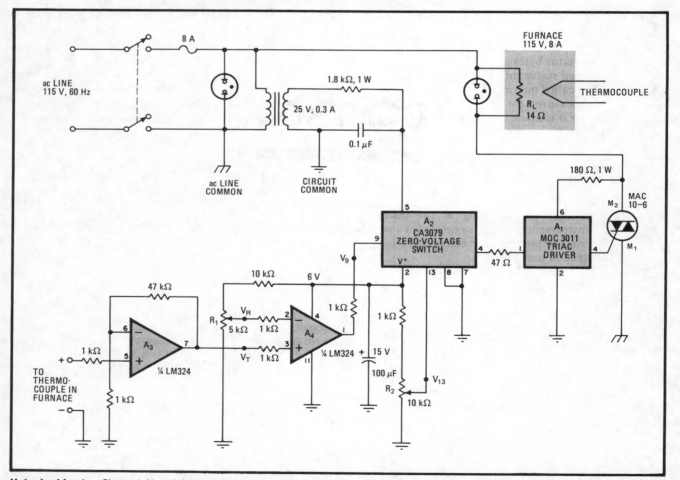

Hot-wired heater. Chromel-Alumel thermocouple eases design of zero-crossing–switched temperature controllers. Potentiometers R_1–R_2 set the reference voltage for switching on furnace from CA3079 switch without the need for setting up a complicated reference scheme. Linear response makes it easy to calibrate R_1 as a direct function of desired temperature. Circuit works to 1,100°C, is accurate to within ±2%.

Lamp dimmer fades
in equiluminous steps

by Mark E. Patton
Sanders Associates, Nashua, N. H.

This programmable light dimmer will serve particularly well as an intensity-control source for vision response testing and in theatrical lighting systems, where it can provide, as perceived by the human eye, a virtually linearly stepped increase or decrease in luminous output (the Munsell curve).[1] Using readily available chips, it can be built for less than $20.

In operation, a triac-driven lamp is triggered by the 60-hertz line input once during each half cycle, at a point determined by an eight-input binary-coded decimal control word derived from a microprocessor or a thumbwheel switch. Thus the lamp brightness may be easily selected and accurately maintained, or alternatively, it can be gradually diminished or increased as desired.

As shown, the LM324, biased to operate from a 5-volt dc supply, works as a comparator to provide 60-Hz square-wave pulses to the CD4046 phase-locked loop and as a buffer to suppress line transients. The PLL and the 4029 up-down counters working together act to

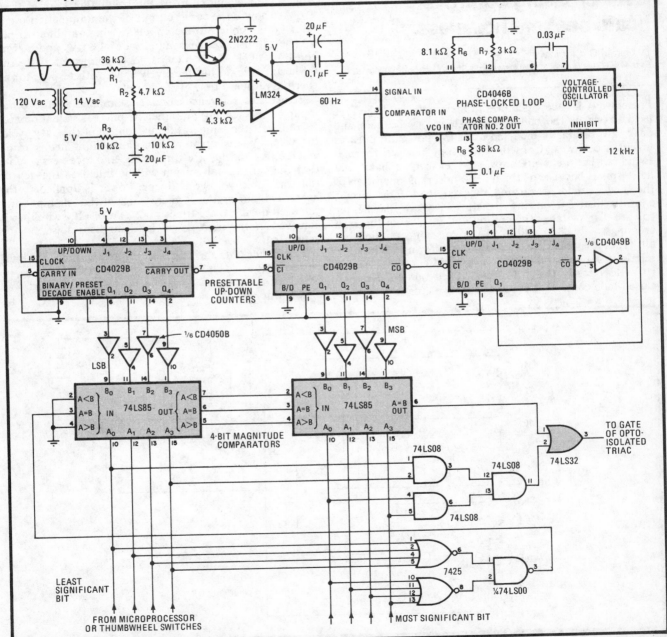

Linear lighting. Programmable lamp dimmer can provide intensity increments and decrements in near-linear steps (as perceived by human eye), virtually meeting Munsell curve specifications. BCD control word, derived from microprocessor, sets switching point on 60-Hz line input.

multiply the line input by 200, so that the counters decrement from 99 toward 0 at a 12-kilohertz rate. This rate permits the selection of $12,000/(60 \times 2) = 100$ brightness levels.

Meanwhile the two-digit BCD control word is introduced to the 74LS85 4-bit magnitude comparators, where it is compared with the output of the counters. When the line-synchronized output of the counter becomes equal to the control word, the opto-isolated triac, which is connected to the ac line, is fired.

The triac should be heavily filtered to prevent switching noise on the line from reaching the logic circuitry. Also, to increase circuit stability near the zero and maximum-voltage switching points of the 60-Hz input signal, the outputs of the 74LS85s are gated for a loaded BCD code of 99 and are disabled for a code of 0. □

References
1. GTE Sylvania, GTE Sylvania Lighting Handbook, 5th ed., 1974.

Zero-crossing controller heats beakers noiselessly

by Gerald D. Clubine
East Texas State University, Fine Instruments Shop, Commerce, Texas

Present-day low-cost heater/dimmer controls of the type used to warm the contents of laboratory beakers and flasks are primarily modeled after the hot-plate burners in electric stoves. Consequently, they feature thermal switches that generate unwanted electronic hash and noise spikes because of the make-and-break operation of the device under a varying thermal load. This circuit controls heat by varying the duty cycle of the heater coil—but it switches the coil on and off during the zero crossings of the 115-volt ac power line, thus eliminating all types of noise. In addition to offering solid-state reliability, it costs no more than the old hot plate. And it is far less costly than the widely used but unnecessary closed-loop controls that use a sensing element.

The heart of the circuit is the CA3059 zero-crossing trigger, A_1, which controls the solid-state switch, triac Q_2. As shown, the ramp output of the unijunction oscillator Q_1 is applied to the on/off sensing amplifier at pin 9. The ramp has a peak amplitude of $\frac{2}{3}$ V_c and a time constant of $R_7 C_3$, which is long compared with the 60-hertz line rate but relatively short with respect to the thermal response time of the hot plate.

A user-set reference voltage is applied to the other input of the sensing amplifier at pin 13. Potentiometer R_2 thus sets the temperature by control of the duty cycle, for when V_{ref} is greater than the instantaneous ramp voltage, A_1 and Q_2 are turned off, and vice versa. Note that the control calibration will be linear to the degree that the ramp voltage is linear. Power is applied to the heater coil during the zero crossings of the line input and removed during these times, too; as a result, switching is achieved at the zero power level, and no noise can be generated.

The choice of the triac will depend upon the amount of current required by the heater coil. In this case, a SC151B has been used, as the heater coil demand was only 6 amperes. □

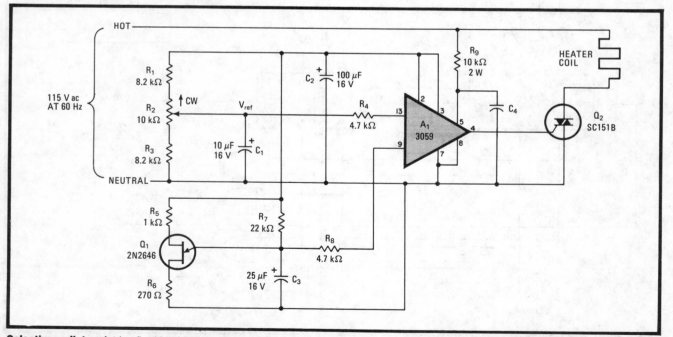

Selective radiator. A triac fired by this controller applies power to and removes power from heater coil of hot plate during zero crossings of the 115-V ac power line, thus eliminating unwanted electrical hash and noise formerly caused by mechanical-type thermal switches. User sets temperature with duty-cycle control R_2, which turns on A_1 and triac when V_{ref} is less than the instantaneous ramp output of oscillator Q_1.

One-chip tachometer simplifies motor controller

by Henrique Sarmento Malvar
Department of Electrical Engineering, University of Brazilia, Brazil

Setting and stabilizing the angular velocity of a dc motor by means of a charge pump and a servoamplifier, one-chip tachometers such as National Semiconductor's LM2917 serve well as a simple but elegant motor-speed controller. Such an arrangement is preferable to the widely used scheme in which both positive and negative feedback is utilized to keep the motor's back electromotive force, and thus its speed, constant by generating a voltage that is proportional to a given load.

As shown in the figure, a magnetic pickup coil detects the angular velocity of a motor-driven flywheel and feeds the low-amplitude pulses, whose frequency is proportional to the motor speed, to the LM2917's charge pump. As a result, the pump generates a current, I_1, whose average value is directly proportional to the input frequency.

The operational amplifier that follows compares this voltage to a user-set reference and, through power transistor Q_1, generates a voltage for the motor's armature of $V_A = (R_2/R_1)(V_{ref} - I_1 R_1)$. Thus, potentiometer R_6 sets the motor's speed, for when $V_1 > V_{ref}$, voltage V_A decreases, and vice versa.

In this application, the gain of the operational amplifier, determined by resistors R_1 and R_2, has been set at approximately 150. The greater the gain, the lower the variation of motor speed with changes in load resistance. However, the setting of very high gains should be avoided, because there will be a reduction in the gain and phase margins—that is to say, a loss of stability in the feedback control loop.

As for the selection of other components to meet any particular application, note that capacitor C_1 serves a double purpose: it integrates pulsed current I_1, thereby performing a smoothing function, and it sets a low-frequency pole for the amplifier, thereby ensuring stability. C_2 sets the conversion factor of the tachometer and should be increased for low-speed motors. R_3 minimizes the offset due to the amplifier's bias currents at pins 4 and 10. Finally, C_3 functions as a noise filter.

As seen, the LM2917's tachometer conversion factor will be almost independent of its supply voltage, as a consequence of the zener diode connected at the device's supply port. The supply voltage should not fall outside the range of 10 to 15 volts, however. □

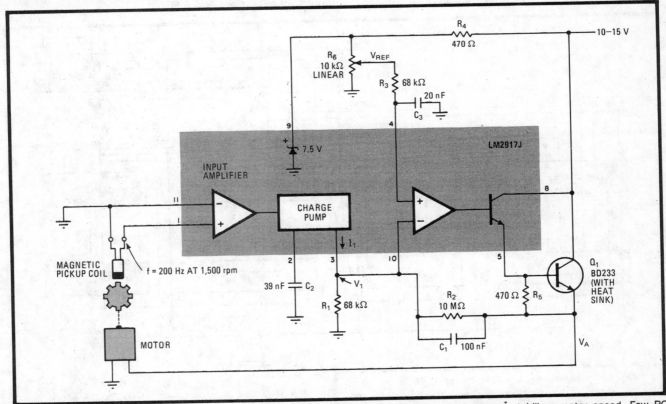

Setting speed. LM2917J tachometer, which is basically a frequency-to-voltage converter, sets and stabilizes motor speed. Few RC components are required, thereby simplifying circuitry. Power transistor Q_1 is the only external active element needed.

On/off timer maintains precision over wide range

by Alfred C. Pinchak, *Cleveland Metropolitan General Hospital, Department of Anesthesiology, Cleveland, Ohio*

This circuit improves in several ways upon available designs for timers whose on and off periods are selectable. Specifically, it provides more precise control of those periods, a wider range over which the time base can be set, and a more flexible range that the supply potentials may assume. The circuit, which is implemented mostly in complementary-MOS, draws a maximum of 20 milliamperes at 5 volts, including relay power.

As shown, the HD4702 bit-rate generators, A_1 and A_2, provide a crystal-controlled clock signal for the ICM7240 timer-counter chips, A_3–A_6. Clock periods of from approximately 100 microseconds to 4 seconds are ordered by A_1 and A_2. The timer-counter outputs are wire-ORed together and are weighted in a binary fashion, with each position increasing in a 1, 2, 4, . . . 32,768 sequence. Thus by adjusting each dip switch appropriately, the on and off periods of the output signal can be independently set over the range $T_c < T_{on} < 65,536T_c$, where T_c is the clock period and $T_{on} = T_{off}$.

A_3 and A_4 form a one-shot that determines the off (low) period. Similarly, one-shot pair A_5–A_6 sets the on (high) period. Because the output of each one-shot (points A and B) are tied back to its own reset terminal and also to the trigger port of the other one-shot pair, the output at A is inverted with respect to B.

The 4702 time-base generators provide a direct clock signal for A_3 and A_5, with A_4 and A_6 driven by pins 8 of A_3 and A_5, respectively. A_3 and A_5, through transistors Q_1 and Q_2, also are part of the wired-OR network. Thus, all portions of each timer chip can be utilized to set the high and low periods. This feature is in contrast to previously published designs that cascade 2240 timers but restrict the T_{off} time to an integral multiple of $128T_c$.

Unfortunately, because of the wired-OR arrangement, the amplitude of the output signals at points A and B does not increase proportionally with supply voltage. In order to increase the effective range of the supply voltage, Q_3 is added to provide a level-shifting function. This extends the maximum supply voltage range from approximately 5.5 to 12 v.

The minimum supply voltage for an electronic output is approximately 3.8 v. However, the actual minimum voltage in cases where a relay is used will depend on the particular relay chosen. In this case, the minimum supply voltage was about 4.6 v. □

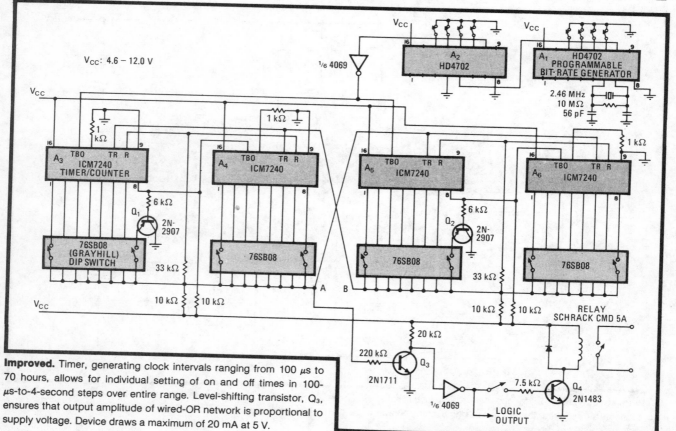

Improved. Timer, generating clock intervals ranging from 100 μs to 70 hours, allows for individual setting of on and off times in 100-μs-to-4-second steps over entire range. Level-shifting transistor, Q_3, ensures that output amplitude of wired-OR network is proportional to supply voltage. Device draws a maximum of 20 mA at 5 V.

Voltage-controlled resistance switches over preset limits

by Chris Tocci
Halifax, Mass.

Using two field-effect transistors as switches, this voltage-controlled resistor network can order up any value of resistance between two preselected limits. It is unlike other circuits in that it does not employ the drain-to-source resistance of matched FETs, whose R_{ds} characteristics are usually proportional to a control voltage. As for circuit linearity, it will far exceed that of conventional networks using a single FET in various feedback configurations.[1]

In operation, oscillator A_1–A_2 generates a 0-to-10-volt triangle wave at 100 kilohertz, which is then compared with the control signal, V_c, at A_3. During the time that the control exceeds switching voltage V_T, FET Q_1 is turned on, and resistor R_1 is placed across resistance R_{out} (disregarding the R_{ds} of Q_1). At all other times, FET Q_2 is on and resistor R_2 is placed across R_{out}. Thus R_{out} is equal to an average value proportional to the time each resistor is placed across the output terminals, with

the actual resistance given by $R_{out} = (R_1 - R_2)V_c/10 + R_2$, for $R_1 > R_2$. This relationship will hold provided any potential applied to the R_{out} port from an external device is less in magnitude than the supply voltages; that any signal processing at R_{out} be done at a frequency at least one decade below the 100-kHz switching frequency; and that the upper and lower resistance limits, R_1 and R_2, are much greater than the on-resistance of Q_1 and Q_2, respectively.

Potentiometer R_{11} adjusts the baseline of V_T to zero so that with $V_c = 0$, $R_{out}n = R_2$, where n is a constant. Further calibration can be carried out by trimming R_1 and R_2 to precise values.

This circuit is readily adapted to many applications, such as a one-quadrant multiplier. This is achieved by connecting a voltage-controlled current source into the R_{out} port to build a dc-shift amplitude modulator whose carrier frequency is the switching frequency. The audio information or data is taken from V_c, but with the signal offset by 5 volts. Thus the dynamic range of the circuit will be 10 v. □

References
1. Thomas L. Clarke, "FET pair and op amp linearize voltage-controlled resistor," *Electronics*, April 28, 1977, p. 111.

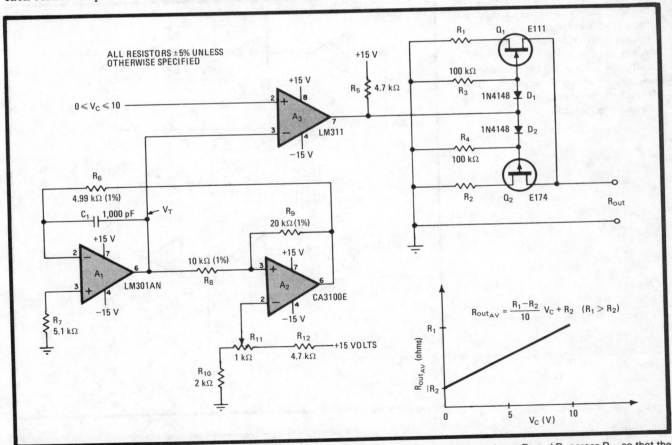

Ohmic linearization. FET switches in voltage-controlled resistor network place maximum-minimum resistors R_1 and R_2 across R_{out} so that the resistance is proportional to the average time each is across output port. Switching technique ensures piecewise-linear operation. This circuit lends itself to many applications, such as a-m modulator, by placing voltage-controlled current source across R_{out}.

Divider sets tuning limits of C-MOS oscillator

by Henno Normet
Diversified Electronics Inc., Leesburg, Fla.

Useful as it is, the square-wave RC oscillator implemented in complementary-MOS has one shortcoming—setting its maximum and minimum frequencies of oscillation independently while also maintaining accuracy is extremely difficult. By placing a voltage divider in the feedback loop of the conventional three-gate circuit, however, a one-time trimming adjustment can accurately set the maximum and minimum frequency excursion and will force the ratio of the upper to the lower limit of oscillation to approach a value virtually determined by the resistors used in the same divider.

The standard RC oscillator generates a frequency of $f \approx 0.482/R_1C$, where $R_1 = R_2$, as shown in (a). Generally, it is not practical or economical to use a variable capacitor for C. A potentiometer could be substituted for R_1 to tune the frequency, but slight differences in integrated-circuit parameters will preclude predicting the maximum and minimum frequencies of oscillation with any degree of accuracy for a particular chip. The only other method for setting the upper and lower frequency limits is to parallel several capacitors across C, a tedious procedure at best.

Alternatively, R_1 can be a potentiometer that is placed virtually in parallel with voltage divider R_4–R_5 through C (b). In this way, capacitor C is no longer charged from the fixed-voltage output of the middle gate in (a), but from the voltage divider across the output. R_1 is thus used to change the circuit's time constant without affecting the potential that is applied to C.

The upper and lower limits of oscillation are determined by the position of R_4's wiper arm and by the values of R_4 and R_5. With the tap at point A, the circuit will oscillate at a frequency given by $f = 1/2.2R_1C$. With the wiper at point B, the frequency will be $f = 1/1.39R_1C$. The frequency ratio to be expected is thus $2.2/1.39 = 1.6$. The actual frequency change measured with the particular chip used for breadboarding was 56%, which is thus very close to the intended value. The ratio will increase as R_4 is made larger with respect to R_5.

The circuit has only one small disadvantage—the load presented by R_4 and R_5 does increase the power-supply drain by approximately 0.5 milliampere. ☐

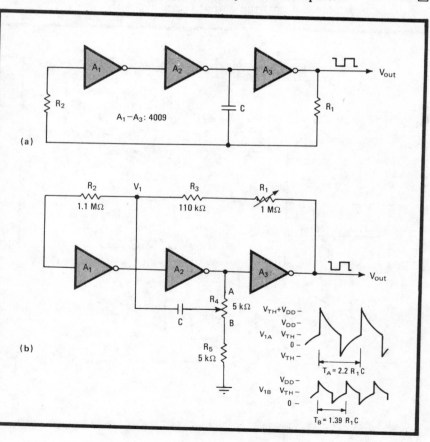

Calibrate. IC anomalies, inherent circuit imbalance, and the expense of making C variable preclude setting upper and lower oscillation limits of typical RC oscillator (a) with any accuracy. Placing R_1 virtually in parallel with voltage divider (b) through C gives circuit one-knob frequency control, with upper-to-lower oscillation ratio in effect determined by R_4 and R_5.

Multiplier increases resolution of standard shaft encoders

by Frank Amthor
School of Optometry, University of Alabama, Birmingham

The resolution that can be attained by two-channel shaft encoders of the type used in speed controllers and optical-positioning devices may be increased by employing a digital frequency multiplier to derive a proportionally greater number of pulses from its TTL-compatible outputs. In this way, an up/down counter, which is normally driven by the encoder in these applications, can position the shaft more accurately and is more responsive to changes in speed and direction. Only two one-shot multivibrators and several logic gates are needed for the multiplier circuitry.

The circuit works well with a typical encoder such as the Digipot (manufactured by Sensor Technology Inc., Chatsworth, Calif.). In this case, the 128 square waves that are generated per channel for each shaft revolution (with output from the other channel in quadrature) are transformed to 512 bits per cycle.

When the shaft rotates in a clockwise direction, the output from port A of the encoder always leads the output from port B by 90°, and the logic will generate pulses only to the up input of the counter on both edges of both channel outputs. Thus, four pulses per square wave are generated. Rotation speed is limited by the duration time of the positive-edge–triggered one-shots, which should be kept to a few microseconds or less. Note that both the count-up and the count-down inputs of the counter are normally held high.

On the other hand, when the shaft's rotation is in a counterclockwise direction, the output of B leads that of A by 90°. In this case, four pulses per square wave are presented to the down input of the counter. □

Increments. Pulse multiplier yields 512 count-up or -down bits for 128 square-wave cycles (one revolution) from two-channel shaft encoder, for more resolution in speed controllers and optical positioning systems. Eliminating tinted area yields 256 bits per revolution.

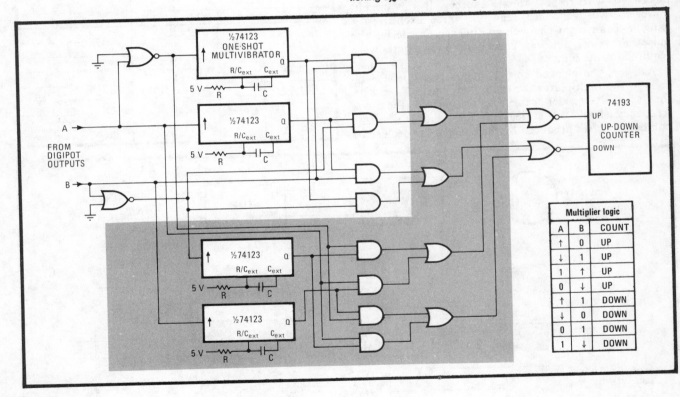

Multiplier logic		
A	B	COUNT
↑	0	UP
↓	1	UP
1	↑	UP
0	↓	UP
↑	1	DOWN
↓	0	DOWN
0	1	DOWN
1	↓	DOWN

Simplified multiplier improves standard shaft encoder

by Michael M. Butler
Minneapolis, Minn.

The pulse multiplier proposed by Amthor [*Electronics*, Sept. 11, p. 139] for increasing the resolution of a standard shaft encoder may be simplified, and improved as well, with this low-power circuit. Using only three complementary-MOS chips to derive a proportionally greater number of pulses from the encoder's output for a positioning up/down counter, it is relatively insensitive to encoder phase errors, uses no temperamental one-shots, and can detect the occurrence of illegal transition states generated by the encoder or circuit. It will serve well in electrically noisy industrial environments.

As in Amthor's circuit, the multiplier (a) used to drive the counter produces four pulses for each square-wave input of the two-phase encoder, whose outputs are displaced 90° with respect to one another. In this circuit, however, two 4-bit shift registers, three exclusive-OR gates, and an eight-channel multiplexer (b) derive the pulses. Previously four one-shots and 16 logic gates were required for the same task.

As seen, the clocked shift registers generate a 4-bit code to the multiplexer for each clock cycle. To ensure that no shaft-encoder transitions are missed, the clock frequency should be at least 8 NS, where N is the number of pulses produced by the encoder for each shaft revolution and S is the maximum speed, in revolutions per second, to be expected. A clock frequency of 1 megahertz or less is recommended for optimum circuit operation.

The code is symmetrical, and so only three exclusive-OR gates are required to fold the data into 3 bits. These bits are then applied to the control ports of the three-input multiplexer, which will generate the truth table shown. □

		MULTIPLIER LOGIC				
A	B	Multiplexer code				Count
		Old A	New A	Old B	New B	
0	0	0	0	0	0	no change
0	↑	0	0	0	1	down
0	↓	0	0	1	0	up
0	1	0	0	1	1	no change
↑	0	0	1	0	0	up
↑	↑	0	1	0	1	error
↑	↓	0	1	1	0	error
↑	1	0	1	1	1	down
↓	0	1	0	0	0	down
↓	↑	1	0	0	1	error
↓	↓	1	0	1	0	error
↓	1	1	0	1	1	up
1	0	1	1	0	0	no change
1	↑	1	1	0	1	up
1	↓	1	1	1	0	down
1	1	1	1	1	1	no change

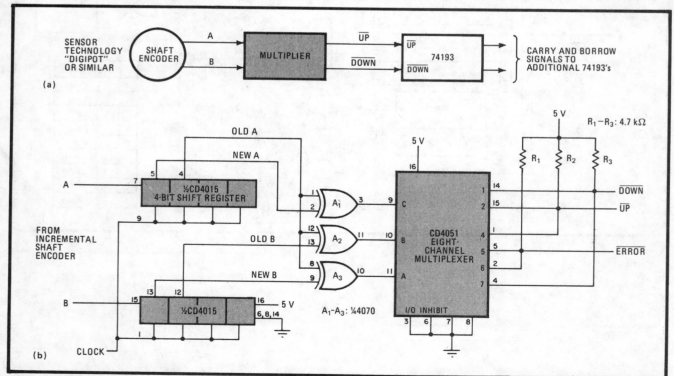

Accretion. Requiring only three chips, pulse multiplier gives better resolution to optical positioning systems that are driven by a shaft encoder. Low-power circuit is relatively insensitive to encoder phase errors. Stability is high because no one-shot multivibrators are used.

Fewer parts resolve shaft encoder data

by Bill McClelland
Digicomp, Darien, Conn.

This circuit achieves the same resolution as the circuit proposed by Amthor [*Electronics*, Sept. 11, 1980, p. 139] but requires only one integrated circuit, instead of seven, and half the number of discrete components.

A standard shaft encoder has two ports, A and B, each generating a square wave as the shaft encoder is turned. The square wave from port A will either lead or follow port B's square wave by 90°, depending on the direction of the rotation of the encoder (a).

To get the maximum resolution out of the shaft encoder, every change of state for both A and B must be counted. Depending on the direction of rotation of the shaft encoder, the counter will count up or down. By exclusive-NOR-ing square waves A and B at gate A_2, a square wave that changes state whenever there is a change of state of either A or B can be obtained. The output of exclusive-NOR gate A_3 is high except when a change of state at gate A_2 occurs. Whenever the output of gate A_2 changes state, the two inputs of gate A_3 will be of opposite state for a time determined by R_2 and C_2, generating a short, low-going pulse. By using complementary-MOS exclusive-NOR gates, the pulse at the output of gate A_3 will have about the same duration for both the positive and negative transitions of gate A_2. The trailing edge of this pulse is used to clock the counter, allowing setup time for the up-down control (b).

The up-down control is generated by R_1, C_1, and gate A_1. R_1 and C_1 act as a latch, holding the value of B prior to a change of state of A or B during the clock pulse at gate A_3. Exclusive-NOR-ing the value of A just after a change of state in A or B, with the value of B set just prior to a change of state of A or B, achieves the proper up-down control.

The operation of gate 1 can be demonstrated as follows: square waves A and B are out of phase with each other by 90°. Adding −90° to B would change the phase shift to 0° or −180°, depending on the direction of rotation of the shaft encoder.

As a result, the output of exclusive-NOR gate A_1 would be high when A and B are in phase and low when A and B are 180° out of phase. Since the only concern is the output of gate A_1 when the counter is clocked, R_1 and C_1 give enough time lag to phase-shift B for the duration of the clock pulse at gate A_3. For this reason the time constant R_1C_1 is greater than R_2C_2.

The polarity of the up-down control may be inverted by swapping the A and B wires or by using the fourth exclusive-NOR gate in the 4077 integrated circuit as a selectable inverter-buffer. If the clock signal needs to be inverted for another type of counter, the entire 4077 exclusive-NOR–gate package can be changed to a 4070 exclusive-OR package. If standard C-MOS rise and fall times at the A and B inputs cannot be guaranteed, it becomes necessary to buffer the A and B inputs with a Schmitt trigger, such as a 74C914. □

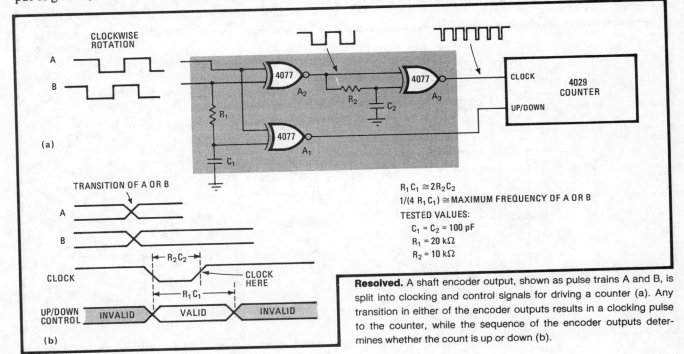

$R_1 C_1 \cong 2R_2C_2$

$1/(4\,R_1C_1) \cong$ MAXIMUM FREQUENCY OF A OR B

TESTED VALUES:
$C_1 = C_2 = 100$ pF
$R_1 = 20$ kΩ
$R_2 = 10$ kΩ

Resolved. A shaft encoder output, shown as pulse trains A and B, is split into clocking and control signals for driving a counter (a). Any transition in either of the encoder outputs results in a clocking pulse to the counter, while the sequence of the encoder outputs determines whether the count is up or down (b).

Train speed controller ignores track resistance

by Stephen H. Burns
U. S. Naval Academy, Electrical Engineering Department, Annapolis, Md.

Because it keeps the voltage applied to any universal motor constant and independent of line resistance for a given line voltage, this circuit will be especially attractive for use with model trains, for which it will maintain speed independently of the resistive joints in the tracks. No modification of the speed-controlling transformer used with the trains is required.

This circuit rides within or near the locomotive and is inserted in the electrical path between the motor and the track pickup and return. Thus it is necessary to connect the ac input of this circuit to the track pickup and frame of the locomotive and to connect the dc output of the circuit across the motor windings. This way the circuit develops a constant average voltage across the motor for a given transformer setting.

This is accomplished with a four-section circuit, with block A containing the supply for powering the unit. Blocks B and C derive a gate pulse inversely proportional to the magnitude of the input voltage and a control

Rail tamer. Controller keeps driving voltage to model trains independent of the resistance in the track joints. Output voltage is derived from pulses whose widths are inversely proportional to the ac input, generated at zero crossings so that load variations on the line are disregarded. Timing diagram details the operation.

voltage proportional to the input signal so that motor speed can be set. Block D handles the power-switching function.

Diode bridge B_1, diodes D_1 and D_2, capacitor C_1, and Norton amplifier A_1 constitute block A, which is actually a three-stage supply. B_1 provides full-wave rectified dc for power stage Q_3 and D_1 and C_1 extract and filter power for A_1–A_4. Zener diode D_2 and A_1 provide a regulated 5 volts for current source Q_1 and to establish a switching reference voltage for amplifier A_2.

In operation, B_1 and Q_3 electrically disconnect the motor from the power source near each zero crossing of the ac input. At this time, a pulse is developed at the output of A_2, its width equal to $P = 2V_r/\omega V_i$, where V_r is the switching reference voltage, ω is 120π radians/sec,

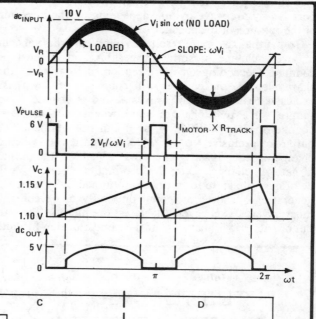

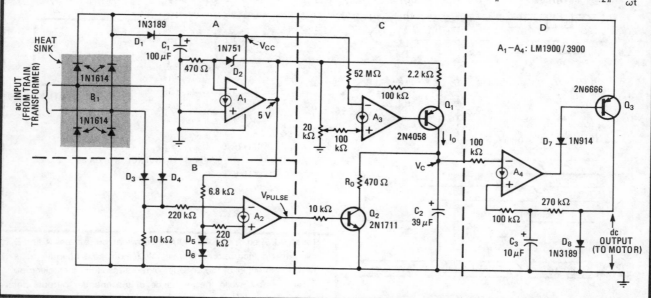

and V_i is the input voltage (see timing diagram). Note that by sampling near the zero crossings, the width of the pulse is made independent of the load on the ac line. One sense diode, D_3 or D_4, reference diodes D_5 and D_6, and one bridge diode set the switching threshold, V_r. This reference voltage is thus equal to four diode drops, or approximately 2 V.

A_3, Q_1, and Q_2 develop from the pulse a control voltage, V_c, whose average value can be expressed as $V_c = \pi I_o R_o V_i / (2V_r)$. A_3 and Q_1 constitute a 0.3-milliampere (I_o) constant-current source. A total resistance of 52 megohms placed in series between V_{cc} and the inverting input of A_3 was found best to compensate for changes in I_o versus supply variations.

The power switching stage includes feedback capacitor C_3, amplifier A_4, isolation diode D_7, damper diode D_8, and Q_3. C_2 and C_3 were selected so that Q_3 switches efficiently under all load conditions. Smaller values of C_2 result in more efficient switching but increase output resistance. Larger values of C_3 will result in greater overshooting in response to a transient.

With a source voltage of from 7 to 25 v rms and a load of 10 ohms, the circuit will generate an output of from 3 to 12 v. Increasing the line resistance from 0 to 4 Ω will cause a typical change in output voltage of only 0.1 v for a line drop of several volts. □

Power-up relays prevent meter from pinning

by Michael Bozoian
Ann Arbor, Mich.

Sensitive microammeters with d'Arsonval movements are still manufactured and used widely today, but surprisingly, there has been little attempt to correct one defect in their design—they are still very prone to pointer damage from input-signal overload and turn-on/turn-off transients. Although ways of protecting the meter movement from input signals of excessive magnitude are well known and universally applied, no convenient means of preventing the pointer from slamming against the full-scale stop during power-up or power-off conditions has so far been introduced or suggested in the literature. However, the problem may be easily solved by the use of a 555 timer and two relays to place a protective shunt across the meter during these periods.

Basically, the 555 timer closes reed relay A's normally open contacts on power up and puts shunt resistor R across the meter for 5 or 6 seconds until the turn-on transients have subsided, as shown in the figure. The normally closed contacts of relay B are also opened at this time.

On power-down, relay B reintroduces the shunt to protect the meter from turn-off transients. Such a scheme is more effective than placing a diode across the meter, as is often done and is much more elegant and less bothersome than manually activating an auxiliary mechanical switch for placing R across the meter each time it is used.

R has been selected for a meter movement having a full-scale output of 200 microamperes and an internal resistance of 1,400 ohms. The complete circuit may be mounted on a 2-by-2¼-inch printed-circuit board. The only design precaution is to ensure that relay B is energized from a source that has a fast decay time during power-off conditions. Here, the voltage has been tapped from the meter's power-supply rectifier. □

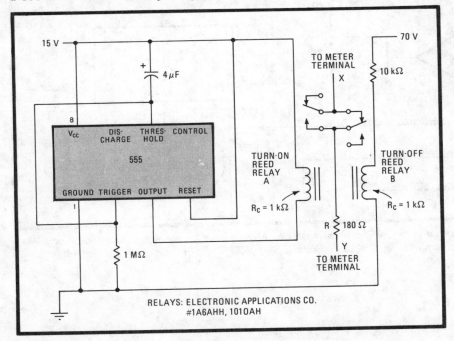

Shunted. Reed relays and 555 timer prevent d'Arsonval movement from slamming against microammeter's full-scale stop during power-up and power-down conditions by introducing shunt resistor across meter terminals until transients die out. Method does not degrade meter's accuracy or its transient response to input signals.

47

Opto-isolated line monitor provides fail-safe control

by Eric G. Breeze and Earl V. Cole
General Instrument Corp., Optoelectronics Division, Palo Alto, Calif.

Because of the degree of isolation they provide, optically coupled ac-line monitors serve well as a small, reliable low-power interface in ac-to-dc control applications, where status information of the ac line is crucial. When a type is used that is TTL- and microprocessor-compatible—like the MID400, which performs the basic monitoring function on a single chip—a circuit can be built that ensures fail-safe control under the most difficult monitoring assignments. And when combined with a 555 timer, the monitor will have improved drive capability, more precise control of the turn-on and turn-off delay times, and better noise immunity than units that are typically available.

As shown in Fig. 1, two gallium arsenide infrared-light–emitting diodes connected back to back and optically coupled to an integrated photodiode and high-gain amplifier make up the MID400, which is encased in an eight-pin dual in-line package. In operation, each LED conducts on alternate half cycles of the ac-input waveform, together producing 120 pulses of light per second. Thus the photodiode periodically conducts, causing the amplifier to drive the npn transistor at the output to its

on state. As the amplifier's switching time has been designed to be slow, it will not respond to an absence of input voltage lasting a few milliseconds; therefore it will not respond to the short zero-crossing period that occurs each half cycle.

The MID400 operates in one of two basic modes: saturated or unsaturated. It operates in the saturated mode when the input signal is above the minimum required current of 4 milliamperes root mean square and the photodiode pulses keep the output of the MID400 low. It operates in the unsaturated mode if the input current drops below 4 mA rms. Under these conditions, a train of pulses will appear at the output. In this way, a clean clock generator, devoid of power-line transients because it is isolated, may be realized.

If the input current drops below 0.15 mA, the device turns off. This causes the output of the MID400 to remain high.

Adding an external capacitor, C, to pin 7 of the device produces a time-delay circuit. The amount of delay on power-up is short because the photodiode has a low impedance when conducting. When ac is removed, however, the delay is long because the capacitor must discharge through the leakage resistance of the amplifier and photodiode. The larger the capacitor, the longer the delay.

In lieu of capacitor C, the use of a 555 timer also provides pulse shaping by yielding faster rise and fall times at the output. Here, the 555 is used as a Schmitt trigger with well-defined thresholds, the high state being $\frac{2}{3}$ V_{cc} and the low state being $\frac{1}{3}$ V_{cc}. Besides providing

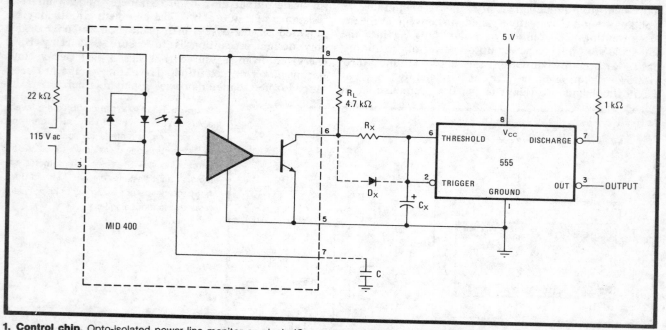

1. Control chip. Opto-isolated power-line monitor on single IC provides hash-free driving signals for ac-to-dc control applications. When united with 555 timer, circuit provides precise control of on and off delay times, improved driving capability, and good noise immunity.

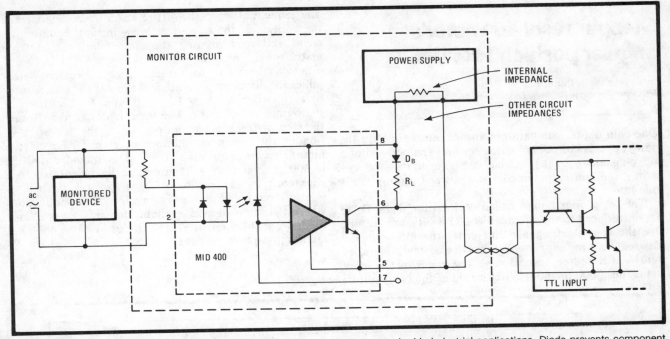

2. Immune. Monitor is easily modified for fail-safe control tasks, such as are required in industrial applications. Diode prevents component failures from creating output glitches. MID400's output circuit design inherently prevents generation of glitches caused by supply anomolies.

noise immunity, use of the 555 also minimizes oscillations that might occur if a TTL device were to drive a minicomputer.

Timing elements R_x and C_x set the delay. With appropriate choice of the time constant, the circuit can be made to respond to, or to ignore, one or more ac input cycles. Diode D_x permits the fast charge and slow discharge of C_x or, if the diode's polarity is reversed, the slow charge and fast discharge of the capacitor. The actual delay time will depend on the operating mode of the MID400.

For industrial, military, or medical applications in which fail-safe operation is important, the circuit's response must also be considered for the cases where either the ac input or the MID400 supply is removed.

Fortunately, the MID400 has been designed so that its output transistor is on (low) only when both the ac input voltage and the supply voltage are present, thus simplifying the problem of providing a valid fail-safe control signal. Consider the case where the MID400 is powered by a separate 5-volt supply and the monitor drives a TTL-compatible interface through a twisted-pair line (Fig. 2). Normally, the inherent truth table of the device will prevent an erroneous output to the TTL interface circuit. Should R_L fall below 1 kilohm for one reason or another, however, and the power supply be off, the TTL input of the minicomputer will appear low because of excessive current flow through R_L. Diode D_B in series with R_L blocks any reverse current, eliminating the problem. □

Stepper resolves motor's angular position to 0.1°

by Jaykumar Sethuram
Electronic Associates Inc., West Long Branch, N. J.

One-chip digital comparators and counters simplify the design of this controller, which resolves the position of a stepping motor to 0.1°. Using complementary-MOS circuitry, the unit is low in cost and power consumption is minimal.

The set of four binary-coded decimal numbers, D_1 to D_4, introduced to the cascaded 40085 4-bit comparators, are the command signals that order the motor to the desired bearing expressed in hundreds, tens, units, or tenths of a degree, respectively. The range of the input set is thus 0000 to 3600. With the aid of the comparators and sequential logic, the 40192 up/down counters track the position of the stepper at every instant, updating its count and thus rotating the motor until its contents match the setting of D_1–D_4.

As can be seen, the sequential logic circuitry determines the direction of rotation of the stepper and counter by monitoring the $A = B$, $A > B$, and $A < B$ outputs of the output comparator. The logic is designed to rotate the stepper from its current position to the desired position in the minimum number of steps. Thus, if the motor's present position is at 5° and the intended position is 300°, the stepper will automatically be rotated in a counterclockwise direction.

The circuit can be easily modified for applications where the input data is available for only a very short time. In such cases, it is only necessary to add input latches to capture the data. □

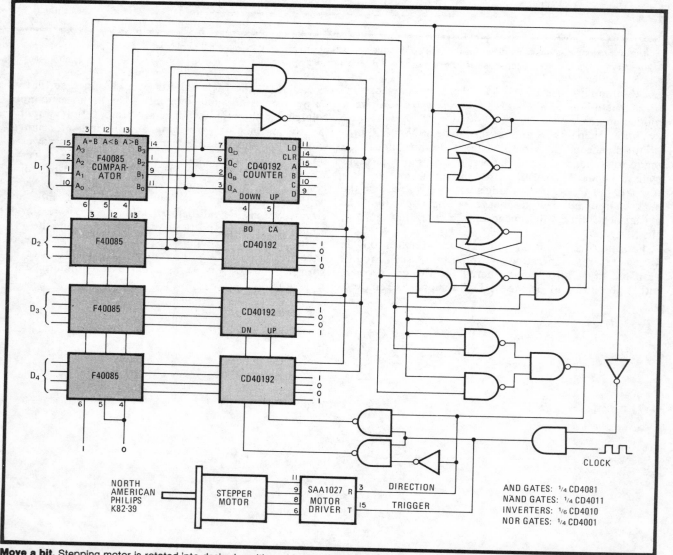

Move a bit. Stepping motor is rotated into desired position with comparators and sequential logic that minimizes the difference between the 4-bit command set D_1–D_4, and the output of the up/down position-tracking counter. Angular position is resolved to 0.1°.

Serial-data interface eases remote use of terminal keyboard

by Robert Nixon
Nixon Engineering Co., San Jose, Calif.

A keyboard that can be detached and operated at a distance from its terminal is often desirable in a computer-based system, but the job of developing the proper cable and connector can be hard and time-consuming. The interconnecting wire count can be reduced to just two leads, however. The trick is to choose a keyboard that generates a serial output for each keystroke and use it with the current-modulating interface shown. A minor modification will adapt the circuit to the RS-232 bus.

Here, the microprocessor-based keyboard is the Micro Switch 103SD24-2, which delivers the serial ASCII data at 110 bits per second. Power to the keyboard, which requires only 5 volts, is provided by the μA7812 voltage regulator. This device also serves as a current limiter, protecting the interface against damage caused by shorts in the connecting cable. A second regulator, the μA7805, smoothes out the small variations in voltage generated by the current modulator.

During the mark states of the data stream, transistor Q_1 is held off because the keyboard output is active—the total current through R_1 and the keyboard is 360 milliamperes, which represents the difference between the supply voltage and the keyboard's optocoupler output stage. During the space interval of the serial data stream, the keyboard output is inactive, and Q_1 is turned on. The total supply current then becomes 610 mA. Diodes D_1 and D_2 allow for the small voltage drop between the Darlington-coupled output of the keyboard, ensuring that Q_1 is switched properly. Capacitors C_1 and C_2 aid in stabilizing the μA7805 regulator during modulation.

The two-state current variation is detected on the receiver side by Q_2, and associated resistors R_3–R_5. During the mark state, the drop across R_3 is about 550 millivolts, which is not enough to turn on the transistor. During the space state, however, the additional current produced will switch on Q_2 and generate a positive voltage level at the output. Note that R_4 and R_5 prevent the transistor from being damaged by a short circuit.

For TTL compatibility, the output signal should be introduced to a Schmitt trigger to eliminate hash and ill-defined switching levels. To interface with the RS-232 bus, it is only necessary to increase R_7's value to 3 kilohms and connect its lower end to −12 V instead of ground. □

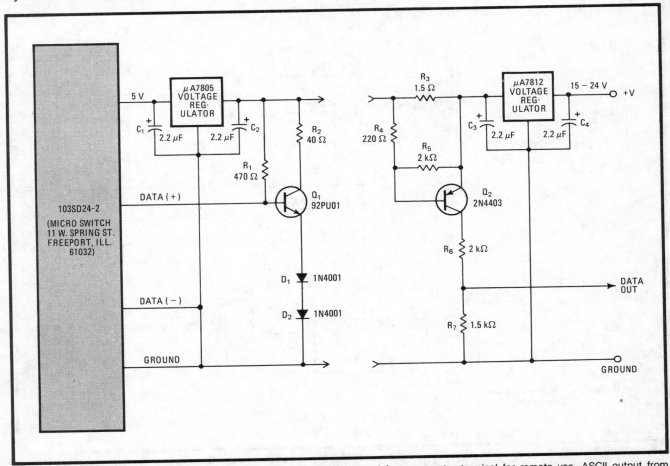

Interim link. Two-wire serial interface makes it simple to remove keyboard from computer terminal for remote use. ASCII output from keyboard is current-modulated by Q_1. Two-state output is recovered by Q_2. Minor modification makes board compatible with RS-232 bus.

One-chip alarm scares auto thieves

by Andrei D. Stoenescu
Bucharest, Rumania

Most of the burglar alarms that have been designed in recent years to discourage automobile thieves contain too many parts (thus raising doubts about their reliability), need special parts, draw too much current, or cost too much. Actually, a circuit that provides the very same features as most alarms now available can be built around only one integrated circuit and a power transistor. Such a circuit is shown here. Its power drain is only 6.2 milliamperes in the idle state, and its cost can be held to under $10.

Once activated by a hidden switch inside the car, the alarm, which uses the LM2900 quad amplifier:
- Will be inhibited for a few seconds to enable the driver and passengers to exit from the vehicle.
- Will sound 10 seconds after the opening of any door and remain on independently of the position of any door.
- Will time out after about 400 seconds unless a door is open, in which case the alarm will continue to sound.

When the circuit is initialized, capacitor C_1 begins to charge and turns the NOR gate A_1 on after a period equal to $R_1 C_1$. After this time, during which the driver leaves the car, a door switch closure to ground is required to set bistable multivibrator A_2 low. The circuit is thus armed.

Opening any door sets the output of the bistable device high, thus allowing capacitor C_3 to charge through resistor R_3. Unless the circuit is disarmed through the hidden switch, the alarm will sound after 10 seconds because the voltage across C_3 will be sufficient to turn on the AND gate A_3, passing the control output of pulse generator A_4 through to the horn relay.

The $R_2 C_2$ combination determines the bistable multivibrator's reset time, which in this case is approximately 400 seconds. Thus the bistable will again be set high if any door is open, and the horn will continue to sound.

Of course, the same logic functions as are needed for this alarm could also be designed using a quad comparator, such as the LM239. The circuit would then require an idling current of only 0.8 mA. Several additional resistors would have to be added, however. □

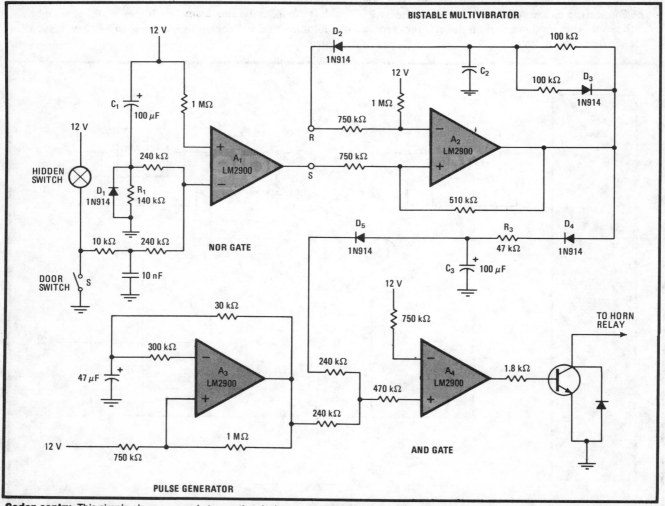

Sedan sentry. This simple alarm uses only two active devices—an LM2900 quad amp and a power transistor—yet performs as efficiently as some of the more complex and expensive circuits. The circuit is activated only after the owner leaves the car and can be disarmed before sounding after he returns. For an intruder, the horn sounds after 10 s and remains on for 400 s. The device can then retrigger.

Dual tones advance slides automatically

by J. A. Connelly and Douglas Martin
Georgia Institute of Technology, School of Electrical Engineering, Atlanta, Ga.

This circuit generates dual audio tones that are recorded on a tape so a slide projector will advance whenever both tones are present during playback. Two LM567 tone decoders are the heart of the circuit and the individual voltage-controlled–oscillator frequencies are set by R_1, C_1 and R_2, C_2.

For the circuit shown, $f_1 = 1/(R_1C_1) = 10$ kilohertz and $f_2 = 1/(R_2C_2) = 7.7$ kHz. The highest frequencies that the recorder can reliably reproduce were chosen to minimize possible annoyance to the listener. Two phase-locked–loop tone decoders prevent false triggering that would allow music or voices to be recorded with the tones.

The VCO frequencies from pin 5 of both tone decoders are summed at the base of Q_3, which buffers the output tones. This prevents any recorder loading from changing the VCO frequencies. When the VCO frequency is present at the pin 3 inputs, the PLL locks and an internal transistor saturates, shorting pin 8, an open-collector output, to ground. The outputs at pin 8 of the two PLLs are diode-OR-ed, so that only when both VCO frequencies are present at the input does the transistor Q_2 switch off.

This action switches Q_1 on, also turning on relay K_1. One set of the contacts of K_1 are used to advance the projector. The other set of contacts serves to turn on a light-emitting diode that provides a visual indication of when the tone is received. This same LED is also connected with switch S_2 so that it indicates when the tones are being recorded onto the tape. This switch, which is used during recording, is pressed for about 1 second at each point on the tape at which it is desired to advance the slide projector.

Switch S_1 prevents feedback between the output and input tones. If both are connected to the recorder at the same time, the outputs at pin 8 will oscillate as the LM567s try to track their own VCO frequencies.

The tone-output–attenuating resistors, R_3 and R_4, should be chosen so that when the tones are recorded at normal levels for music and voice, their playback level is close to 200 millivolts peak to peak. This level will assure reliable phase lock by the PLLs.

The circuit draws a small standby current of 17 milliamperes and can therefore run off a battery. □

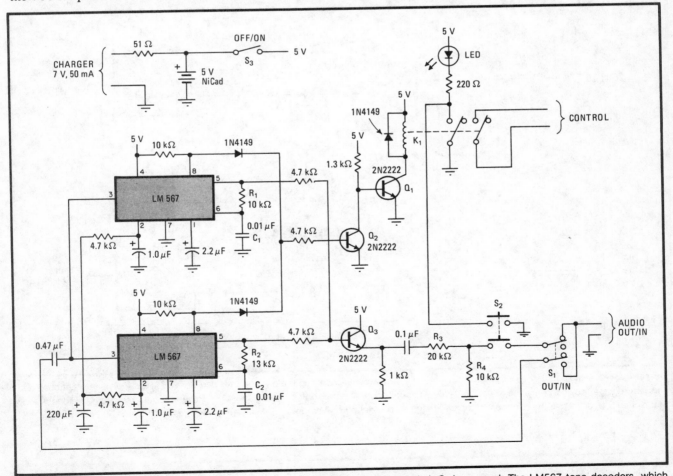

Double duty. Two tones are simultaneously recorded onto a cassette tape when switch S_2 is pressed. The LM567 tone decoders, which generate the tones, also decode them from the tape and trigger Q_2 to energize relay K_1, which in turn advances a slide projector.

Current mirror linearizes remote-controlled timer

by George Hughes and S. A. Hawley
Eye Research Institute, Boston, Mass.

Although setting the pulse duration of timers of the 555 variety by remote means is most conveniently done with a single control such as a potentiometer, often there is an undesired nonlinear relationship between wiper-arm setting and output width because of the simple methods employed to achieve control. Adding a current mirror and feedback loop to the basic circuit solves the problem of linearity with little additional complexity or cost.

In general, any current passing through the pot's wiper should be minimized and the pot placed as close as possible to the circuit's interfacing operational amplifier, especially in remote-control applications, where the effects of stray coupling from various processing circuits can be considerable. A typical configuration is shown in (a). In this type of circuit, however, difficulties arise because the op amp's output voltage supplies charging currents to the one-shot's timing capacitor through a fixed resistor. As a result, the pulse capacitor width will be inversely proportional to the current driving C_T and will not be a linear function of the wiper-arm position.

Adding the current mirror and the feedback loop to the circuit, as shown in (b), overcomes this drawback. Here, the mirror's charging current is made a constant whose magnitude is proportional to only the voltage at the amp's noninverting input, V_i, and hence to the potentiometer's setting. In the feedback loop, the average value of the timer's output is compared with a voltage that represents the wiper-arm position, where current injected into timing capacitor C_T is such that the difference is kept small by the virtual-ground properties of the op amp. The average value of the timer's output is itself a linear representation of pulse duration, so that overall linear control is maintained.

This circuit will function with any TTL timer. Parts values are not critical and can be varied to suit a wide range of triggering rates and pulse durations. Substitution of matched dual transistors or packaged current mirrors is recommended to improve the circuit's temperature stability. □

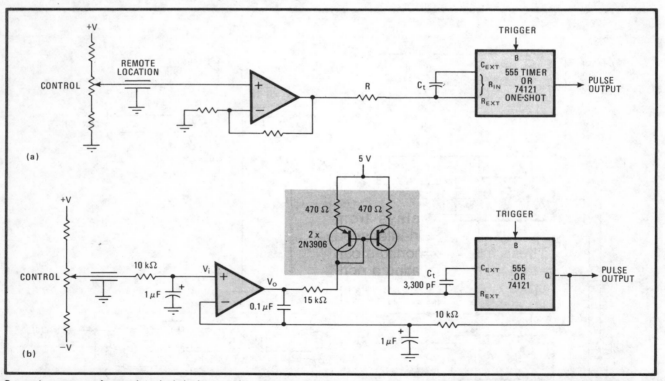

Current correspondence. A typical single-control pot arrangement for setting the on-time of a one-shot (a) has a nonlinear relationship of duration to wiper position because the current-driving capacitor, C_T, is proportional to $V_i(R + R_{IN})$. Adding a current mirror and feedback loop to the circuit (b) linearizes the relationship by generating a constant current set by V_i. The values shown are for $8 < T_{out} < 50$ μs.

Low-cost controller stabilizes heater-type cryostats

by S. K. Paghdar, K. J. Menon, R. Nagarajan, and J. Srivastava, *Tata Institute of Fundamental Research, Bombay, India*

Controllers for maintaining small objects at a low temperature use either complicated gas-flow techniques, that regulate gas pressure or costly commercial units that are built for general applications and must be modified to suit a particular need. Finger-type cryostats, in contrast, which control a heater on the principle of error-sensing and feedback techniques, are extremely simple, easy to implement, and inexpensive. As for stability, this circuit holds the temperature to ±0.2°K over 24 hours (short-term variation is ±0.01 K) in the range of 80 to 200 K.

As shown in the figure, the circuit may be built around an OC23 or other power transistor, that has a fairly linear base-current–to–collector-current characteristic, eliminating the need for the additional amplification usual in circuits of this type. Error signals from a Wheatstone bridge are applied to the 741 operational amplifier act as the temperature control. The signal is then amplified by transistor Q_1 and passes to Q_2, which drives a resistive load and associated container that, placed inside the liquid-nitrogen–filled cryostat, heats the environment.

Thermal changes are sensed by a copper resistance thermometer, also located inside the cryostat. This element, placed in one arm of the Wheatstone bridge, reflects changes in the equilibrium temperature between the container and environment and in effect acts to cancel the original error signal applied to the op amp.

This part of the circuit serves only to correct temperature variations and does not set the temperature of the cryostat. Potentiometer R_1 fulfills this task by setting the bias current at the output without affecting the base-driving circuit of the power transistor.

To calibrate the system, switch S_1 is placed in the manual position and R_1 adjusted to obtain the desired cryostat temperature. Next, the Wheatstone bridge should be balanced by adjusting the standard resistor, whose value will be determined by the center value of the circuit's copper resistance thermometer.

The gain of the amplifier stage, R_3/R_2, should be matched to the response of the cryostat. A nominal value might be 1,200, as in this circuit.

The system can handle heater currents of up to 850 milliamperes. Above this value, however, the current gain of the power transistor begins to fall, so that the circuit will not function effectively in the specified temperature range. □

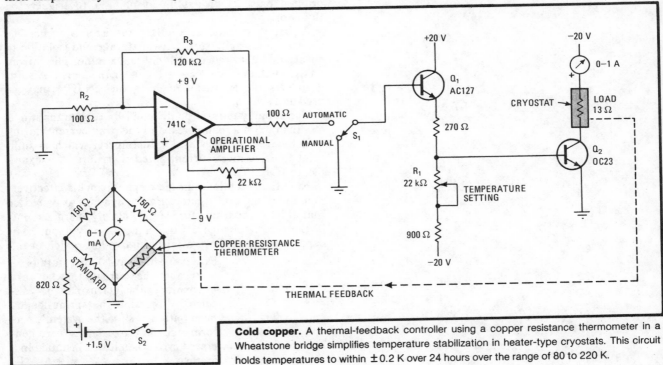

Cold copper. A thermal-feedback controller using a copper resistance thermometer in a Wheatstone bridge simplifies temperature stabilization in heater-type cryostats. This circuit holds temperatures to within ±0.2 K over 24 hours over the range of 80 to 220 K.

Noise-immunized annunciator sounds change-of-state alarm

by K. Soma
Singapore Electronic & Engineering Ltd., Sembawang, Singapore

To determine the status of a multichanneled telemetry receiver, relays are usually employed to activate lamps or light-emitting diodes set in the face of a remotely sited operator panel. However, if the call annunciator must sound an alarm each time a change occurs in the receiver's state, it often becomes vulnerable to noise pickup from external sources and produces false alarms. This circuit immunizes the receiver panel against the effects of that noise.

The simplest way to sense a change in status would be to link 39 capacitors at points P_1 through P_{39} in the figure and to connect their common output to the gate of a thyristor at point J. Indeed, this method is often used. But although the circuit will work, it is extremely susceptible to noise pickup from such sources as an electrical drill because all 39 capacitors form a series-parallel network that filters out most of the 12-volt pulse switchover signal when a lamp changes from green to red or *vice versa*. Thus, only about 100 millivolts of the original pulse is picked up at point J to trigger the thyristor.

A better method is to use transistor switches, as shown, for capacitor-to-thyristor storage and isolation to ensure that a sizable spike—not just a minor glitch from an external noise source—will trigger the alarm. A standard versatile transistor such as the 2N3904 may be used as a switch.

The standby current contributed by each transistor is less than 3.5 microamperes, and the peak current during switch-on is as much as 1 milliampere, which is sufficient to drive most current-gated thyristors—for example, the C103YY.

Note that each lamp in the display panel is effectively monitored by a transistor. Each capacitor is wired so that at least one transistor is momentarily energized only if there is a change in the lamp display input. The capacitors should have a fairly high value, which in this case is specified at 10 microfarads.

Because the currents that flow are momentary, the alarm can be canceled by pressing the spring-loaded push button. As for the system's performance, no false alarms were generated even when it was installed in a factory. □

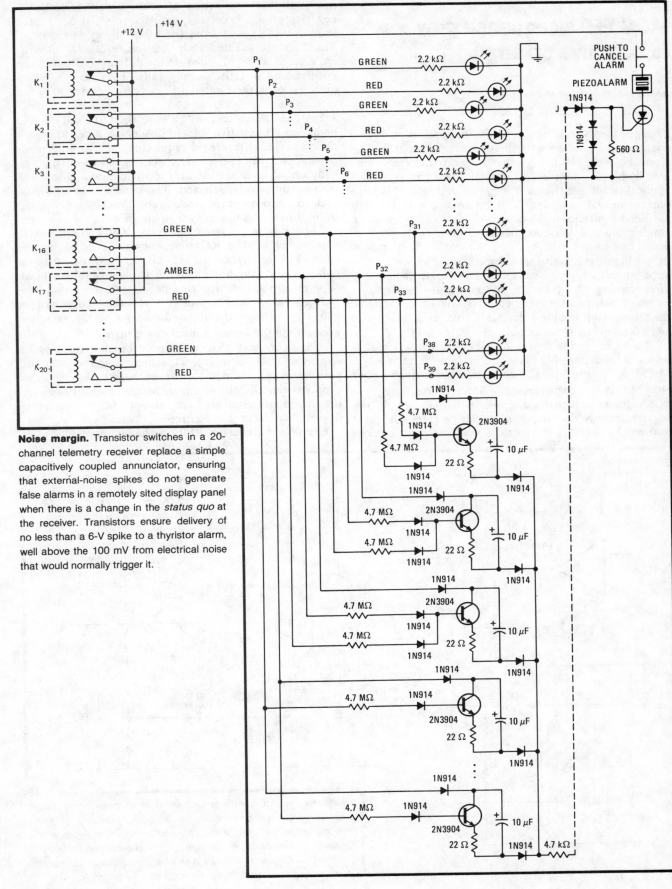

Noise margin. Transistor switches in a 20-channel telemetry receiver replace a simple capacitively coupled annunciator, ensuring that external-noise spikes do not generate false alarms in a remotely sited display panel when there is a change in the *status quo* at the receiver. Transistors ensure delivery of no less than a 6-V spike to a thyristor alarm, well above the 100 mV from electrical noise that would normally trigger it.

MOS FETs sequence power to sensitive op amps

by J. E. Buchanan
Westinghouse Electric Corp., Baltimore, Md.

Though hardly mentioned, even in application notes, operational amplifiers with double-diffused input devices often require—like many other integrated circuits powered by bipolar supplies—the simultaneous or sequential application of positive and negative voltage. This is to prevent device degradation or burnout due to forward biasing of various input-circuit diodes and transistors. One simple and low-cost means to meet these requirements can be achieved by using MOS field-effect transistors, which have high input impedance and low output impedance, to apply power to one terminal of the op amp after sensing the presence of power at the opposite terminal. Such an arrangement is not only more reliable than any using double-pole relays, but uses less power and takes up less space as well.

The basic circuit shown in (a) ensures the simultaneous application of plus and minus voltage to a MC1556 op amp. The p-channel, enhancement-mode MOS FET in the positive supply line requires a negative gate voltage to turn on and the n-channel unit in the negative supply line requires a positive gate voltage to turn on. Therefore, this cross-coupled configuration does not allow the application of positive voltage unless a negative voltage is present, and vice versa. If one supply fails, power applied from the other supply is removed. The FETs are selected such that the threshold, or turn-on, voltage is roughly equal to the difference between the positive and negative supply rails. Thus both supplies must be near their rated values before either FET can turn on.

In actual operation, the gates of the FETs will have to be biased via resistive voltage dividers in order to match their individual threshold requirements, and other supporting circuitry is needed as well, as shown in (b). The addition of a capacitor at the divider will allow the turn-on time to be selected. The capacitor can also be used to compensate for a relatively slower FET in one leg or for differences in supply turn-on times.

The delay in applying the voltages to the op amp is determined by the RC time constant formed by the equivalent resistance of the divider and the turn-on delay. The decoupling capacitor is also useful for noise suppression and in supplying peak (transient) load currents. A diode may be required across the MOS switch, as shown, to ensure the rapid discharge of the switched nodes when the system's supplies are turned off.

A basic circuit that will apply bipolar voltages in sequence is shown in (c). This circuit ensures that the positive supply is not turned on unless the negative supply is established. A similar arrangement is used for positive-supply predominance, except that an n-channel device is placed in the negative-supply lead.

Use of the Supertex VP01 p-channel MOS FET (and

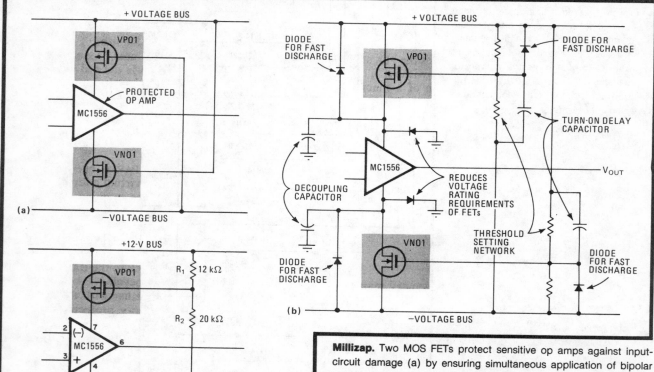

Millizap. Two MOS FETs protect sensitive op amps against input-circuit damage (a) by ensuring simultaneous application of bipolar supply voltages. Practical circuit configuration (b) includes various capacitors and diodes for controlling turn-on delay and for transient protection. Only one MOS FET is required for applications where the plus and minus voltages are to be supplied in sequence (c).

the n-channel VN01) is ideal for all applications. They have a specified on-resistance of about 10 ohms, which is low enough to ensure that there is little voltage drop across them when they are on; in this case, the drop is only 50 mV for a supply current of 0.5 mA, and it will not increase greatly despite rather heavy current flow.

Again, voltage divider R_1–R_2 is selected so that the VP01 will be fully on with minimum operational supply levels. Circuitry as seen in (b) is also needed. □

Audio-visual controller synchronizes museum display

by William S. Wagner
Northern Kentucky Unversity, Highland Heights, Ky.

A synchronized sound-and-transparency show that may be placed in any convenient area of a museum or science building can be created with this interface. Built entirely with off-the-shelf components, the cost of the circuit is below $20.

The interface controls a cassette player and a display having several illuminated panels. Each panel contains a color transparency and a source of light (in this case, a light bulb). The circuit causes these transparencies to light in sequence, while advancing the cassette tape, which contains a recorded message for each panel. Pairs of recorded audio tones control panel sequencing and thus synchronize the audio-visual display.

When the show ends, a second pair of audio tones shuts the entire display off. Because a continuous tape loop is used, the show may be restarted by pressing a start button. A pause button is included to extend the viewing period of any panel.

As for circuit operation, when the start button is pressed, the 4043 reset-set flip-flop sets, turning on the 2N2222 transistor and pulling in the double-pole, double-throw relay. Its normally open contact closes, turning on the cassette player's motor. At the same time, the relay's normally closed contact opens, allowing the audio signal to reach the LM324 amplifier. A 667- and a 1,200-hertz tone combine to form the initial sound heard and to activate their respective 567 phase-locked loops.

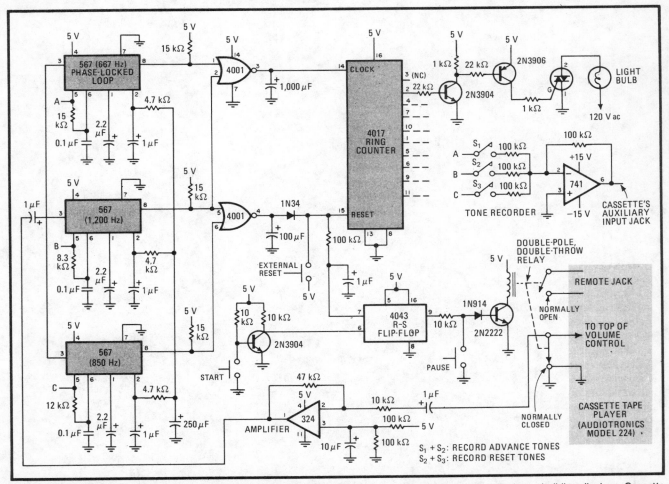

Show and tell. This interface synchronizes sound with illuminated panels and can be used in museum or science building displays. Cassette tapes hold recorded segments corresponding to information seen on illuminated display panels. When the circuit detects a chord preceding a given segment of text, the following panel is illuminated. Also, the interface has an automatic shut-down feature.

This causes pin 3 of the first 4001 NOR gate to go high and advance the 4017 ring counter.

When pin 2 of the counter goes high, the 2N3904 and 2N3906 transistors turn on and the triac fires, causing the first light bulb to illuminate the first transparency. Then the recorded message corresponding to that transparency is played. At the end of the message a second pair of recorded tones (667 and 1,200 Hz) causes the 4017 counter to advance to pin 4, turning off the first light and turning on the second with its appropriate interfacing transistors and triac.

This process is repeated until all transparencies have been displayed and described. At the end of the show, recorded tones at 850 and 1,200 Hz activate their respective PLLs and the 4017 is reset so that all lights are turned off. The 4043 R-S flip-flop is also reset and turns off the 2N2222, which deactivates the relay and turns off the cassette player. □

DESIGN

Two-chip radio link pilots toys and models

Transmitter and receiver ICs for multichannel remote control give low-cost digital and proportional system a 100-meter range

by Martin Giles, Kerry Lacanette. Dennis Monticelli, and Ron Page, *National Semiconductor Corp., Santa Clara, Calif.*

☐ Toys and model vehicles with radio-frequency remote control have long been limited to committed hobbyists and radio amateurs working with expensive control terminals. But the price of radio control will drop enough to spur a consumer boom now that inexpensive but sophisticated integrated circuits are moving into the field.

Penetration of this high-volume, low-cost market is helped considerably by ICs designed for easy, reliable assembly and operation. Two of the first such chips, introduced at the end of 1978 and now in volume production, are the LM1871 encoder-transmitter and the LM1872 receiver-decoder. They make it possible to build a complete radio control system for only $10.

The LM1871 encoder-transmitter contains all the circuitry required to modulate an rf carrier as high in frequency as 80 megahertz with up to six analog channels of control information. The LM1872 receiver-decoder uses a combination of pulse-width and pulse-count techniques to recover two analog signals and to accommodate two others for digital (latched) service. Alternatively, simple external circuitry provides for handling a total of four independent channels in any combination of analog or digital formats. The versatile chip pair thus may be adapted to many other tasks such as activating burglar alarms or the remote switching of lights, TV channels, or data links, to name just a few.

With or without a license

While sharing many of the features of the typical 0.75-watt, $200-to-$400 radio control set used by the serious hobbyist in the licensed portion of the spectrum at 72 MHz, the LM1871/LM1872 combination is also designed to provide superior performance over the frequencies where no operator license is required (see Table 1). The modulation technique used is compatible with the requirements of the Federal Communications Commission for all allocated frequencies. The decoding technique, suitable for use in the licensed bands at the

REMOTE-CONTROL FREQUENCY ALLOCATIONS AND GENERAL REQUIREMENTS					
Frequency (MHz)	Carrier tolerance	Maximum power or field strength	Band-width	Modulation	Notes
26.995 27.045 27.095 27.145 27.195 27.255	0.01%	10,000 μV/m measured at 3 meters.	± 10 kHz	On/off keying or amplitude tone modulation only	• Low power. Licensed operators permitted transmitting powers to 2.5 W • Frequency, phase and amplitude modulation prohibited • Maximum out-of-band emission: 500 μV/m at 3 m • Channel spacing: 50 kHz
49.830 49.845 49.860 49.875 49.890	0.01%	10,000 μV/m at 3 m	± 10 kHz	Any type	• No license required • Maximum out-of-band emission: 500 μV/m at 3 m • Channel spacing: 15 kHz
72.160 72.320 72.960	0.005%	0.75 W	± 4 kHz	On/off and tone	• License required
72.080 75.640 72.240 72.400	0.005%	0.75 W	± 4 kHz	On/off and tone	• Remote control of model aircraft only • License required

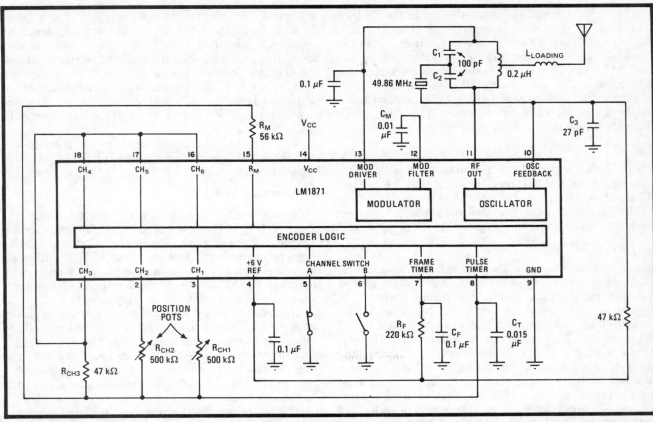

1. Guidance. LM1871 encoder-transmitter guides toys and models at 27, 49, and 72 MHz. Digital and proportional unit, shown configured for two channels each of digital and analog data, can be set up to deliver up to six channels of pulse-width–modulated information.

allowed higher power levels, works equally well in the low-power unlicensed segments at 27 and 49 MHz.

The LM1871 is a six-channel combination digital and proportional type encoder and rf transmitter (Fig. 1). A bipolar linear device, it is designed to generate a field with a strength of 10,000 microvolts per meter at a distance of 3 meters from its antenna at frequencies up to 50 MHz. This is the maximum field strength permitted for unlicensed transmitters. Encoding involves a pulse-width modulation scheme: analog information is converted into a train of pulses whose widths are proportional to the corresponding channel inputs.

In practice, the analog information at each channel input, and thus the output pulse width, can be set by a potentiometer that corresponds to a given control variable. Each of up to six pots may be sequentially switched to discharge the timing capacitor at pin 8, which is periodically charged by the 1871. The setting of switches A and B (pins 5 and 6) determines the number of channels sent in the transmitted pulse train. This number may vary from three to six. Each frame of six pulses lasts about 20 milliseconds, which includes a terminating sync pulse 5 ms long to allow the receiver to discriminate between one set of pulses and the next.

In operation, capacitor C_T at pin 8 is charged to two thirds of the supply voltage (V_{cc}) through the pulse timer in a time determined by both R_M and C_T. This time corresponds to the carrier-off period. The capacitor is then discharged back down to one third of V_{cc} through external potentiometer R_{CH1}, which sets the carrier-on

period for the corresponding channel, with the sum of the on and off periods constituting the pulse width for the channel. This width is usually between 1 and 2 ms, with a nominal 1.5-ms value. At the receiver, a corresponding potentiometer connected into a pulse recovery circuit is mechanically set in position by a servo, the servo rotating until the pulse widths at receiver and transmitter match.

Closed loop or open

This pulse-width matching is a form of closed-loop analog control: the rotation of the receiver's servo is proportional to the control position of the transmitter's potentiometer—that is, a steering, or positional function. Alternatively, open-loop control can be obtained for any channel by omitting the corresponding receiver potentiometer and comparing the transmitted pulse with a fixed pulse width at the receiver (usually a 1.5-ms monostable vibrator triggered by the leading edge of the transmit pulse). A shorter transmitted pulse will cause the servo to rotate in one direction. Matching pulses will result in a stationary motor, and a wider transmitted pulse causes rotation in the other direction. The motor speed can either be fixed for positional control or variable, depending on the actual difference in the pulse widths for speed control. Because this open-loop method initially requires matched pulses for a stationary motor, the LM-1871/1872 can also use another method, described later, that avoids the need for a time reference to control latched channel controls (digital channels).

The typical transmitting antenna used in the field will be a telescoping or fixed wire antenna about 0.6 m in length. At 27 and 49 MHz, this length is less than one tenth of a carrier wavelength, so the antenna is capacitive. At 49 MHz, a 0.6-m, 5.6-mm-diameter antenna can be represented by a 6.2-picofarad capacitor. The ability of such an antenna to radiate power can be represented by an equivalent radiation resistance (R_A) that would dissipate the same power. R_A is given by:

$$R_A = 40 (\pi L/\lambda)^2 \text{ ohms}$$

where L is the length of the antenna and λ is the wavelength, both in meters. For an antenna 0.6 m long, R_A equals 3.78 Ω.

The current through R_A needed to generate a given field strength, E (in μV/m), is given by:

$$I_A = Ed\lambda/(120\pi L)$$

where d is the distance in meters from the antenna. Plugging in the FCC limit for E of 10,000 μV/m at d = 3 m, it is seen that the antenna current is 0.8 mA. If the capacitive reactance of the antenna is tuned out with a loading coil (resonating with 6 pF at 49 MHz) less than 3 mV is required from the oscillator tank circuit, in theory. The loss resistance, R_L, is considerable, however, and must be taken into account. This resistance will be a function of the terrain, transmitter height, load mismatch, and other factors. For a typical hand-held transmitter with a consequently poor ground return, R_L will vary from several hundred ohms to kilohms. Practical experience indicates that the tank coil should be suitably tapped to deliver 20 mV peak to peak at 49 MHz and about 200 mV p-p at 27 MHz to the antenna loading coil in order for the 1871 to deliver the maximum field strength. The transmitter is regulated so that the maximum power output is maintained for a supply voltage variation extending from 16 down to 5 volts.

The extremely low radiated power permitted in the unlicensed bands does indicate one difficulty in utilizing these frequencies, apart from the limited range. Specifically, FCC regulations mandate that out-of-band emissions must be at least 26 dB below the peak permitted carrier level: that is, less than 500 μV/m. Because of the substantial losses encountered in the antenna circuit, the oscillator power level must usually be made high to achieve the maximum permitted field strength. This means that the level of harmonics being radiated directly by the oscillator can easily be above the FCC limit if care in circuit layout is not exercised. Oscillator and output leads, including ground returns, should be kept as short as possible. Design and evaluation kits for both the 1871 and 1872 are now available for those who wish to eliminate construction-phase headaches.

Range versus terrain

The range to be expected with this low-power transmitter is dependent on the transmitting and receiving antenna heights and the local geography. Outdoors, the transmitted field strength can be expected to be similar to that of the color curves of Fig. 3, taken across an asphalt parking lot with a transmitter 3 feet above the ground. Wet grass or water and higher antenna locations

will yield an increase in field strength for a given distance from the transmitter. In contrast, operation within buildings can drastically reduce range if they contain much metal. Metal furniture, refrigerators, filing cabinets or steel beams will cause dramatic local variations in field strength making any range predictions subject to large errors. However, in domestic environments, a range of at least 10 to 20 m can usually be attained.

But while the permissible output power is an important factor in determining the control range, of equal importance is the sensitivity of the LM1872 receiver.

Sensitive superhet

To obtain sensitivity along with good selectivity, the LM1872 (Fig. 2a) is configured as a single-conversion superheterodyne receiver. The local-oscillator and mixer stages are capable of operation up to 80 MHz with good conversion gain and low intrinsic noise. The intermediate frequency is 455 kHz, and a wide-range (97-dB) automatic-gain-control circuit is employed in the i-f amplifier to handle the wide range of input voltages typically encountered. This circuit also provides good immunity to voltage transients on the supply line. The active digital detector that follows raises the system gain to 88 dB. The resulting baseband signal is then applied to the decoding logic, so that the original signal information sent on each channel can be retrieved.

A high-gain precision comparator, a 30-μs integrator, and a 25-mv reference make up the unique digital detector. When the signal voltage from the i-f amplifier exceeds 25 mV (the detector threshold level), the comparator will drive transistor Q_{11} to discharge the envelope-detection capacitor, C_{12}. A period of 30 μs is normally required for the 1-μA current source to linearly charge C_{12} to the 3 V ($V_{cc}/2$) level necessary to fire the Schmitt trigger. But the presence of the 455-kHz carrier waveform (2.2-μs period) prevents C_{12} from reaching this threshold until the carrier signal goes to zero during the interchannel time. The Schmitt will respond 30 μs later. This delay does not upset system sync since the LM1872 decoder responds only to the negative edges of the modulation envelope.

Recovering the data

The decoder (Fig. 2b) extracts the timing information from the carrier for the analog channels (of which there are normally two) and the pulse-count information for the digital channels (normally two). At the heart of the decoder is a three-stage binary (flip-flop) counter, A–C, that is advanced by one count on each negative transition of the modulated carrier envelope.

When the rf carrier drops out for the first modulation pulse, its falling edge advances the counter. During this time the sync capacitor C_6 is held low by transistor Q_{12}.

When the carrier comes high again for the variable channel interval, C_6 ramps toward $V_{cc}/2$ through the 100-kΩ resistor but is unable to reach it in the short time that is available. At the end of the pulse, the carrier drops out and the counters advance once again. The sequence is repeated for the second analog channel.

Gates G_1 and G_2 decode the analog channels by exam-

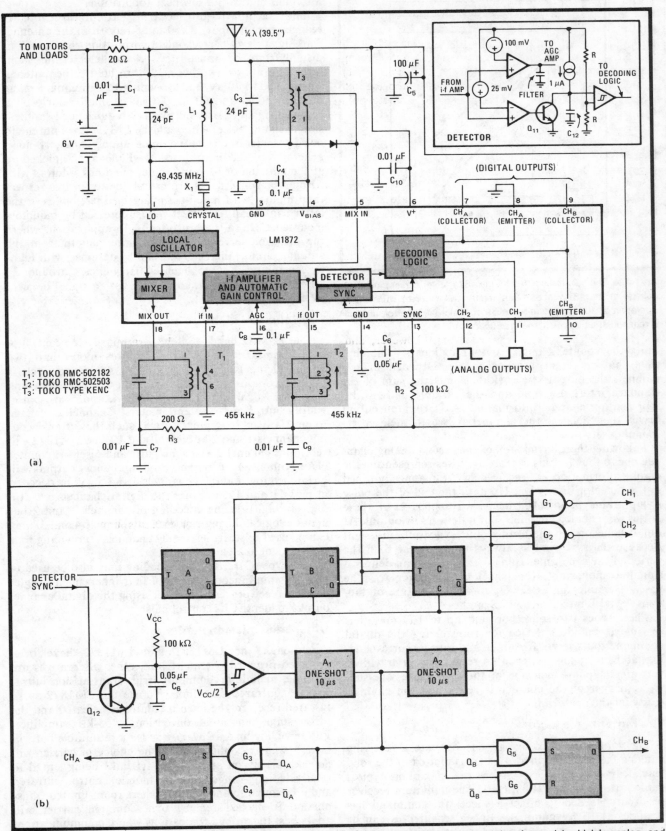

2. Linkage. LM1872 (a) demodulates up to four channels of incoming data, converting it into positional data for model vehicle's analog- and digital-channel servos. Single-conversion superhet is built on par with standard a-m receiver, except for digital decoder (b), which is needed for extracting the timing and pulse-count data from carrier in order to deliver the proper channel command to its corresponding servo.

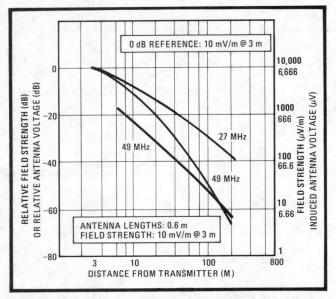

3. Profile. The field transmitted by the 1871 (color curves) induces a voltage at the 1872 receiver's antenna (black curve) sufficient for operation at 100 m. The receiver's automatic-gain-control threshold is reached at an input voltage of 250–280 μV.

ining the counter's binary output to identify the time slots that represent those channels. Decoded in this manner, the output pulse width equals the sum of the standard interpulse time and the variable pulse width representing channel information. A Darlington output driver then delivers the channel pulses to their corresponding servos.

Following the transmission of the second analog channel, one to four (in this case, two) pulses representing the digital information are received in the manner outlined in the detector discussion. Up until the end of the pulse group frame period, the decoder responds as if these pulses were analog channels, but it delivers no output. At the conclusion of the frame, the sync pulse is sent. Because the sync time is always made longer than the period of the sync timer (pin 13), the timer can deliver a signal to monostable (one-shot) multivibrator A_1. The first A_1 enables gates G_3–G_6 to read the state of flip-flops A and B into a pair of RS latches.

The latches can source or sink up to 100 mA, thus serving as an ideal device for transferring the digital command to its servo. If A or B, and thus its corresponding latch, is at logic 1, then its respective servo will be activated. Upon conclusion of the read pulse, one-shot A_2 is triggered, the counter is reset, and the chain is ready for the next frame.

The motor noise factor

The voltage induced by this encoder into a receiving antenna 0.6 m in length at 49 MHz is plotted in the solid black curve of Fig. 3. As seen, the maximum typical outdoor range will be 100 meters. The minimum receiver sensitivity needed to effect a successful command has been set at 15 μV nominal. Higher sensitivities can be easily achieved and the range possibly increased significantly, but the high-noise environment created by inexpensive servo motors themselves makes this consider-

ation impractical for low-cost applications.

The automatic-gain-control (AGC) threshold is reached for an input of 250 to 280 μV from the antenna. This signal level corresponds to a position roughly 25 m distant from the transmitter. At the detector threshold level (12 dB below the AGC threshold), the antenna signal is 60 to 70 μV, corresponding to a minimum range between 50 m and 60 m. To run a small vehicle on a received signal of only 60 μV does require good suppression of motor noise. Although the LM1972 is immune to noise transients on the common supply lines, rf noise generated by the motor brushes will always be picked up at the antenna or i-f transformer windings. Motors with wire or carbon brushes are usually better in this respect than motors with metal-stamping brushes, but even the latter can usually be effectively suppressed by inductors mounted close to the brush leads. In applications where the drive or servo motors are more remote from the antenna circuit, the LM1872 can be designed with higher sensitivity. At the licensed frequencies around 72 MHz, the circuit is able to operate with a signal below 2 μV at the antenna input.

Four-channel flight

The 72-MHz band is intended primarily for control of model aircraft, which often requires more than two analog channels. Expansion to four analog channels is easily accomplished by modifying the LM1871 encoding waveform such that channels 1, 2, 4, and 5 are pulse-width–controlled by potentiometers. Channel 2 is made to emit a fixed long pulse (5 ms) such that after decoding channels 1 and 2 at pins 11 and 12, the LM1872 will recognize channel 3 as a sync pulse and reset the counter chain. Simultaneously, both digital channel outputs will be latched low and then channels 4 and 5 will be decoded at pins 11 and 12. Because the digital channels are at a logic 1 (high) during encoding of channels 1 and 2 but are at a logic 0 during encoding of channels 4 and 5, they can be used to steer the analog channels—providing four independent analog controls.

This type of transmitter encoding may also be used to provide simultaneous control of four independent single-channel receivers, each receiver using the digital channel output to identify its control pulse.

Other transmission media

Although the LM1871 and LM1872 have been designed primarily as an rf link, other alternatives are possible, including common carrier transmission, ultrasonic, or infrared data links. To use the LM1872 as an infrared receiver, the local oscillator is defeated and the mixer stage runs as a conventional 455-kHz amplifier. For an ac line link, a 262-kHz i-f is more suitable but will have a similar configuration. The choice of carrier will depend largely on application—rf links being suited to relatively long-range outdoor mobile control, infrared and ultrasound to applications where room-limited transmission is needed for privacy. Common carrier will apply best to stationary locations where communications is desired without additional wiring around a building. Additional information is available in the application notes for the 1871 and 1872. □

Transformerless inverter cuts photovoltaic system losses

Design eliminates the iron-core losses that hurt efficiency during long low-load periods

by Geert J. Naaijer
Laboratoires d'Electronique et de Physique Appliquée,
Limeil-Brévannes, France

☐ The eventual viability of photovoltaic power systems for the home depends on more than the development of efficient solar cells. Any losses that can be eliminated from the system reduce solar-cell area requirements, making the system more competitive.

One place in the power system where significant losses occur is the dc-to-ac inverter. Iron-core losses in a typical inverter's transformer can impair a solar power system's efficiency during the long off-peak hours of a daily load cycle. Thus a transformerless inverter design was developed to boost the efficiency of a photovoltaic system and reduce its solar-cell area requirements substantially [*Electronics*, Dec. 6, 1979, p. 69].

The 2-kilovolt-ampere prototype stepped–sine-wave inverter described here is the result of approaching the classic problem of dc-to-ac conversion in a new way. A 2-kVA production version will be marketed this fall by OMERA (Société d'Optique, de Mécanique, d'Electricité et de Radio) in Argenteuil, France, a subsidiary of NV Philips Gloeilampenfabrieken (as are the Laboratoires d'Electronique et de Physique Appliquée).

This design yields a conversion efficiency that is high on the average because its no-load losses are low. The following example demonstrates the importance of reducing no-load losses in a photovoltaic system.

A solar-powered house

It is reasonable to assume that with thermal collectors providing central heating and hot water, a family of four could live comfortably using about 10 kilowatt-hours of electrical energy per day. This example also assumes a sunny climate such as that in the south of France, a 5-kilowatt peak photovoltaic array, and 200 kwh of backup battery storage.

If inverter losses are considered negligible, 70 square

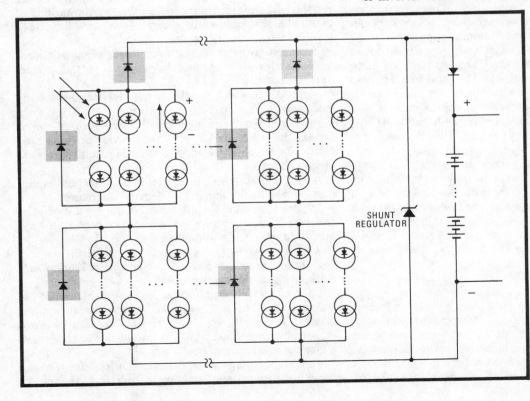

1. Diode protection. Stacked arrays of photocells require protective diodes if the array is large. Parallel diodes across series cells prevent excessive power dissipation should the accumulated voltage reverse-bias a weak cell. Series diodes between parallel arrays further isolate the branches and reduce the chance of damage.

SHUNT REGULATOR

2. Switched on. Eight separate battery modules are switched onto the bridge circuit in a sequence dictated by the control electronics. Output voltage is determined by the number of modules on line; the bridge section adds polarity reversals. Part numbers are European.

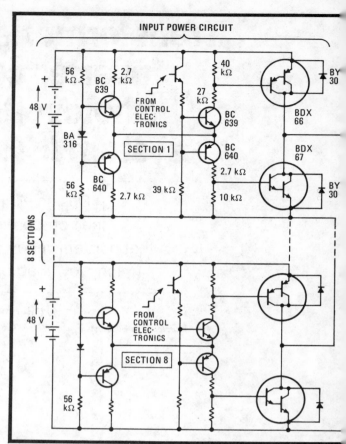

meters (84 square yards) of silicon photovoltaic panel are required. A typical commercial photocell module measures 38 by 102 centimeters (15 by 40 inches) and generates 33 watts peak at about 16 volts. Each module contains 36 monocrystalline silicon cells in a clear silicone resin sandwiched between two glass plates.

The 5 kw required would be produced by 150 such panels. The array of cells would constitute a major part of the system cost. Yet by using an off-the-shelf inverter with a 90% full-load efficiency, photovoltaic array requirements would double.

The reason is that in this application, the inverter will operate, on the average, at a power level less than one-tenth of what it is rated to handle. This is similar to the situation faced by the utility companies, which must meet peak power demands and then run their generators underutilized for a large portion of time. As a result the no-load, or fixed, losses of the inverter become an important factor in determining the overall system efficiency, and hence the cost. For example a 10-kwh daily demand, an average demand of only 417 watts, would nevertheless require a 7.5-kw inverter—large enough to handle the possible simultaneous load demands from a washing machine and other heavy equipment. In fact, the inverter would need to withstand occasional transient demands as high as 10 kVA.

To determine the losses, recall that efficiency, η, is given as:

$$\eta = P_{out}/P_{in} = P_{out}/(P_{out} + \text{losses})$$

where P_{in} and P_{out} are input and output power, respectively. If η is 90% and P_{out} is taken as 7.5 kw, losses work out to 833.3 w, or 11.1% of the nominal output. Assuming for the example that fixed losses and proportional losses are equal at full load, then each constitutes 5.5% additional input power required, and the total input energy required to supply the 10-kwh demand can be derived.

Continuous 24-hour operation of the inverter is also assumed, so the daily fixed losses are 24 hours × 417 w, or about 10 kwh, and daily proportional losses are 0.055×10 kwh = 0.550 kwh.

The total daily input energy to supply a 10-kwh demand is then 20.55 kwh, and overall system efficiency is therefore about 50%. Furthermore, demanding only 10 kwh from an inverter that is designed to supply 180 kwh per day is wasteful. The total energy could be supplied only by increasing the number of photovoltaic panels from 150 to 300, doubling the investment in arrays of photovoltaic cells.

No-load losses

The major contributors to no-load losses in power inverters are transformer magnetizing currents, hysteresis, and eddy currents. In contrast, proportional losses are due to semiconductor voltage drops, switching losses, and IR drops and have relatively little impact on overall system efficiency; for practical purposes they can be neglected. The key to efficient low-power inverter operation rests, therefore, in the reduction of iron losses.

Before abandoning the transformer-based power inverter, however, several solutions that do use the device should be considered, since the inherent limitations of these alternatives are the stepped–sine-wave inverter's justification in the first place.

To sidestep the imposing fixed losses of conventional ac power inverters for widely varying loads, a system designer could:
■ Automatically cut off the inverter when there is no electrical demand.
■ Provide two or more inverters of different rated power, for example, 4, 2, and 1 kVA, and provide an automatic circuit for selecting the most appropriate combination at any given time.
■ Assign a high-power inverter for high-demand equipment and a smaller one to low-demand appliances.
■ Impose a particular time schedule on the use of various equipment in order to have the inverter always operating near its optimum working point.
■ Assign an inverter to each piece of equipment.
■ Install a mixed ac and dc electrical distribution network, using dc wherever possible.

Each of these alternatives adds expense, and some are not very effective. It is clear that with a transformerless inverter design it would be possible to obtain much higher efficiencies, especially at output power levels well under the rated maximum.

The stepped–sine-wave inverter differs from more common designs not only by eliminating the power

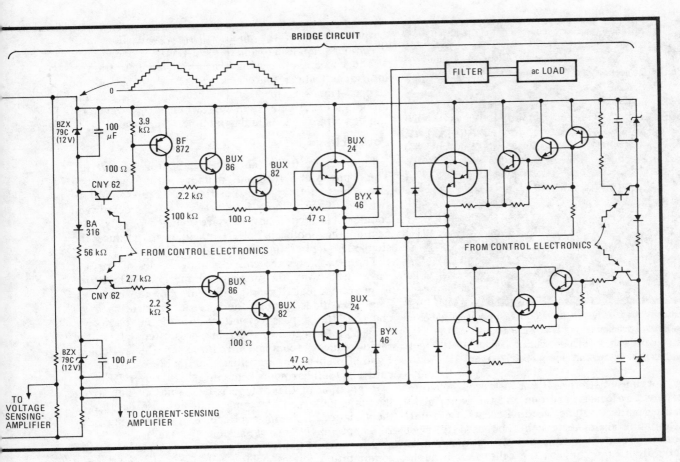

BRIDGE CIRCUIT

transformer. It also exploits a feature peculiar to photovoltaic power plants, that of modularity.

The stepped–sine-wave inverter develops an ac output from an array of dc sources, in this case batteries, photocells, or both. The output voltage is varied by rapidly changing the connections between each source in the array into different series and parallel circuits. The output is stepped higher and lower, positive and negative as the interconnecting switches rearrange the connections between sources.

Actually the output is not a pure sine wave, but a staircase function simulating a sine wave. By smoothing the edges of the staircase with filters and providing a sufficient number of steps, a sine wave, for all practical purposes, is produced.

Multiple dc inputs

Unlike conventional transformer-equipped inverters with two input lines to accept dc and two output lines supplying single-phase ac, the stepped–sine-wave device accepts a multisource, reconfigurable arrangement at its input. This is what most photovoltaic power plants with stacked solar panels look like.

There are limitations on the stacking of photovoltaic panels beyond which protective measures should be taken. Protective diodes must be strategically placed in series and parallel, as shown in Fig. 1, to prevent damage and breakdown.

Parallel diodes are placed across series-connected photocell branches because, as the total series voltage accumulates in the string, single cells may become reverse-

biased, causing excessive local power dissipation. Also, in parallel-connected photocell branches, sometimes one or more branches become a load for the others, again dissipating excessive power. This is prevented by isolating the interconnected solar panels with series diodes.

Typically, the unprotected array is safe for up to 10 branches connected in parallel, with each branch at a nominal voltage of 48 v for battery loads. If a higher voltage is desired, subassemblies of photocells or batteries may be connected in series. For example, 10 36-v assemblies connected in series are sufficient to drive the input of a transformerless power inverter capable of delivering 220 v ac.

Rapid electronic commutation of voltage sources is the basis of the stepped–sine-wave inverter. However, even relatively slow, time-dependent commutation of array interconnections can prove very useful. Being able to modify the interconnection of separate arrays allows the system to adapt to changes in photocell output.

Consider as an example the application of six photocell subassemblies to the task of charging a battery. Two parallel rows of three subassemblies each would be configured in series at high light levels and reconfigured as three parallel rows of two for low light levels. Note that judiciously adding steering diodes to the network reduces the complexity of the array wiring.

Another case of stepwise commutation of a photocell array is one where its output is defined over a period of one day. The array might be used, for example, to match the output variations of a nontracking photocell array to loads such as pumping and irrigation systems where it is

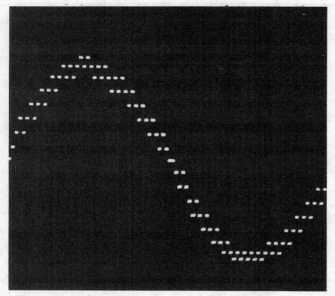

3. Many possibilities. A hybrid waveform incorporating staircase and pulse-width modulation is one of an infinite variety of simulated waveforms possible with the stepped-output inverter. The 50-hertz wave shown has peak-to-peak voltage of about 700 volts.

preferable not to use batteries. If, for instance, the pump is a lift type with a constant torque and the motor a dc type with a permanent magnet needing constant-current drive, a commutation scheme could be used to give near-constant current at optimum power output while the available light impinging on the cells goes through daily half-wave sinusoidal variations. In this case, the

output voltage of the photocell array will show daily variations very close to a half-wave–rectified sine wave.

The concept of varying the wiring configuration of individual voltage sources is the principle behind the stepped–sine-wave inverter. By speeding up the commutation and using semiconductor switches, any waveform can be synthesized, including a 60-hertz sine wave.

Power circuit

Figure 2 illustrates the power section of the inverter. The contents of a read-only memory within the control electronics defines the position of the solid-state switches. This memory is addressed by a clock-driven counter. The switch positions are changed rapidly, connecting the photocell/battery modules to produce the stepped 60-Hz output.

The ROM stores the code for many cycles of the sine wave. In this way, the source commutation can be varied to guarantee equal average discharge of the batteries. The zener diodes protect the batteries from being overcharged, the bypass capacitors isolate the photocells from high frequencies, and a low-pass filter reduces the radio-frequency content introduced by the switching. Figure 3 depicts the waveform obtainable with this circuit. The total harmonic content is slightly over 5%.

Regulation of the voltage is desirable not only from the standpoint of a changing load, but also because of the variations in battery voltage, which can swing from 20% above to 10% below its nominal value.

One way to achieve regulation is to modulate the commutation angles, which will increase slightly the total harmonic distortion. Another way is to pulse-width-

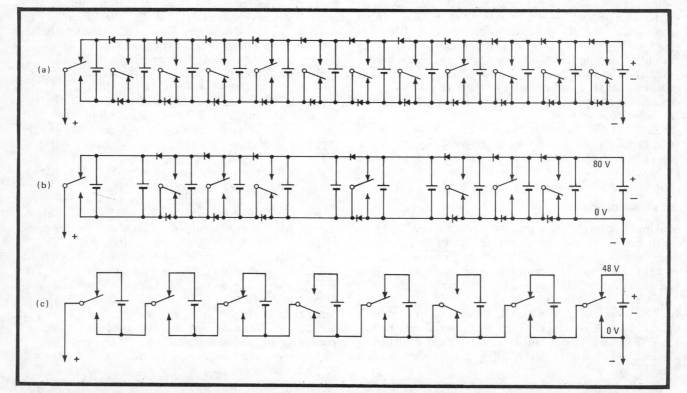

4. Commutation schemes. The general form for wiring sources (a) can be simplified, giving fewer combinations of series and parallel connections (b) but retaining equal discharge rate for each source. Further simplification is possible (c), but the equal discharge rate is lost.

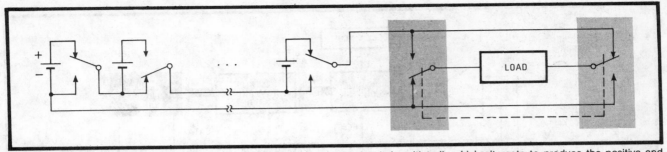

5. Polarity reversal. Bridge circuit operation is depicted here by the load switches (tinted), which alternate to produce the positive and negative excursions of the sine wave. In the actual circuit, optically coupled silicon switches are driven by the control circuit.

modulate the voltage steps so that particular steps dwell around the ideal sine curve. Both methods require some feedback arrangement, but it need not be complex.

In comparison with conventional PWM switched-mode power supplies, transient amplitude and commutation frequencies are lower. These lower frequencies ease the tasks of filtering and of reducing iron losses in the filters.

The basic operation of the inverter in Fig. 2 can be understood by considering Fig. 4a. A multiple-source arrangement is shown wherein each battery connects to a single-pole, double-throw switch and is coupled to adjacent batteries by diodes.

Flexible switching

A special simplified case of this general structure was described in the example of the commutated photocells, using subarrays with values that are not necessarily equal and with fewer, simpler switches. With 12 identical 80-v batteries, the circuit in Fig. 4b allows six different output voltages through the use of appropriate switching combinations, namely, 0, 80, 160, 240, 320, and 480 V. In the configuration shown, batteries are discharged at an equal rate, obviating the need to keep track of different levels of charge in each battery. Other configurations may result in unequal discharge rates. However, since the circuit is reconfigurable, periodic changes can be made to balance the overall discharging of each battery.

The point is that there are numerous ways to configure an array of voltage sources to make stepped changes in output voltage. In fact, almost any waveform can be generated. It is this concept of time-dependent commutation from which the design of the stepped–sine-wave inverter is drawn.

The circuit of Fig. 4c omits all diodes and uses eight identical 48-v batteries. This allows output steps of $n \times 48$ v, where $n = 0, 1, 2, 3, \ldots 8$, and is the circuit on which the 2-kVA prototype stepped–sine-wave inverter is based. Cyclic commutation of the batteries ensures equal average discharge of all batteries. Going one step further, it is possible to monitor the batteries and electronically reconfigure them according to need or to isolate bad cells entirely from the system.

But these circuits simulate only positive- or negative-going waves, not both. To simulate a full sine wave, the voltage output must go positive and negative, and this can be accomplished in at least two ways. A complete sine wave may be synthesized using two sets of batteries and switches, so that positive and negative battery assemblies are switched at 60 Hz. Alternatively, a single bank of batteries and switches can be switched by an electronically controlled full-wave bridge circuit (Fig. 5). The latter technique was selected for the prototype.

Isolation between the prototype inverter's control electronics and its power circuitry is achieved with optical couplers (Fig. 6). The power switch associated with each battery consists of complementary Darlington power switches shunted by power diodes that bypass inductive spikes. The bridge that performs the polarity reversals has four identical power Darlington transistors, each shunted by power diodes. All power for the switching and bridge circuitry is drawn directly from the source voltage, and no auxiliary power supplies are needed.

Feedback resistors sense the output voltage and current. This information is compared with the reference signal generated in the control electronics and is used for error correction in the power switches.

The control electronics are very simple and contain less than 10 common integrated circuits such as LM339 quad comparators, LM324 quad operational amplifiers, complementary-MOS gates, one-shots, an up-down counter, and a 32-byte ROM controlling the optical couplers. The clock frequency applied to the counter is on the order of several kilohertz. The counter's output addresses the ROM, whose output controls the optical couplers and therefore drives the power circuitry that determines the output voltage.

Comparison of the actual inverter output voltage with the reference sine wave generates a control signal that determines the operating mode of the up-down counter. The up-down counter is also controlled by feedback from the output current of the inverter. If the current exceeds a preset threshold, the counter is made to decrement rapidly, bringing the output voltage to zero. Regulation is excellent and the waveform is clean enough to run a color television receiver.

Efficiency is also excellent. At full load, it exceeds 93%. At a 100-VA output, 5% of rated output, efficiency still exceeds 90%. No-load power consumption is just 5 W and would not be much higher for a similar 10-kVA design. Total harmonic distortion is under 15%, typically 12% without any filtering.

Potential for photovoltaics

In a system for providing sun-generated electricity, the dc photocell array and ac inverter output can be isolated by splitting the battery assembly into identical halves, each capable of supplying power for prolonged

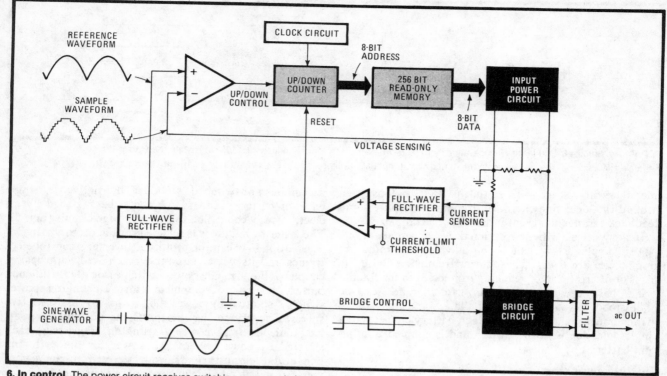

6. In control. The power circuit receives switching commands from a read-only memory coded for the desired waveform. Polarity reversals are triggered by a reference sine-wave generator but may also be in ROM. Voltage- and current-sensing taps guard the output limits.

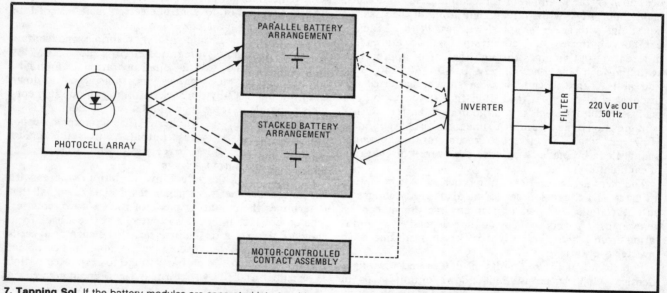

7. Tapping Sol. If the battery modules are separated into two blocks, one may be charged by photovoltaic cells while the other powers the inverter load. The two halves exchange roles when a block approaches either an upper limit of charge or a lower limit of discharge.

sunless periods. As one half is charged by the photocells, the other is connected to the load via the inverter. When either bank is close to its upper limit of charge or to its lower limit of discharge, the halves are switched. Automatic commutation can be performed at night during low-load conditions by a motor-driven contact assembly.

Such a twofold battery arrangement (Fig. 7) simplifies battery inspection, maintenance, and replacement. Since each half will have several days' capacity, daily commutation will ensure practically identical states of charge for the two banks, and sufficient reserve capacity is available to bridge maintenance periods. As batteries are kept at nominal voltage levels (between 1.85 and 2.05 v per cell), regulation is held within ±5% without additional feedback circuitry.

If necessary the inverter can also operate as a battery charger supplying power from the main power lines. Additional flexibility and built-in functions may be implemented by replacing the ROM in the inverter with a microprocessor. □

Achieving stability
in IC oscillators

Waveform-generator chips that operate above 1 megahertz rely on
emitter-coupled circuits needing sophisticated temperature compensation

by Ilhan Refioglu, *Exar Integrated Systems Inc., Sunnyvale, Calif.*

□ Monolithic waveform and function generators form
the backbone of circuits in a wide range of applications—telecommunications, data transmission, and test-
equipment design and calibration. These integrated-
circuit oscillators are characterized by an output waveform that is well-defined, repeatable, and stable despite
changes in ambient temperature and power-supply level.

Modern waveform- and function-generator ICs are
overcoming the limitations of older IC oscillators like
phase-locked loops and voltage-to-frequency converters.
The latter type of device is limited in performance by the
fact that it provides only pulse-train or square-wave
outputs. Waveform and function-generator chips, on the
other hand, provide a wider variety of output waveforms,
and do so at lower cost.

A function-generator IC generally consists of a cur-
rent- or voltage-controlled oscillator section that generates the periodic waveform and allows for frequency
variation, a wave-shaping section—basically, a sine-wave
shaper—and a modulator (Fig. 1).

The heart of any function-generator IC is the oscillator
section. This circuit determines the chip's most important performance characteristics. These include stability

with power-supply voltage and temperature changes,
frequency range, sweep linearity, and so on.

There are two major types of IC oscillators, differentiated mainly by their ability or inability to operate at
frequencies above 1 megahertz. Oscillators that operate
under 1 MHz generally employ lateral pnp transistors for
switching and saturated logic. Their operating frequencies are limited in practice to several hundred kilohertz.
But they also feature high stabilities of 50 parts per
million per °C or less, thanks to careful compensation
techniques employed in their designs.

Speed versus stability

Oscillators that operate above 1 MHz employ emitter-
coupled multivibrators and npn transistors. They are
inherently capable of operation up to 10 MHz. But they
also suffer from frequency instabilities of more than 150
ppm/°C and low-frequency inaccuracy.

Figure 2a shows a basic RC multivibrator low-
frequency oscillator circuit that has gained wide accept-
ance among IC oscillator designers. Capacitor C_0 is
exponentially charged through resistor R_1 to the supply-
voltage level. When the voltage across C_0 ramps up to

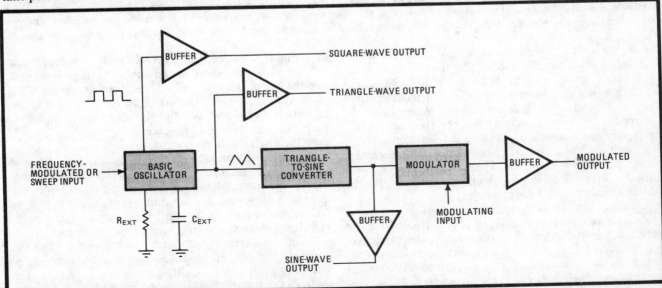

1. Functions. Generating waveform functions involves three major circuit elements: a basic oscillator to produce a periodic and variable-
frequency wave, a wave-shaping section, and a modulator. The oscillator frequency is controlled by either a voltage or a current.

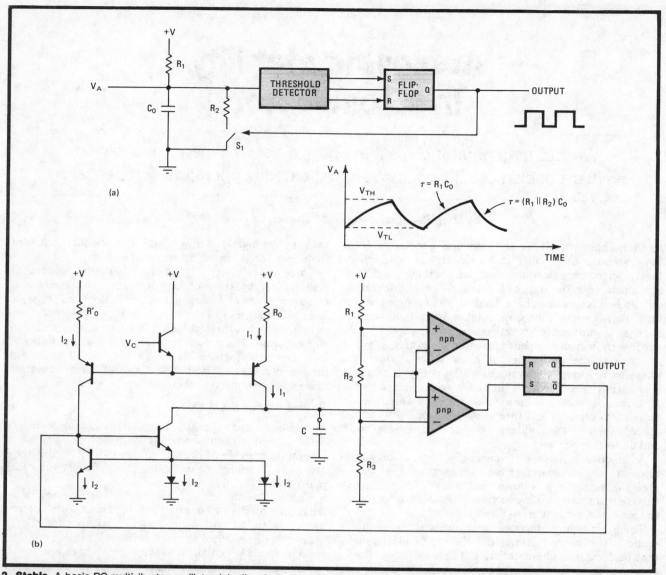

2. Stable. A basic RC multivibrator oscillator (a) offers high stabilities, but its lateral pnp transistors limit it in operating frequency to about 100 kilohertz. An implementation similar in concept (b) differs in that two current sources, I_1 and I_2, are used in place of resistors R_1 and R_2.

the higher of two threshold values, V_{TH}, the threshold detector changes the flip-flop's state, thus closing switch S_1 (usually a transistor). With S_1 closed, C_0 starts discharging its voltage exponentially to ground through the parallel combination of R_1 and R_2. When C_0's voltage reaches a lower threshold, V_{TL}, the threshold detector is once again activated, causing the flip-flop to revert to its original state, and the charging process is repeated. Note that if R_1 is small, an exponential sawtooth waveform is obtained. If R_2 is much larger than R_1, the output waveform will be symmetrical.

A circuit similar in principle to that of Fig. 2a uses two current sources, I_1 and I_2, in place of R_1 and R_2 to generate a linear ramp waveform across the capacitor. When current I_2 is equal to $2I_1$, a symmetrical-output triangular or square waveform is obtained. A practical implementation of this circuit is shown in Fig. 2b. This type of circuit is employed in the ICM8038 IC oscillator from Intersil Inc., Cupertino, Calif. Charging and dis-

charging of capacitor C are performed by currents I_1 and I_2. I_1 and I_2 are equal to the supply voltage minus V_C divided by resistors R_0 and R_0', respectively. Although I_1 is always on, I_2, which is doubled by the current mirrors, is switched on and off by the flip-flop's output. I_1 performs the charging function while current $2I_2 - I_1$ does the discharging.

If resistors R_0 and R_0' are equal, then I_1 equals I_2 and C is charged and discharged by identical currents, leading to symmetrical output waveforms. Oscillator frequency for this case is a constant value, k, multiplied by I_1C. Since current is set up by a control voltage, this circuit is known as a voltage-controlled oscillator.

A different type of VCO circuit is the one used in the popular type NE566 function-generator IC from Signetics Corp., Sunnyvale, Calif., and others. It is also used as the VCO for the Signetics 565 phase-locked loop IC. The circuit and its implementation are shown in Fig. 3. The same voltage-controlled current, I_0, is used to

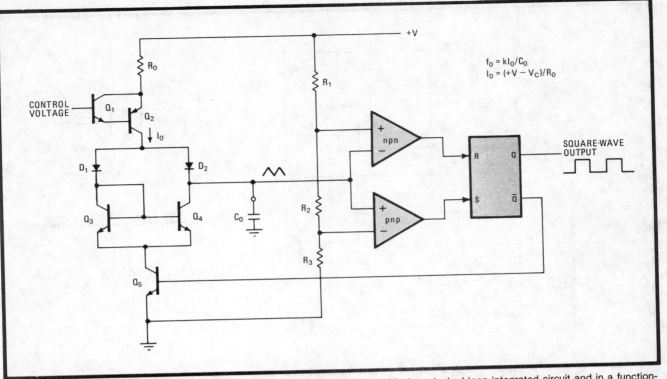

$$f_0 = kI_0/C_0$$
$$I_0 = (+V - V_C)/R_0$$

3. Voltage-controlled. This voltage-controlled oscillator is used in the popular 565 phase-locked-loop integrated circuit and in a function-generator IC, Signetics' NE566. Another astable multivibrator, it uses one voltage-controlled current, I_0, to charge and discharge capacitor C_0.

charge and discharge capacitor C_0 via the actions of the flip-flop circuit.

When transistor Q_5 is off, I_0 charges C_0 through diode D_2. When the voltage across C_0 reaches the trip point of the comparator, the flip-flop changes state and Q_5 is turned on. At this point D_2 becomes back-biased and C_0 is discharged through Q_4 by the mirrored current, I_0, until the voltage across C_0 reaches the lower threshold level. Then the flip-flop reverts to its original state, turning off Q_5 and repeating the charge-discharge cycle. Since the same current is used for charging and discharging, the circuit's duty cycle cannot be varied.

The oscillators of Figs. 2 and 3 are astable multivibrator circuits. They exhibit good stabilities, in the range of 50 to 100 ppm/°C. Unfortunately, they are limited to a maximum frequency of about 100 kHz due to the use of lateral pnp transistors.

Emitter coupling for higher frequency

Figure 4a shows a simplified schematic of an emitter-coupled multivibrator oscillator capable of 20-MHz operation. This circuit is difficult to compensate for changes in temperature, however, for very good frequency stability at high operating frequencies.

Transistors Q_1 and Q_2, resistors R_{L1} and R_{L2}, and the timing capacitor C form the heart of the multivibrator. The clamping action of D_1 and D_2 and the level shift of emitter-followers Q_3 and Q_4 (which are always conducting) keep the circuit from saturating and firmly establish the voltage swings. At a given time, either Q_1 and D_1 or Q_2 and D_2 are conducting, so that C is alternately charged and discharged by constant current I_1, which is generated by Q_5 and Q_6. When Q_1 is on, the output V_A is

constant at $V_{CC} - 2V_{BE}$ (where V_{CC} is supply voltage and V_{BE} is Q_1's base-emitter voltage), and the output V_B is a linear ramp with a slope equal to $-I_1/C$, since Q_2 is off. When V_B is pulled low enough (1 V_{BE} below Q_2's base, which is at $V_{CC} - 2V_{BE}$) by I_1, Q_2 turns on and regenerative switching occurs. The collector of Q_2 is pulled down to a diode drop below V_{CC} and the base of Q_1 is pulled down to $V_{CC} - V_{BE}$, turning off Q_1 and raising its collector rapidly by 1 V_{BE} to the supply level. This step of 1 V_{BE} appears at the emitter of Q_2 and is transmitted to the emitter of Q_1 by C. The emitter of Q_1 is now 1 V_{BE} above its base and must slew a full $2V_{BE}$ at I_1, with a slope equal to $-I_1/C$, before the oscillator changes state again.

The waveforms generated by this oscillator circuit are shown in Fig. 4b. The voltage at the collectors of Q_1 and Q_2 are two symmetrical square waves, with peaks between V_{CC} and $V_{CC} - V_{BE}$. The differential output V_0 across diodes D_1 and D_2 corresponds to a symmetrical square wave, with a peak-to-peak amplitude of $2V_{BE}$. $V_A(t)$ and $V_B(t)$ are linear ramp waveforms with peak-to-peak amplitudes of $2V_{BE}$. They can be subtracted from each other to produce a linear triangular waveform, which is the voltage across the capacitor. Subtraction can be performed by a simple differential amplifier stage whose output voltage is a triangular waveform. The same differential amplifier circuit can also be used to obtain a sinusoidal output.

The frequency of oscillation f_0 of the emitter-coupled multivibrator of Fig. 4a can be expressed as:

$$f_0 = I_1/(4V_{BE}C)$$

The frequency can be controlled by varying I_1 by means

75

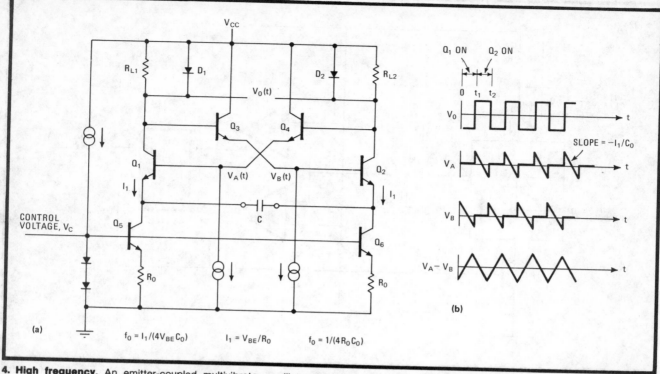

$$f_0 = I_1/(4V_{BE}C_0) \qquad I_1 = V_{BE}/R_0 \qquad f_0 = 1/(4R_0C_0)$$

4. High frequency. An emitter-coupled multivibrator oscillator (a) allows the generation of waveforms (b) of up to 20 megahertz. Unfortunately, this type of circuit is difficult to compensate for changes in temperature, leading to poor stabilities at high frequencies.

of a control voltage, V_C. The symmetry of the triangular- and square-wave outputs can be offset by changing the ratio of emitter resistors of Q_5 and Q_6. This ratio effectively changes the ratio of the current that charges capacitor C to the current that discharges it. In this manner, the triangular- and square-wave outputs can be converted to sawtooth or pulse waveforms.

The emitter-coupled multivibrator circuit shown is widely used for high-frequency applications. Oscillator types NE560 and NE562 from Signetics and others, as well as Exar phase-locked loops type XR-S200, XR-210 and XR-215, use it. The Exar XR-205 monolithic waveform generator also uses a similar emitter-coupled astable multivibrator design.

Strong temperature dependence

The frequency of this emitter-coupled multivibrator circuit is a function of V_{BE}, which in turn is strongly dependent on temperature. To overcome this strong temperature dependence, the timing current I_1 is also made a function of V_{BE}, such that $I_1 = V_{BE}/R_0$. Thus to a first-order degree, f_0 is temperature-compensated and is expressed as:

$$f_0 = (V_{BE}/R_0)/(4V_{BE}C) = 1/(4R_0C)$$

This compensation is only effective at the center frequency. Since the control current that modulates the frequency is not compensated, even very small control-current deviations degrade the temperature coefficient drastically (typically ±300 ppm/°C at $\pm10\%$ current deviation).

Despite center-frequency compensation, the emitter-coupled multivibrator still exhibits a temperature coeffi-

cient of 200 to 300 ppm/°C. The culprits are the charging-current imbalance in Q_1 and Q_2 near the switching thresholds and the switching transients. The transients depend on circuit resistances, transistor transconductances, and input resistances, which all are temperature-sensitive. Temperature drift of the circuit is inherent in its emitter-coupled multivibrators. There are other compensation techniques that can be used to make a high-stability (typically 50 ppm/°C or less) oscillator out of the circuit in Fig. 4a, but this is usually achieved at the expense of speed.

Improving temperature compensation

Two very stable temperature-compensated oscillator configurations are used in Exar's XR-2206 and XR-2207 function-generator ICs as well as in the company's XR-2211 and XR-2212 phase-locked-loop ICs. They use a temperature-compensated emitter-coupled astable multivibrator circuit that has a typical temperature stability of 30 ppm/°C (Fig. 5).

Timing current, I, set up by R_{ext}, flows in Q_2, C, and Q_3 when transistors Q_5, Q_7, and Q_9 are on. The timing current is inverted by the current balance and establishes an identical emitter current density in Q_7. The voltage at the control input B is thus held at 0 over a wide range of timing currents. At an optimum current value, point A is also at 0 v, eliminating the temperature coefficient introduced in this area. When the state changes, I flows in Q_1, C, and Q_4; all the compensation transistors on the right are turned on; and I is inverted by a current balance. As a result, I establishes an identical emitter current density in Q_{10}.

The instability introduced by a shift in the regenera-

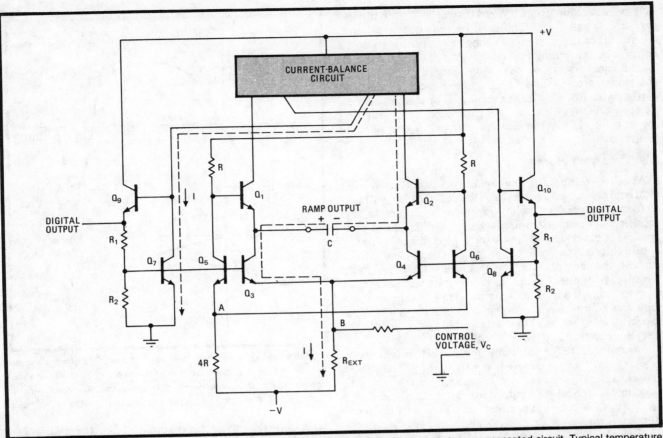

5. Compensation. Emitter-coupled astable multivibrators can be stabilized using this temperature-compensated circuit. Typical temperature stabilities of 30 parts per million per °C are possible. This circuit is used in Exar's XR2207 function-generator and XR2211 PLL chips.

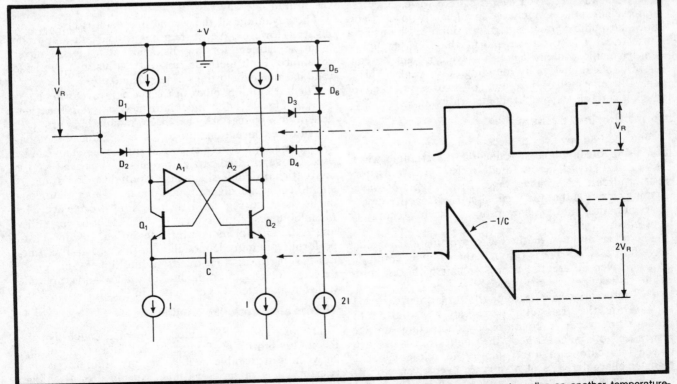

6. Clamped. The emitter-coupled multivibrator in Analog Devices' AD537 voltage-to-frequency converter relies on another temperature-compensation method. The collectors of Q_1 and Q_2 are clamped and a differential reference voltage across them charges capacitor C.

tion point arising from dV_{BE}/dT (where T is temperature) in Q_1 and Q_2 is minimized by the current balance, which forces the currents in these two transistors to be equal at the switching point.

The square-wave output is obtained differentially at the emitters of Q_9 and Q_{10}. A linear ramp is obtained across capacitor C. The frequency of operation is given by $f = 1/(CR_{ext})$ and can be controlled by modulating the current, I, via the control voltage, V_C, applied to control node B.

Clamped collectors

Another temperature-compensated emitter-coupled multivibrator, used in Analog Devices' AD537 voltage-to-frequency converter chip, is shown in Fig. 6. In this precision collector-clamping scheme, a differential voltage, V_R, generated by a bandgap reference circuit, appears across the collectors. V_R is independent of the current, the temperature, the absolute value of V_{BE}, and the supply voltage. This precise reference voltage is then transferred to the timing capacitor via two-stage emitter-followers A_1 and A_2 and transistors Q_1 and Q_2. Thus, the capacitor charges to $2V_R$ twice each cycle, yielding a frequency expression of $f = 1/(4CV_R)$.

To compensate for the temperature drift mechanisms inherent in emitter-coupled multivibrators mentioned earlier, a small temperature coefficient in the opposite direction is deliberately added to the voltage reference V_R. Using this technique, excellent stabilities of around 20 ppm/°C are possible.

After the generation of a basic waveform such as a triangular or square wave, the next step is to convert the waveform into a low-distortion sine wave. A triangular wave is usually preferred over a square wave, since the former's harmonic content is significantly lower. This initial harmonic content is further minimized by using a symmetrical triangular waveform that has negligible even-harmonic content. Such a waveform can be converted into a sine wave by rounding off its peaks. This is generally accomplished in one of two ways, each of which is suitable to monolithic integration.

Converting into a sine wave

One method involves a piece-wise linear approximation using breakpoints to round off the triangle wave. This is usually done by diode-resistor or transistor-resistor circuits. A disadvantage of these types of wave-shaping circuit is that the input signal level, active device characteristics, and resistor ratios must be accurately controlled.

The other common method of converting a triangular wave into a sine wave is through the gradual cutoff of an overdriven differential transistor pair with an appropriate value of emitter resistance.

The differential gain state of the transistor pair used to generate the triangular wave can be adjusted to produce an overdrive condition by decreasing emitter resistance to a point where the input transistors are driven into cutoff. Figure 7 shows the voltage-current transfer characteristics of a such an overdriven circuit, with a triangular-wave input and a resulting sinusoidal output. The gradual transition between the active and

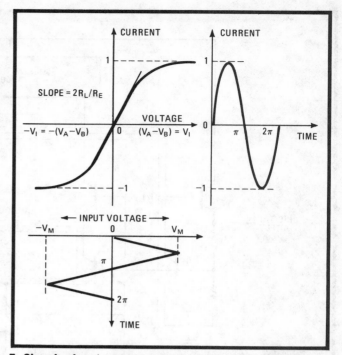

7. Sine shaping. A common method of converting a triangular wave (bottom left) into a low-distortion sine wave (right) is through the gradual cutoff of an overdriven differential transistor pair, whose transfer function is at top left, with an appropriate emitter resistance.

the cutoff regions is logarithmic. Thus the triangular wave is amplified linearly near the center but logarithmically at the peaks. As a result, the sharp peaks of the input signal are rounded off and it is transformed into the desired sine wave.

The advantage of the second approach is circuit simplicity. However, it also requires a constant-amplitude input adjustment for low distortion at a given emitter resistance. Both methods can, with adjustment, provide total harmonic distortions of less than 0.5%.

The last building block of the typical waveform generator in Fig. 1 is the modulator section. For function-generator applications, balanced modulators are preferred over conventional mixer types. Balanced modulators offer a high degree of carrier suppression and can be used for suppressed-carrier modulation, as well as for conventional double-sideband amplitude modulation. A simplified circuit diagram of a balanced modulator circut is shown in Fig. 8a. It is used almost exclusively by manufacturers of this type of IC because of its versatility and suitability for monolithic integration. In addition to performing amplitude modulation, this circuit also functions as a linear four-quadrant multiplier and phase detector. The balanced modulator's phase and amplitude transfer characteristics are shown in Fig. 8b.

Timers also work like oscillators

The well-known 555 timer IC operates much like the RC multivibrator low-frequency oscillator circuit of Fig. 2a when in its astable mode. The only difference is that resistor R_2 is in series with R_1, in place of R_1 alone. Switch S_1 is hooked up between ground and the connection between R_1 and R_2. Again, operation is by the same

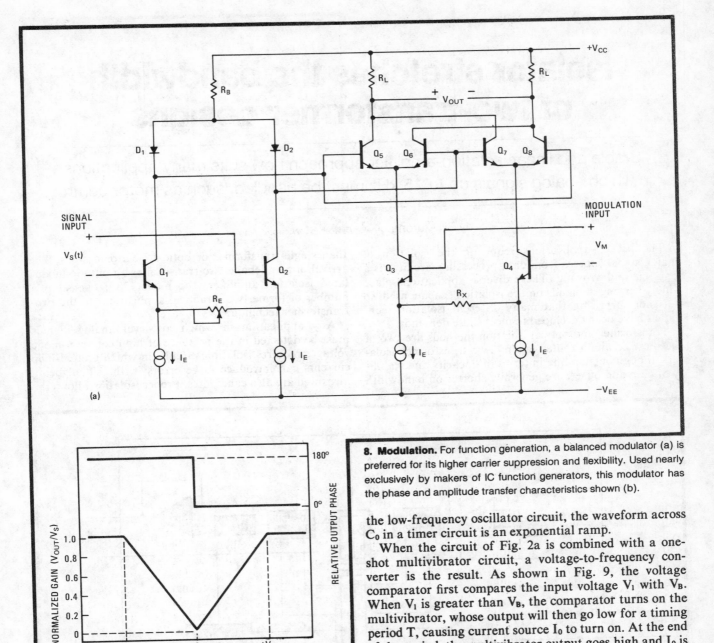

(a)

(b)

8. Modulation. For function generation, a balanced modulator (a) is preferred for its higher carrier suppression and flexibility. Used nearly exclusively by makers of IC function generators, this modulator has the phase and amplitude transfer characteristics shown (b).

the low-frequency oscillator circuit, the waveform across C_0 in a timer circuit is an exponential ramp.

When the circuit of Fig. 2a is combined with a one-shot multivibrator circuit, a voltage-to-frequency converter is the result. As shown in Fig. 9, the voltage comparator first compares the input voltage V_1 with V_B. When V_1 is greater than V_B, the comparator turns on the multivibrator, whose output will then go low for a timing period T, causing current source I_0 to turn on. At the end of the period, the multivibrator output goes high and I_0 is turned off.

V-f converter cycling

As long as V_B is not greater than V_1, the multivibrator keeps turning on and off for T-length durations until a sufficient charge (determined by the product of I_0 and T) is injected into the R_B and C_B network to cause V_B to become higher than V_1. When that happens, I_0 stays off and V_B decays until it equals V_1. This completes one cycle, and the V-f converter runs in a steady-state mode.

In the steady-state mode, I_0 charges C_B fast enough to keep V_B equal to or greater than V_1. Since the discharge rate of C_B is proportional to V_B/R_B, the frequency at which the circuit runs is proportional to the input voltage. The circuit's output is a series of pulses, with the length of durations, T, determined by the external RC components of the multivibrator.   □

charge-and-discharge cycle of capacitor C_0, except that the charging voltage is passed through the series combination of R_1 and R_2, instead of R_1 only. The output of the timer circuit is thus determined by the total resistance of R_1 and R_2 divided by the capacitance of C_0.

When the upper threshold of the timer circuit is reached, the circuit's output goes low and S_1 is turned on, discharging C_0 to ground through R_2. When the voltage reaches the lower threshold level, the threshold detector is triggered to begin a new cycle. During the discharge period, which is determined by R_2C_0, the output stays low, allowing a digital output waveform to be generated. If R_1 is made very small in value compared with R_2, the output becomes a square wave. As it is in

Isolator stretches the bandwidth of two-transformer designs

Stable and linear isolation-amplifier approach now suits many applications in which analog signals up to 15 kHz must be handled, such as motor control

by Bill Morong, *Analog Devices Inc., Norwood, Mass.*

☐ The list of applications requiring the isolation of analog signal sources from data-processing circuitry is a long one and growing. These diverse applications place widely varying demands on the isolation scheme used, so it is not surprising that many different isolation techniques have been developed to meet those demands.

Transformer and optical isolation methods are two of the most common routes taken. Two-transformer isolators, though outstanding in terms of linearity and stability of gain and offset, are generally shorter on bandwidth

than single-transformer or optical isolator designs. The arrival of a wideband two-transformer amplitude-modulated isolation amplifier, the model 289, opens up a number of formerly impractical applications to the two-transformer technique.

Any application in which low-level analog signals must be detected in the presence of high common-mode voltages requires isolation; circuits in which ground-loop currents can introduce large errors in the signal being measured are also candidates. Proper isolation allows the

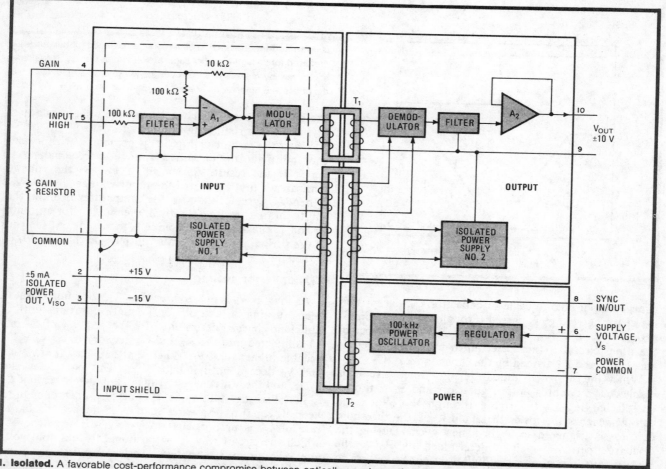

1. Isolated. A favorable cost-performance compromise between optically coupled and single-transformer isolation amplifiers is achieved by the wideband two-transformer model 289 isolation amplifier. It owes much of its high performance to its input and power isolation schemes.

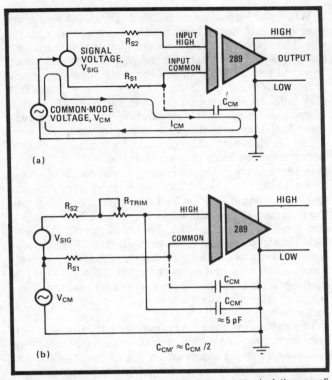

2. Common-mode. Finite capacitance across an isolation amplifier's isolation barrier limits common-mode rejection (a). Adding capacitor $C_{CM'}$ and resistor R_{TRIM} as in (b) causes the common-mode voltage across R_{S2} to cancel the common-mode voltage across R_{S1}.

transmission of a signal across a nonconducting barrier without a galvanic or electrical connection.

Of the wide variety of isolation techniques now in use, optical and magnetic isolation schemes are by far the most common in all but highly specialized applications. A knowledge of their strengths and weaknesses is important for a designer faced with isolation problems.

A typical transformer-coupled isolation amplifier incorporates an oscillator to generate the carrier signal. The isolation amplifier's input modulates this carrier. The input signal can be any frequency within the passband of the isolation amplifier—including dc. The modulated carrier is passed through a signal transformer and demodulated, where a replica of the input signal is reconstructed at the isolation amplifier's output port.

The second transformer

Transformer-coupled isolation amplifiers often contain a second transformer that makes the unmodulated carrier signal available on both sides of the isolation barrier. This unmodulated carrier signal is used to facilitate modulation and demodulation and to generate dc power to energize the isolation amplifier's input or output circuitry. It can sometimes be used for powering external circuits.

Two-transformer isolation amplifiers have been available for a long time and are convenient to use. They feature input-offset drifts of a few microvolts per °C, gain-temperature coefficients under 50 parts per million per °C, and gain nonlinearities of less than 0.01%. Long-

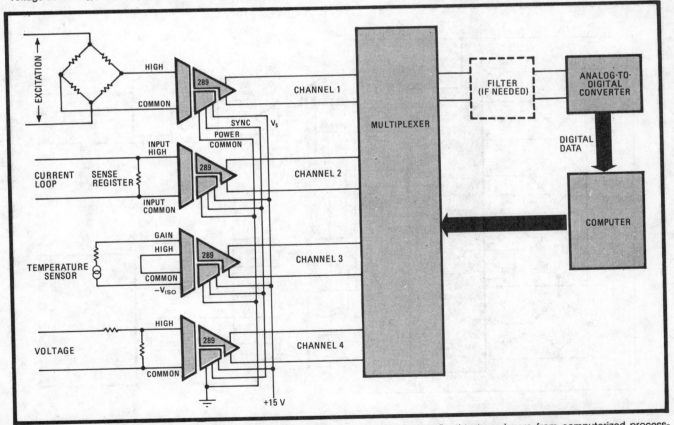

3. Process control. A two-transformer isolation amplifier is sufficiently linear to isolate floating transducers from computerized process-control equipment. The analog-to-digital converter used must be monotonic to guard against instability in closed-loop systems.

term stability of these parameters is also excellent. But they have had one major limitation: bandwidths of not much more than 3 or 4 kilohertz.

For higher bandwidths, optically coupled isolation amplifiers were developed that have bandwidths up to 15 kHz. In such isolation amplifiers, the input signal modulates the intensity of beams of light generated by light-emitting diodes. The modulated light beams impinge upon light-sensitive diodes that generate output currents roughly proportional to the intensity of the impinging light. In optically coupled isolation amplifiers, the current from the light-sensitive diodes is fed to circuitry that converts it into an isolation-amplifier output voltage. Other light-sensitive diode currents are fed back to the isolation amplifier's input circuit to help remove gain nonlinearity and instability normally introduced by the variations in the transfer efficiency of the LEDs, the optical path, and the light-sensitive diodes.

Besides extending bandwidths, optical isolation amplifiers also have input offset drifts and gain temperature coefficients similar to those of transformer-coupled units. One drawback, however, is a long-term gain shift that is typically an order of magnitude greater than that of transformer-coupled isolators. That shift is caused by aging of the optical components.

Another drawback is that although optical isolators require no carrier signal, a separate dc-dc converter is needed to power the amplifier's input and output circuits. This hurts the cost advantage of an optically coupled isolator over a transformer-coupled one.

Wideband transformer-coupled isolation amplifiers have been introduced in which the functions of separate signal and power transformers are combined into a single transformer. Such isolation amplifiers feature about twice the bandwidth of optically coupled units and comparable nonlinearities. They are also less expensive. But they suffer from increased offset drift and the generation of excessive noise in the modulation-demodulation process. And they are also susceptible to semipermanent shifts of electrical characteristics when subjected to strong magnetic fields that are later removed.

Improvements in the design and construction of transformers allow the model 289 two-transformer isolation-amplifier module to offer 15-kHz bandwidth and retain the approach's traditional strengths—excellent isolation and good dc characteristics. Packaged in a 2.25-cubic-inch plastic case, this three-port isolator (Fig. 1) contains a dc-dc converter for isolated ±15-volt power-supply lines, an output-port buffer, and a current-limiting regulator that allows operation over a wide range of supply voltages without any degradation in performance.

The 289 represents a favorable cost-performance compromise between optically coupled and single-transformer isolation designs. An error budget has been calculated for all three approaches (see "A comparison of error budgets," p. 156). Although the small-signal bandwidth of the dual-transformer method employed in the model 289 is less than that of the single-transformer design, gain nonlinearity and gain change with temperature of

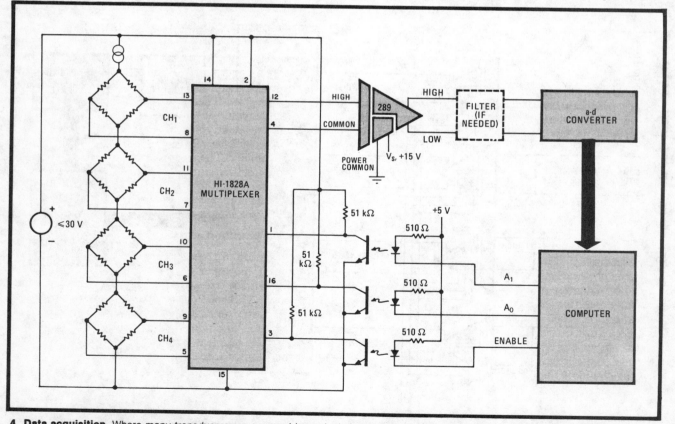

4. Data acquisition. Where many transducers are powered by a single low-voltage supply, a multiplexer can be used to feed into a single isolation amplifier. This circuit is only useful for cases in which the potential between transducers does not exceed 30 volts.

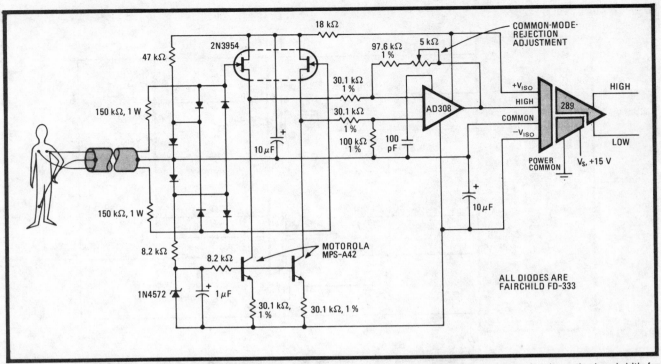

5. Patient isolation. Although many isolation amplifiers are used in electrocardiograph patient-lead isolation, few have the bandwidth for applications like electromyography and pacemaker-pulse analysis — but the 289 is wideband enough for these medical uses.

the former method are as good, if not better. Moreover, offset-voltage changes with temperature are by far the lowest with the two-transformer design.

The presence of a carrier signal in a transformer-coupled isolation amplifier inevitably leads to a carrier-ripple component in the isolation-amplifier's output. As the bandwidth of an isolation amplifer becomes a larger fraction of its carrier frequency, ripple becomes more difficult to control. Despite this fact, the 289 isolation amplifier produces less ripple than many other transformer-coupled isolation amplifiers having much less bandwidth. This low ripple level means less need for output filtering.

Holding down ripple

To keep power-supply ripple from modulating the isolation-amplifier's carrier signal, voltage regulators should be used. Some isolation amplifiers have built-in regulators, not only to eliminate power-supply ripple effects, but also prevent carrier-frequency spikes from being broadcast to the rest of the system via the isolation amplifier's power terminal.

Another potential problem is that of output loading. For many isolation amplifiers with unbuffered output impedances of 1,000 ohms or more, the use of low-impedance loads can lead to large gain errors. The use of external output buffering is recommended in such cases. Of course, those isolation amplifers with internal output buffering eliminate the need to do so.

Three-port isolation amplifiers are easier to apply than two-port ones, since the latter have their power-supply and output-port returns through a common terminal. But even three-port ones are not all of the same construction and thus offer differing degrees of isolation

between output and power ports. For example, some three-port isolation amplifiers have their power-supply and output ports connected by a capacitor. The capacitor permits carrier current to pass but blocks dc, allowing moderate levels of output common-mode voltages. However, the carrier signal's return through external circuits can introduce ripple currents into those external circuits.

True three-port isolation amplifiers like the model 289 have galvanically isolated ports between which neither ac nor dc can flow. Their outputs can be connected to common-mode voltages of either polarity, within the output common-mode voltage range of the isolator.

Certain precautions must be observed when applying isolation amplifiers. The most obvious is that the circuit in which the isolation amplifier is used must be wired in such a manner that the amplifier's isolation properties are not lost. This means that adequate spacing must be provided between input and output circuits.

Maximizing common-mode rejection

The conversion of common-mode signals into normal-mode ones at the input to an isolation amplifier limits the common-mode rejection of the amplifier to some finite value. A certain amount of capacitance exists between circuitry on either side of the isolation barrier, and it causes a common-mode current to flow when a common-mode voltage is applied across the barrier (Fig. 2a). This common-mode current is proportional to the applied voltage of the common-mode signal, its frequency, and the barrier capacitance.

For most isolation amplifiers, the common input terminal forms a more direct path for the common-mode current caused by the barrier capacitance than the high input terminal, so most of the common-mode current

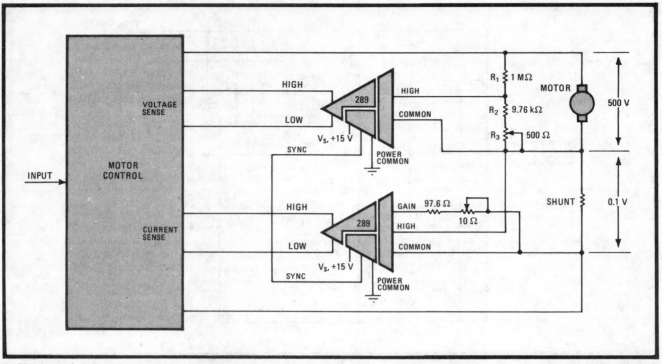

6. Motor control. The 289 isolation amplifier has sufficient bandwidth and low enough phase shift to be used in motor and ac load-control applications. Two isolators are used, one to sense motor current and another to feed armature-voltage information to the controller.

flows through the common input terminal. If a normal-mode signal source with two equal output resistors is connected to an isolation amplifier as shown in Fig. 2a, a common-mode–induced normal-mode signal appears in series with the signal source and is treated by the system as a normal-mode signal.

One way to minimize the effects of common-mode currents is to interpose a shield in the isolation barrier to intercept common-mode currents and divert them around the input-source resistance. Another method is to employ a differential input stage ahead of the isolation amplifier. These techniques, however, may be limited for those cases where physical space is at a premium and little room is available for shields or additional input stages. In such cases, common-mode rejection can be maximized by minimizing the capacitance value across the isolation barrier.

For applications in which the source resistance is known and is relatively constant, large common-mode-rejection improvements can be obtained at little extra cost using the circuit of Fig. 2b. Adding capacitor $C_{CM'}$ causes more common-mode current to flow in R_{S2} and R_{TRIM}. The proper adjustment of R_{TRIM} can develop a voltage in series with the high input terminal that can cancel the common-mode–induced voltage across R_{S1}. The penalty for this approach is a small increase in common-mode current (about 0.25 microampere at 117 volts, 60 hertz). $C_{CM'}$ must be capable of withstanding the full common-mode voltage across the isolation amplifier.

Using a lengthy cable to connect a high-impedance device to the input of an isolator exacerbates the problem of converting common-mode signals into normal-mode ones and opposes the cancellation obtained in

Fig. 2b. The use of a long cable between signal source and isolation amplifier should therefore be avoided.

When data must be acquired from floating transducers for computerized process-control systems, a two-transformer isolation amplifier like the model 289 may be used for potential differences or to interrupt ground loops among transducers or between transducers and local ground levels (Fig. 3).

In process control

Since the isolation amplifier and the analog-to-digital converter are likely to be included in a large feedback loop, the converter must be monotonic and isolation must be sufficiently linear not to induce non-monotonic behavior. Lack of monotonicity can cause instability in the feedback loop.

In using the circuit of Fig. 3, it is desirable that the isolation amplifiers be protected against differential input overloads. Otherwise, miswiring the amplifiers to the ac power line can cause them to fail. Furthermore, the isolation amplifiers should be synchronized to avoid errors caused by beat-frequency signals generated by the mixing of the amplifiers' individual carrier frequencies. The connection of the synchronization terminals in Fig. 3 achieves this purpose. This circuit suffices for common-mode voltages up to 2,500 v peak, ac or dc.

In a data-acquisition system in which multiple transducers are powered by a single supply and the voltage level of that supply is sufficiently low that a multiplexer can handle all of the transducers' voltages, a lone isolation amplifier and a multiplexer can be used (Fig. 4). In the past, such a configuration has not been generally possible because of the speed limitations of the isolation amplifiers available. The model 289 isolation amplifier,

A comparison of error budgets

A comparison of error budgets for the three most common analog isolation schemes—two-transformer designs such as the model 289, optically coupled hybrid amplifiers, and single-transformer amplifiers—shows clearly the first technique's advantages over the other two. The following calculations are based on the summary of major specifications listed in the table. For the sake of brevity, only major error sources are treated. Calculations are for a circuit with unity gain, with an output of 10 volts full scale (±5 V). Operation is at 25°C±25°C, and it is assumed that initial gain and offset errors are trimmed out.

A gain temperature coefficient of 0.005%/°C multiplied by a 25°C span yields 0.125% of full scale for the dual-transformer scheme (listed first in the table). Next, input and output offset voltages as a function of temperature, ±10 and +50 microvolts/°C yield 1,500 μV, which is 0.015% of the 10-V full-scale output. The new error sum is now 0.125% (gain temperature coefficient) plus 0.015% (offset voltage), which equals 0.14%. Add to this gain nonlinearity of 0.01%, and the total error becomes 0.15% of full scale.

The gain temperature coefficient of the second design, with optical coupling, is the same as that of the dual-transformer scheme—0.125% for a 25°C span. The 455-μV/°C offset voltage multiplied by 25°C yields 11,375 μV, which is 0.114% of 10 V. When the linearity error of 0.05% of full scale is added, the total (0.125%+0.114%+0.05%) is 0.289%.

For the third, single-transformer design, the gain tem-perature coefficient of 0.006%/°C multiplied by a 25°C span yields 0.15% of full scale. The 525-μV/°C offset voltage multiplied by 25°C yields 13,125 μV, which is 0.13% of 10 V. When the linearity error of 0.05% of full scale is added, the total (0.15%+0.13%+0.05%) comes to 0.33%.

For gains other than unity, the calculations become more complicated. The stability of user-supplied gain resistors can affect the amplifier's gain stability, so the effects of these must be included. (This is also true at unity gain for isolation amplifiers in which gain is set to unity by user-supplied resistors.) At different levels of isolation-amplifier gain, offset drift varies, further complicating error-budget calculations. For example, the first isolation scheme has less total offset drift below a gain of 80 than the second. Above a gain of 80, the second scheme has less total offset drift than the first. And the third, the single-transformer design, has more offset drift at all levels of gain than the other two.

Other complicating factors include errors caused by input-difference current and by noise. For applications involving low source resistance, these errors are small enough to be negligible. If, however, it becomes necessary to add resistors in series with the input of an isolation amplifier for differential-overload protection, these errors may become large enough to merit consideration. Because the input structures of different isolation amplifiers vary greatly, including these errors in the above calculations is very difficult if not impossible.

| | | | | PERFORMANCE COMPARISON OF THREE ISOLATION AMPLIFIER TYPES |
Isolator type	Small-signal bandwidth (kHz)	Maximum gain nonlinearity (percentage of full scale)	Maximum gain temperature coefficient (percentage of full scale/°C)	Maximum offset-voltage temperature coefficient (μV/°C, G = gain)
Two-transformer plastic module	15	0.01	0.005	±10 ±50/G
Optically coupled hybrid	15	0.05	0.005	±5 ±450/G
Single-transformer hybrid	30	0.05	0.006	±25 ±500/G

however, has a sufficiently short settling time to make its use practical in this circuit.

The approach shown in Fig. 4 is useful when the voltage difference between any two terminals of the transducers does not exceed 30 v. A limitation of this circuit is that, though the input of the isolation amplifier is protected against ac power-line voltages, the amplifier's power terminals as well as the multiplexer are not.

Addressing of the multiplexer in Fig. 4 is binary, with an enable signal being provided for the selection of the signal-source circuit. Digital signals are optically isolated. For several groups of transducers, several circuits may be used as in Fig. 4, in which case the isolation amplifiers are synchronized for operation. And if several transducers share the same common terminal, that terminal can be attached to the input common of the isolator, halving the number of switching elements.

In wideband vibration analysis, a strain gage may be bonded to a mechanical member that is subject to stress. Strain produced in the mechanical member is transmitted to the strain gage. Since the gage must be intimately connected to the mechanical member, it may be desirable to isolate its output. For cases in which the frequencies of interest extend much beyond a few hundred hertz, a wideband isolation amplifier like the model 289 can be used. The use of variable filters at the isolation amplifier's output stage makes it possible to view on an oscilloscope particular frequency spectra.

Medical applications

The 289 is useful in medical applications such as patient isolation. Although many isolation amplifiers are used in electrocardiograph patient-lead isolation, few have the bandwidth necessary for use in electro-

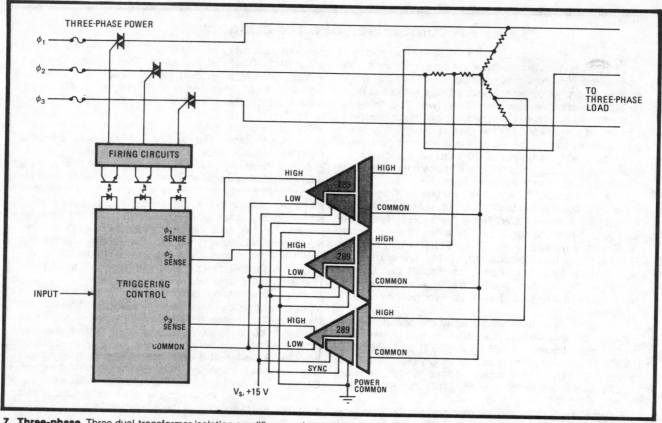

7. Three-phase. Three dual-transformer isolation amplifiers can be used in a control circuit for a three-phase ac load. Each amplifier senses a line's voltage, produces a replica of the waveform sensed, and provides this replica waveform to the trigger-control circuit.

myography or for the analysis of pacemaker pulses.

The circuit of Fig. 5 is useful for such applications. A differential amplifier is connected to the isolation amplifier's input. This allows the 289's common input to be connected to the patient so that the patient's common-mode voltage drives the amplifier. A balanced input structure reduces the normal-mode noise that is converted from common-mode noise.

The circuit's FET inputs allow the use of large-value input-protection resistors without affecting noise performance. These input resistors, along with the clamping diodes, protect the isolation amplifier's input structure from defibrillator pulses and protect the patient from fault currents that can develop in the event of the failure of a preamplifier component.

The differential input of Fig. 5 is converted into a single-ended input suitable for use by the isolation amplifier. The gain stage used for this conversion does not make use of unduly high impedance values, thus minimizing noise generation. The input diode should be of a low-leakage type and must not be light-sensitive lest photocurrents be generated in the input structure.

In any patient-lead isolation application, wiring on the patient's side of the isolation amplifier is as critical as the isolation properties of the amplifier itself. Since this wiring is an extension of the patient's vulnerable area, its proper selection is critical. For example, some cables produce copious noise when flexed, thus ruining the otherwise noise-free performance of an isolation system. Cable length can also be a problem. A few tens of feet of

patient cable along a concrete floor can entirely bypass the capacitive isolation of the amplifier.

For motor and ac load control, the use of two-transformer-coupled isolation amplifiers has not usually been possible because of such amplifiers' bandwidth limitations. Thus optically coupled isolation amplifiers equipped with floating power sources to energize their input amplifiers have been used. The two-transformer design used in the model 289 makes it possible to use transformer-coupled isolation amplifiers for motor and ac load-control applications. This amplifier possesses sufficient bandwidth and low enough phase shift to make its use practical in such applications.

Faithful replication

Figure 6 shows two dual-transformer isolation amplifiers sensing the armature voltage and current of a motor. Faithful replicas of the waveforms of these variables are delivered to the motor control. Isolation amplifier A_1 operates at unity gain from divider R_1–R_3 to deliver an output that is 1/100 of the armature voltage. Isolation amplifier A_2 operates at a gain of 100 to deliver a voltage that is 100 times that developed across the current-sensing resistor.

Figure 7 shows three dual-transformer isolation amplifiers sensing the voltages on the three lines of a three-phase ac load. The Y network divides the voltages of the three phases and creates a neutral for the input commons of the isolation amplifiers. The output of each isolation amplifier is a faithful replica of the waveform

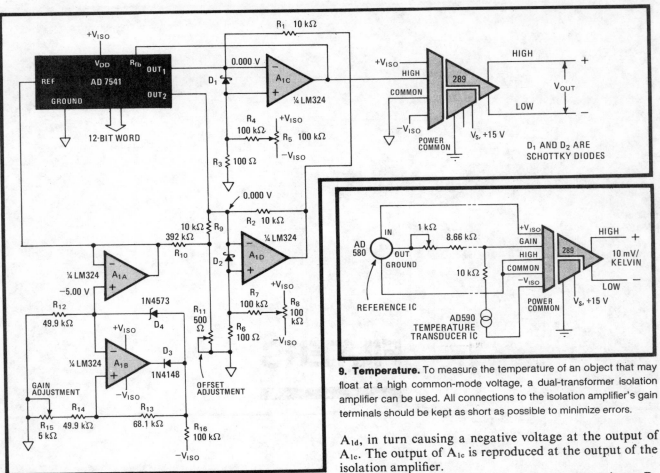

8. Converter. The 289 two-transformer isolation amplifier can be used to isolate the output of a 12-bit digital-to-analog converter. Resistors R_5 and R_8 should be adjusted to produce less than 0.5 millivolt at both d-a converter outputs for this circuit to work properly.

of the phase that it senses. The isolation-amplifier outputs provide the feedback necessary for the trigger control to correctly fire the triacs. These same outputs could also be fed to root-mean-square-to-dc converters in similar ac load-control applications.

A note of caution on the use of the circuit of Fig. 7: since transformer-coupled isolation amplifiers are susceptible to applied magnetic fields, it is best to place them outside the leakage fields of motors, transformers and other sources of magnetic interference. If this is not done, these magnetic fields can modulate the signals passing through the isolation amplifiers.

Figure 8 shows a dual-transformer isolation amplifier providing a 12-bit d-a converter with isolated output-voltage capability. A buffered −5-v reference voltage is provided to the converter by amplifiers A_{1a} and A_{1b} and their associated circuitry. The fractional value of a digital-word input to the converter causes a proportional fraction of the d-a converter current to flow in the converter's OUT$_1$ output terminal. The remaining converter current flows into the converter's OUT$_2$ terminal. Current flowing into OUT$_1$ causes a positive voltage at the output of amplifier A_{1c}. Current flowing into OUT$_2$ of the converter causes a positive voltage at the output of

A_{1d}, in turn causing a negative voltage at the output of A_{1c}. The output of A_{1c} is reproduced at the output of the isolation amplifier.

For the circuit of Fig. 8 to work properly, resistors R_5 and R_8 must be adjusted to produce less than 0.5 millivolt at both d-a converter outputs. Resistor R_{15} can be used for gain adjustment, while resistor R_{11} can be used to adjust the output offset between an input binary code of 100000000000 and one of 0. Circuit operation is bipolar with a ±5-v swing.

Measuring floating temperatures

A dual-transformer isolation amplifier like the 289 may be used in applications where it is necessary to measure the temperature of an object that may float at a high common-mode voltage, as shown in Fig. 9. The isolation amplifier provides a ground-referenced output.

In the circuit of Fig. 9, the temperature sensor sinks a current of −1 microampere per kelvin. This current flows from the gain terminal of the isolation amplifier, developing across the amplifier's internal feedback resistor a voltage of +10 millivolts/K. This voltage appears at the isolation amplifier's output.

For an output of 10 mv/°C, the circuitry shown with a dotted connection can be used. A current of +273 μA is sourced through the 8.66-kilohm resistor and the 1-kΩ potentiometer, canceling the temperature-sensor current at 0°C (273 K). This results in 0 mv at the amplifier output at 0°C.

For proper operation of the circuit in Fig. 9, all connections to the isolation amplifier's gain terminals should be kept as short as possible. □

9. Temperature. To measure the temperature of an object that may float at a high common-mode voltage, a dual-transformer isolation amplifier can be used. All connections to the isolation amplifier's gain terminals should be kept as short as possible to minimize errors.

FILTERS

Tracking filters demodulate two audio-band fm signals

by Stephen Barnes
Center for Bioengineering, University of Washington, Seattle

Because of the way in which they retrieve recorded data, many systems designed for monitoring biomedical functions have to demodulate two closely spaced fm carrier signals in the audio-frequency band. The original data signals could be recovered with low-pass filters, but they are an expensive solution since their cutoff must be sharp to prevent cross modulation, signal blocking, or undue limiting of the bandwidth needed by one or both signals. The low-cost solution shown here, however, uses a dividing phase-locked loop to demodulate one signal and to provide the clock signal for a tracking notch filter that recovers the other channel of data.

The advantages of the circuit may be seen for a typical monitoring case in which a 30-hertz electrocardiogram signal (having a frequency too low to be recorded directly on cassette tape) is placed on a 9-kilohertz carrier. This signal is applied to the LF356 amplifier along with a 0-to-6-kHz signal from an ultrasonic doppler flowmeter that provides data on blood circulation.

Block A, the dividing phase-locked loop module, oscillates at a free-running frequency equal to $8f_m$. It is here that the 9-kHz carrier is directly demodulated. Also included in block A is a 74C193 divide-by-8 counter in the PLL's feedback loop, which provides the driving signals for the CD4051 multiplexer in block B. This block contains the sampling filter which passes frequencies equal to 1/8 the sampling frequency, $8f_m$, and its harmonics. Thus the doppler data is notched out by the sampling filter. But signal $\vec{f}_m$ is subtracted from the original input signal $\vec{f}_o + \vec{f}_m$ by the differential amplifier in block C. Therefore, only signal f_o will appear at the output.

Resistor R_Q, which is in the PLL's feedback loop, controls the width of the notch, which is given by $B = 1/8\pi\ R_Q C_Q$, where B is the width defined by the filter's upper 3-decibel frequency minus its lower 3-dB frequency. Potentiometer R_B is used for balancing the differential amplifier by nulling the 9-kHz feedthrough signal.

When the circuit is in the locked state, the minimum attenuation of the fm signal will be approximately 33 dB for input signals ranging from 540 millivolts to 8 volts peak to peak. Below signal levels of 540 mV, feedthrough from the multiplexer will reduce the attenuation.

Because the filter is a sampling device, it is subject to aliasing if any input-frequency components approach the Nyquist limit of $4f_m$, so that precautions should be taken to prevent this. Spurious output components that are higher harmonics of the 9-kHz fm signal or the clock signal can be removed easily.

Phase jitter in the PLL should also be minimized, for it causes narrow noise sidebands centered about the 9-kHz fm signal and separated from it by a frequency equal to the loop bandwidth of the PLL. The amplitude of these noise sidebands in a properly adjusted circuit should be down at least 33 dB from the level of the fm signals at the input. □

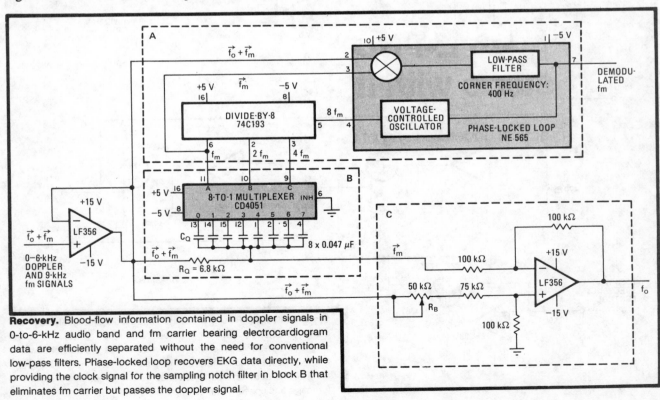

Recovery. Blood-flow information contained in doppler signals in 0-to-6-kHz audio band and fm carrier bearing electrocardiogram data are efficiently separated without the need for conventional low-pass filters. Phase-locked loop recovers EKG data directly, while providing the clock signal for the sampling notch filter in block B that eliminates fm carrier but passes the doppler signal.

Voltage-controlled integrator sets filter's bandwidth

by Henrique Sarmento Malvar
Department of Electrical Engineering, University of Brazilia, Brazil

Because it uses operational transconductance amplifiers as electrically tuned integrators for selecting a state-variable filter's center frequency and bandwidth virtually independently of one another, this circuit is ideal for use in music and speech synthesizers that require individual voltage-controlled setting of these parameters.

As shown, input signals to be processed are applied to transconductance amplifier A_1, whose bias current is derived from voltage-to-current driver A_5Q_5. The bias current, in turn, is set by control voltage V_ω, which ultimately determines the filter's center frequency. In general, $I_{bias} = V_\omega/2R_{11}$.

Placing the capacitor C_ω across the output of the operational transconductance amplifiers A_1 and A_2 converts the two-stage network into a noninverting integrator, the transfer function becoming $V_o(s)/V_i(s) = k/s$, where k is the 3080's transconductance factor k'/C, and transconductance k' as given in its data sheets is $k' = 19.2\ I_{bias}$. Substituting for I_{bias}, $V_o(s)/V_i(s) = 19.2\ V_\omega/sRC_\omega$.

Placing integrator A_3 in the feedback loop of A_1 and A_2 equips the basic filter with the capability to control bandwidth. As seen from inspection of the circuit:

$$V_x(s) = R_1\|R_2\|R_3\|R_4\left[\frac{V_1(s)}{R_1} + \frac{V_y(s)}{R_3} + \frac{V_{LP}(s)}{R_4}\right]$$

where the low-pass function is given by:
$$V_{LP}(s) = -(k_2/s)^2 V_x(s)R_6/(R_5+R_6)$$
and where $V_y(s) = -k_1 V_x(s)/s$. Constants k_1 and k_2 are given by:
$$k_1 = 19.2\ V_B/R_7C_B$$
$$k_2 = 19.2\ V_\omega/2R_{11}C_\omega$$
and the bandpass function, $V_{BP}(s)$, equals $-k_2V_x(s)/s$.

Assuming $R_1 = R_3 = R_4 = R_5 = R'$ and $R_2 = R_6 = R''$, with $R''/R' = a \ll 1$, it follows that $R_1\|R_2\|R_3\|R_4 = R_2$. Substituting the appropriate quantities back into all the above equations, it is seen that:
$$V_{LP}(s)/V_i(s) = -1/[(s/\omega_o)^2 + (B/\omega_o)(s/\omega_o) + 1]$$
$$V_{BP}(s)/V_i(s) = -(s/\omega_o)/[(s/\omega_o)^2 + (B/\omega_o)(s/\omega_o) + 1]$$

where the resonant frequency and the bandwidth are given by:
$$\omega_o(rad/s) = ak_2 = 19.2aV_\omega/2R_{11}C_\omega$$
$$B(rad/s) = ak_1 = 19.2aV_B/R_7C_B$$

Parameter a should be near 0.01, to ensure the best compromise between distortion and signal-to-noise ratio. The bias current of the operational transconductance amplifier should not be more than 500 microamperes. □

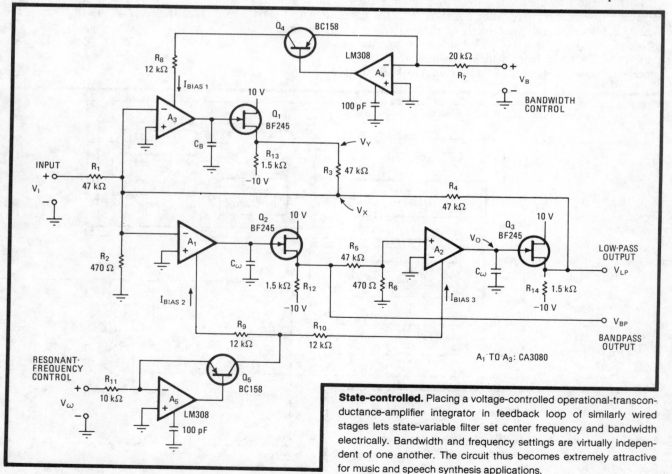

State-controlled. Placing a voltage-controlled operational-transconductance-amplifier integrator in feedback loop of similarly wired stages lets state-variable filter set center frequency and bandwidth electrically. Bandwidth and frequency settings are virtually independent of one another. The circuit thus becomes extremely attractive for music and speech synthesis applications.

Inverting amplifier flips filter's response curve

by Henrique Sarmento Malvar
Department of Electrical Engineering, University of Brazilia, Brazil

The voltage-controlled bandpass filter so popular in music synthesizers and useful in remote-tuned receivers can be also made to work in the band-reject mode by placing an inverting operational amplifier stage in the existing filter's input/output feedback loop. In that way, a controlled notch, which is often equally valuable in the aforementioned applications, may be put together at low cost.

The transfer function of the typical VCF is given by:

$$H(s) = (s/\omega_o)/[(s/\omega_o)^2 + 2k(s/\omega_o) + 1]$$

where ω_o is the voltage-controlled resonant frequency and k is the damping factor, which is usually adjusted with a potentiometer. It is seen that when k is at its maximum, the response approaches that of a wideband filter. As k decreases, the filter's Q increases, and the bandwidth therefore decreases. At the limit, for a value of k that is slightly negative, the system oscillates at ω_o.

By adding the operational amplifier and its gain-controlling resistors to the feedback loop of the VCF as shown in (a), the output voltage generated is:

$$V_o(s) = -V_o(s)H(s) - V_i(s)$$

This expression leads to the transfer function:

$$H'(s) = \frac{V_o(s)}{V_i(s)} = \frac{(s/\omega_o)^2 + 2k(s/\omega_o) + 1}{(s/\omega_o)^2 + (2k+1)(s/\omega_o) + 1}$$

This function has two zeros and two correspondingly equal poles. But although the absolute value of both pairs is the same, for $k > -0.25$ the poles will be more damped than the zeros, and thus the filter's frequency response will be mainly determined by the zeros. Therefore, the system will operate as a band-reject filter (b).

The deepest null is attained at k = 0, and a theoretically infinite attenuation is thereby achieved at $\omega = \omega_o$. Thus the filter can be tuned to null the fundamental frequency of any synthesized signal, leaving only its harmonics. If the frequency control is simultaneously fed with a low-frequency sine or triangle wave, the so-called phaser sound used for special effects is obtained.

As k is increased toward infinity, the null becomes less sharp and the filter offers almost no attenuation at any frequency, thereby behaving as a quasi–all-pass network. Note that as k increases beyond k = 10, the filter response approaches that of k = -0.25. Clearly, k should not be less than -0.25, because the poles of the function will again become prominent and the system will once more behave as a bandpass filter. At $k < -0.50$, the system will oscillate. □

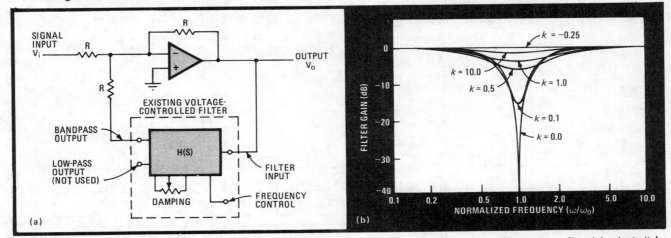

Double duty. Adding inverting op-amp stage into feedback loop of music synthesizer voltage-controlled bandpass filter (a) adapts it for band-rejection duties. Notch depth (b), selected by filter's damping potentiometer, may be adjusted for a maximum value of −60 dB.

Logic-gate filter handles digital signals

by Andrzej M. Cisek
Electronics for Medicine, Honeywell Inc., Pleasantville, N. Y.

Performing the digital counterpart of electric-wave filtering in the analog domain, this unit can function as a low-pass, high-pass, bandpass, or band-reject filter of a square-wave pulse train. No RC integrating networks or comparators are needed, the all-digital filter being tuned simply by adjusting the reference frequency. Built originally for biomedical applications, it can find much broader use in the field of communications.

Consider the case of the band-reject filter shown in (a) in the figure. As seen with the aid of the timing diagram, the Q output of the edge-triggered set-reset flip-flop formed by the gates of the CD4011, A_1–A_4, and the 4013 D flip-flop (B_1) is brought high by the training edge of reference frequency f_0 and brought low by the falling edge of signal f_1. The combined output of the flip-flop and f_0 appears at gate C_1, moving low if $f_0 > f_1$.

Similarly, C_2 moves low if $f_1 > f_0$. Therefore, signals from the output of the NAND gate formed by NOR gates D_1–D_4 appear whenever $f_0 \neq f_1$. Each pulse sets flip-flop B_2 high if it is not already so, permitting signal f_1 to pass through to the output.

Meanwhile, the 12-stage 4040 ripple counter advances on each pulse from f_0. The counter will reach the Q_n state if $f_0 = f_1$, because no reset pulse can emanate from gate D_4 under that condition. These events will disable gate C_3 and prevent f_1 from reaching the output.

The steepness of the filter's roll-off characteristic will be determined by which stage of the counter resets flip-flop B_2. The filter's reaction time to changes in the input and reference frequencies will vary accordingly—that is, the steeper the slope, the longer the response time, this delay being the major drawback of the filter. The corner frequencies are $f_{1 min} = (N-1)f_0/N$ and $f_{1 max} = (N+1)f_0/N$, where N is the number of pulses of f_0 required for the counter to produce a reset pulse. The quality factor is $Q = f_0/\Delta f_1 = N/2$.

The stop-band filter can be easily modified to a bandpass type if the $\overline{Q}$ output of flip-flop B_2 is wired to serve as the inhibit line. To convert the filter for low-pass duties C_2 is removed and both inputs of D_3 are connected to D_1. In like fashion, C_1 is removed and both inputs of

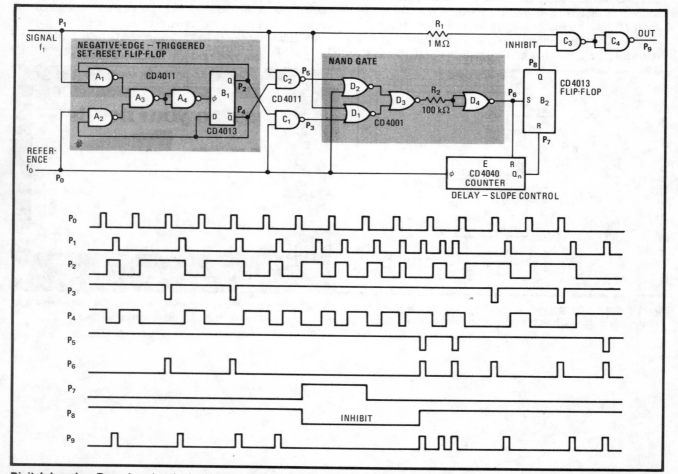

Digital damping. To perform band-reject function, this combinational logic circuit ascertains the frequency relationship of two square-wave signals. Tuning is done by adjusting the reference frequency. Selectivity is determined by tap position Q_n of the counter. Waveforms for given points in circuit show timing relationships. With minor changes, the filter is easily adapted for high-pass, low-pass, and bandpass duties.

D₃ are connected to D₂ if a high-pass response is desired. Note that the NOR-gate circuitry is required to avoid any ambiguity of output state when pulses of input and reference signals overlap. Also, resistors R_1 and R_2 neutralize the effect of variable propagation-time differences of f_0 and f_1 through the gates ☐

Low-pass Chebyshev filters use standard-value capacitors

by Ed Wetherhold
Honeywell Inc., Signal Analysis Center, Annapolis, Md.

If a low-pass filtering requirement is such that a roll-off attenuation of 40 decibels per octave is adequate, this table will enable rapid design of seven-element filters of the Chebyshev variety using standard-value capacitors. Both L and C values are given directly for operation in the 1-to-10-megahertz region and are scaled for frequencies outside this range. Element values, specified for filters having a source and load impedance of 50 ohms, are easily calculated for any impedance.

Component values for the Chebyshev filter (see table), which is characterized by low-level equi-ripple response throughout its passband, have been derived by an 85-line program written in Basic. In this configuration and for the equally terminated case, $C_1 = C_7$, $C_3 = C_5$ and $L_2 = L_6$. Once a standard-capacitor value for C_3/C_5 is specified, capacitors C_1/C_7 and inductors L_2, L_4, and L_6 are found for a given reflection coefficient selected to ensure that C_1 is also a standard value. The frequencies corresponding to the 1-, 3-, and 50-dB attenuation points are also calculated.

A simple example illustrates the use of the table. Consider the case of a filter whose 3-dB cutoff frequency, F_3^x, is 6 megahertz and whose terminating impedance, Z_x, is 75 ohms. The user must:

■ Find the scaled impedance factor $R = Z_x/50$.

■ Calculate the 3-dB cutoff frequency of the 50-Ω filter from $F_3^{50} = R \cdot F_3^x$, dividing Z_x by 10^n where $n = 1, 2, \ldots$ if necessary to ensure $F_3^{50} < 10$ MHz.

■ From the table, select the design closest to that meeting the calculated F_3^{50} requirement. Note the tabulated values of C will be used directly in this design, and the L values will be scaled.

■ Calculate the exact value of $F_3^x = F_3'^{50}/R$, where $F_3'^{50}$ is the tabulated value.

■ Calculate the new L_2/L_6 and L_4 values for the given terminating impedance from $L = R^2 L_{50}$.

Given $F_3^x = 6.0$ MHz and $Z_x = 75\ \Omega$, it is seen that $R = 75/50 = 1.5$, $R^2 = 2.25$ and $F_3^{50} = 1.5(6)$ MHz $= 9.0$ MHz. Filter number 109 is selected because its F_3^{50} value is closest to the desired specified value. Thus $C_{1,7} = 390$ pF, and $C_{3,5} = 750$ pF. Inductors $L_{2,6} = R^2(1.39) = 3.13$ microhenries; $L_4 = R^2(1.57) = 3.53\ \mu H$. These components may be conveniently hand-wound on standard toroidal cores that are readily available. Note that design 109 has a reflection coefficient of 9.99%. If the filter must be operated at a low voltage standing-wave ratio, then design 113, which has a reflection coefficient of only 1.93%, should be used. □

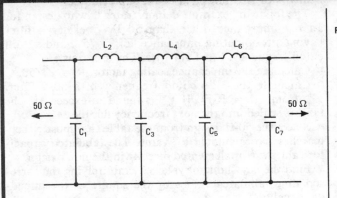

Filter No.	Frequency (MHz) 1 dB	3 dB	50 dB	Reflection coefficient %	$C_{1,7}$ (pF)	$C_{3,5}$ (pF)	$L_{2,6}$ (µH)	L_4 (µH)
1	.95	1.04	2.28	.455E-02	1500	5600	10.1	15.3
2	.99	1.06	2.17	.255E 00	1800	5600	10.9	14.8
3	1.04	1.10	2.08	.178E 01	2200	5600	11.4	14.0
4	1.12	1.16	2.06	.663E 01	2700	5600	10.9	12.6
5	1.29	1.33	2.19	.189E 02	3300	5600	8.86	9.69
6	1.07	1.15	2.43	.630E-01	1500	5100	9.61	13.7
7	1.11	1.18	2.33	.720E 00	1800	5100	10.2	13.2
8	1.17	1.23	2.26	.341E 01	2200	5100	10.3	12.3
9	1.29	1.34	2.30	.110E 02	2700	5100	9.29	10.4
10	1.61	1.64	2.62	.302E 02	3300	5100	6.45	6.92
11	1.12	1.23	2.75	.206E-03	1200	4700	8.28	12.9
12	1.18	1.26	2.58	.233E 00	1500	4700	9.14	12.4
13	1.23	1.30	2.49	.147E 01	1800	4700	9.52	11.9
14	1.31	1.37	2.45	.560E 01	2200	4700	9.27	10.8
15	1.50	1.54	2.57	.166E 02	2700	4700	7.75	8.53
16	1.25	1.36	2.93	.185E-01	1200	4300	7.92	11.6
17	1.31	1.40	2.77	.643E 00	1500	4300	8.58	11.1
18	1.38	1.45	2.69	.280E 01	1800	4300	8.71	10.5
19	1.50	1.56	2.70	.917E 01	2200	4300	8.06	9.14
20	1.82	1.86	3.01	.260E 02	2700	4300	5.93	6.40
21	1.35	1.48	3.31	.314E-03	1000	3900	6.89	10.7
22	1.41	1.52	3.14	.138E 00	1200	3900	7.49	10.4
23	1.48	1.57	2.99	.151E 01	1500	3900	7.90	9.85
24	1.57	1.64	2.95	.516E 01	1800	3900	7.73	9.04
25	1.77	1.83	3.07	.152E 02	2200	3900	6.60	7.30
26	1.49	1.62	3.50	.162E-01	1000	3600	6.62	9.74
27	1.55	1.66	3.34	.397E 00	1200	3600	7.10	9.43
28	1.64	1.73	3.21	.271E 01	1500	3600	7.29	8.82
29	1.77	1.84	3.22	.810E 01	1800	3600	6.86	7.83
30	2.09	2.15	3.50	.227E 02	2200	3600	5.30	5.75
31	1.58	1.74	3.95	.554E-06	820	3300	5.73	9.14
32	1.66	1.79	3.73	.108E 00	1000	3300	6.30	8.80
33	1.73	1.83	3.57	.949E 00	1200	3300	6.64	8.47
34	1.85	1.93	3.49	.471E 01	1500	3300	6.58	7.72
35	2.04	2.11	3.58	.128E 02	1800	3300	5.83	6.50
36	1.78	1.94	4.22	.978E-02	820	3000	5.47	8.15
37	1.87	1.99	4.01	.397E 00	1000	3000	5.91	7.85
38	1.95	2.05	3.87	.204E 01	1200	3000	6.09	7.47
39	2.12	2.20	3.86	.810E 01	1500	3000	5.72	6.52
40	2.46	2.52	4.14	.207E 02	1800	3000	4.59	5.00
41	1.94	2.13	4.81	.326E-04	680	2700	4.72	7.46
42	2.03	2.19	4.56	.112E 00	820	2700	5.16	7.19
43	2.12	2.25	4.35	.111E 01	1000	2700	5.45	6.90
44	2.24	2.34	4.26	.411E 01	1200	2700	5.41	6.40
45	2.53	2.61	4.41	.141E 02	1500	2700	4.66	5.18
46	2.25	2.44	5.23	.277E-01	680	2400	4.45	6.47
47	2.34	2.50	4.98	.520E 00	820	2400	4.76	6.25
48	2.46	2.59	4.82	.271E 01	1000	2400	4.86	5.88
49	2.65	2.76	4.82	.810E 01	1200	2400	4.57	5.22
50	3.24	3.31	5.36	.254E 02	1500	2400	3.35	3.62
51	2.39	2.62	5.88	.148E-03	560	2200	3.87	6.06
52	2.50	2.69	5.57	.148E 00	680	2200	4.23	5.84
53	2.61	2.76	5.34	.117E 01	820	2200	4.44	5.61
54	2.77	2.89	5.23	.471E 01	1000	2200	4.38	5.15
55	3.06	3.16	5.38	.128E 02	1200	2200	3.88	4.33
56	2.69	2.92	6.29	.203E-01	560	2000	3.69	5.41
57	2.81	3.00	5.98	.494E 00	680	2000	3.96	5.22
58	2.94	3.09	5.79	.243E 01	820	2000	4.06	4.93
59	3.18	3.31	5.79	.810E 01	1000	2000	3.81	4.35
60	3.68	3.78	6.22	.207E 02	1200	2000	3.06	3.33
61	2.94	3.22	7.13	.124E-02	470	1800	3.21	4.93
62	3.06	3.29	6.79	.163E 00	560	1800	3.47	4.78
63	3.20	3.38	6.51	.131E 01	680	1800	3.64	4.57
64	3.39	3.54	6.39	.478E 01	820	1800	3.59	4.21
65	3.80	3.92	6.62	.141E 02	1000	1800	3.11	3.45
66	3.40	3.68	7.76	.614E-01	470	1600	3.01	4.29
67	3.53	3.76	7.43	.664E 00	560	1600	3.19	4.15
68	3.72	3.90	7.21	.309E 01	680	1600	3.24	3.88
69	4.04	4.19	7.27	.925E 01	820	1600	3.00	3.39
70	4.85	4.97	8.04	.254E 02	1000	1600	2.23	2.41
71	3.52	3.86	8.57	.938E-03	390	1500	2.67	4.11
72	3.68	3.95	8.14	.181E 00	470	1500	2.90	3.97
73	3.83	4.05	7.82	.119E 01	560	1500	3.03	3.82
74	4.06	4.24	7.67	.464E 01	680	1500	2.99	3.52
75	4.50	4.65	7.89	.129E 02	820	1500	2.64	2.94
76	4.04	4.43	9.96	.106E-03	330	1300	2.28	3.58
77	4.21	4.54	9.50	.908E-01	390	1300	2.47	3.47
78	4.38	4.65	9.08	.901E 00	470	1300	2.61	3.34
79	4.60	4.82	8.87	.338E 01	560	1300	2.62	3.14
80	5.03	5.21	8.99	.103E 02	680	1300	2.39	2.70
81	4.47	4.86	10.5	.119E-01	330	1200	2.19	3.25
82	4.64	4.97	10.1	.294E 00	390	1200	2.35	3.16
83	4.84	5.11	9.70	.174E 01	470	1200	2.43	3.01
84	5.13	5.35	9.59	.550E 01	560	1200	2.37	2.76
85	5.79	5.97	10.0	.155E 02	680	1200	2.02	2.23
86	4.97	5.36	11.2	.908E-01	330	1100	2.09	2.94
87	5.16	5.48	10.8	.752E 00	390	1100	2.20	2.84
88	5.42	5.68	10.5	.320E 01	470	1100	2.22	2.66
89	5.85	6.07	10.6	.893E 01	560	1100	2.07	2.35
90	6.95	7.13	11.6	.240E 02	680	1100	1.58	1.71
91	5.34	5.82	12.7	.628E-02	270	1000	1.81	2.72
92	5.58	5.97	12.0	.353E 00	330	1000	1.97	2.62
93	5.80	6.13	11.7	.169E 01	390	1000	2.03	2.51
94	6.18	6.44	11.5	.573E 01	470	1000	1.97	2.29
95	6.88	7.09	12.0	.146E 02	560	1000	1.71	1.89
96	6.00	6.47	13.6	.744E-01	270	910	1.72	2.43
97	6.26	6.65	13.0	.926E 00	330	910	1.83	2.34
98	6.56	6.88	12.7	.327E 01	390	910	1.84	2.20
99	7.13	7.39	12.8	.964E 01	470	910	1.69	1.91
100	8.35	8.56	13.9	.235E 02	560	910	1.32	1.43
101	6.50	7.09	15.5	.487E-02	220	820	1.48	2.23
102	6.81	7.28	14.7	.344E 00	270	820	1.61	2.15
103	7.14	7.52	14.1	.213E 01	330	820	1.66	2.04
104	7.58	7.89	14.0	.614E 01	390	820	1.61	1.86
105	8.56	8.82	14.7	.165E 02	470	820	1.36	1.49
106	7.26	7.84	16.6	.598E-01	220	750	1.41	2.01
107	7.59	8.06	15.8	.867E 00	270	750	1.51	1.93
108	8.03	8.40	15.4	.386E 01	330	750	1.51	1.79
109	8.69	9.00	15.6	.999E 01	390	750	1.39	1.57
110	10.39	10.6	17.2	.257E 02	470	750	1.04	1.12
111	7.81	8.53	18.8	.264E-02	180	680	1.22	1.86
112	8.18	8.76	17.8	.278E 00	220	680	1.33	1.79
113	8.58	9.04	17.1	.193E 01	270	680	1.38	1.70
114	9.22	9.60	17.0	.687E 01	330	680	1.32	1.52
115	10.33	10.6	17.8	.165E 02	390	680	1.12	1.24
116	8.76	9.48	20.1	.484E-01	180	620	1.16	1.67
117	9.15	9.73	19.1	.758E 00	220	620	1.24	1.60
118	9.68	10.1	18.6	.362E 01	270	620	1.25	1.49
119	10.67	11.0	18.9	.113E 02	330	620	1.12	1.26
120	12.64	12.9	20.9	.262E 02	390	620	.851	.918

High-pass Chebyshev filters use standard-value capacitors

by Ed Wetherhold
Honeywell Inc., Signal Analysis Center, Annapolis, Md.

Complementing the computer-generated design table for low-pass Chebyshev networks having standard-value capacitors [*Electronics*, June 19, 1980, p. 160], this listing is useful for building seven-element filters of the high-pass type that provide a roll-off attenuation of at least 42 decibels per octave. Both L and C values for 120 filters were found by an 85-line program written in Basic and were tabulated for an operating range of 1 to 10 megahertz. These components can be scaled for frequencies outside this range. Element values are specified for a source and load impedance of 50 ohms, but values for any input/output impedance are easily determined.

The high-pass filter (see table) uses a capacitive input and output configuration to minimize the number of inductors and to provide dc isolation with respect to ground. In this configuration and for the equally terminated condition, $C_1 = C_7$, $C_3 = C_5$, and $L_2 = L_6$. Given a standard capacitor value for C_3 and C_5, the program calculates all capacitor and inductor values for those unique values of the reflection coefficient that make C_1 and C_7 a standard value. The frequencies corresponding to the 3- and 50-dB attenuation levels are also listed.

To scale the tabulated frequency and component values into the 10-to-100- or 100-to-1,000-MHz frequency range decades, the user must multiply the frequency by 10 or 100, respectively, and divide all C and L values by the same number. Similarly, for the 1-to-10-, 10-to-100- and 100-to-1,000-kilohertz decades, the frequency is divided by 1,000, 100 or 10, respectively, and the component values are multiplied by the same number.

The following example demonstrates how to design for an I/O impedance other than 50 Ω. Consider a filter having a terminating impedance, Z_x, of 75 Ω and a 3-dB cutoff frequency, F_3^x, of 9.4 MHz. The user must:

■ Calculate the impedance scaling factor, $R = Z_x/50$.

■ Calculate the 3-dB cutoff frequency of a 50-Ω filter, F_3^{50}, from $F_3^{50} = R \cdot F_3^x$. If F_3^{50} is found to exceed 10, the table is scaled into the next frequency decade.

■ Select the 50-Ω design from the table that most closely matches the calculated F_3^{50} value. The tabulated capacitor values are implemented directly in the new design.

■ Find the new inductor values by multiplying the corresponding tabulated values by the square of the impedance-scaling factor, R.

■ Find the corresponding 3- and 50-dB attenuation points by dividing the tabulated frequencies by the impedance-scaling factor.

Thus, for an F_3^x of 9.4 MHz and a Z_x of 75 Ω, $R = 75/50 = 1.5$, $R^2 = 2.25$, and $F_3^{50} = 1.5(9.4) = 14.1$ MHz. Because F_3^{50} is greater than 10 MHz, the 50-Ω tabulation is scaled to the 10-to-100-MHz decade by multiplying all frequencies by 10 and dividing all component values by 10. The user should select filter number 17 because its F_3^{50} value is closest to 14.1 MHz.

Therefore, $C_{1,7} = 360$ picofarads, and $C_{3,5} = 120$ pF. Inductor $L_{2,6} = R^2(0.380) = 0.855$ microhenry, and $L_4 = R^2(0.286) = 0.644$ μH. Further, $F_3^{75} = 14.1/1.5 = 9.4$ MHz and $F_{50}^{75} = 4.69$ MHz. To construct the filter, polystyrene capacitors with a 2.5% tolerance, such as Mallory type SXM, are suitable. The inductors may be conveniently hand-wound on standard powdered-iron toroidal cores. □

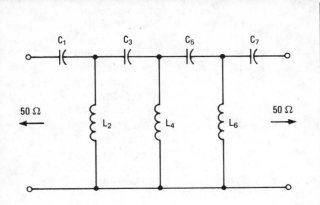

Filter No.	Frequency (MHz) 3 dB	Frequency (MHz) 50 dB	Reflection coefficient (%)	$C_{1,7}$ (pF)	$C_{3,5}$ (pF)	$L_{2,6}$ (μH)	L_4 (μH)
1	.849	.525	.254E 02	2400	1500	6.72	6.22
2	.958	.567	.141E 02	2700	1500	5.43	4.89
3	1.02	.583	.810E 01	3000	1500	4.92	4.31
4	1.06	.587	.471E 01	3300	1500	4.70	4.01
5	1.09	.584	.271E 01	3600	1500	4.63	3.83
6	1.11	.578	.151E 01	3900	1500	4.63	3.71
7	1.12	.568	.643E 00	4300	1500	4.70	3.62
8	1.14	.556	.233E 00	4700	1500	4.82	3.55
9	1.15	.544	.630E-01	5100	1500	4.97	3.50
10	1.16	.530	.455E-02	5600	1500	5.19	3.44
11	1.12	.679	.207E 02	2000	1200	4.90	4.50
12	1.21	.714	.128E 02	2200	1200	4.25	3.81
13	1.28	.729	.810E 01	2400	1200	3.94	3.45
14	1.34	.734	.411E 01	2700	1200	3.74	3.16
15	1.37	.727	.204E 01	3000	1200	3.70	3.01
16	1.40	.716	.949E 00	3300	1200	3.73	2.92
17	1.41	.703	.397E 00	3600	1200	3.80	2.86
18	1.43	.689	.138E 00	3900	1200	3.91	2.82
19	1.44	.670	.185E-01	4300	1200	4.07	2.77
20	1.46	.653	.206E-03	4700	1200	4.26	2.72
21	1.27	.787	.254E 02	1600	1000	4.48	4.15
22	1.44	.851	.141E 02	1800	1000	3.62	3.26
23	1.53	.875	.810E 01	2000	1000	3.28	2.87
24	1.59	.881	.471E 01	2200	1000	3.14	2.67
25	1.63	.877	.271E 01	2400	1000	3.08	2.55
26	1.67	.862	.111E 01	2700	1000	3.10	2.45
27	1.69	.843	.397E 00	3000	1000	3.17	2.39
28	1.72	.823	.108E 00	3300	1000	3.28	2.34
29	1.73	.803	.162E-01	3600	1000	3.40	2.31
30	1.76	.785	.314E-03	3900	1000	3.54	2.27
31	1.53	.951	.266E 02	1300	820	3.76	3.49
32	1.77	1.04	.129E 02	1500	820	2.91	2.61
33	1.85	1.06	.925E 01	1600	820	2.74	2.42
34	1.94	1.07	.478E 01	1800	820	2.57	2.19
35	2.00	1.07	.243E 01	2000	820	2.53	2.08
36	2.03	1.05	.117E 01	2200	820	2.54	2.01
37	2.06	1.03	.520E 00	2400	820	2.58	1.97
38	2.09	1.00	.152E 00	2700	820	2.68	1.92
39	2.12	.975	.978E-02	3000	820	2.81	1.89
40	2.15	.948	.554E-06	3300	820	2.95	1.85
41	1.90	1.17	.240E 02	1100	680	2.96	2.74
42	2.08	1.24	.155E 02	1200	680	2.53	2.29
43	2.20	1.28	.103E 02	1300	680	2.31	2.05
44	2.34	1.30	.464E 01	1500	680	2.13	1.81
45	2.39	1.29	.309E 01	1600	680	2.10	1.75
46	2.45	1.27	.131E 01	1800	680	2.10	1.67
47	2.49	1.25	.494E 00	2000	680	2.14	1.63
48	2.52	1.22	.148E 00	2200	680	2.21	1.60
49	2.54	1.19	.277E-01	2400	680	2.29	1.58
50	2.59	1.15	.326E-04	2700	680	2.43	1.54
51	2.32	1.43	.235E 02	910	560	2.42	2.23
52	2.55	1.51	.146E 02	1000	560	2.05	1.85
53	2.71	1.56	.893E 01	1100	560	1.86	1.64
54	2.82	1.57	.550E 01	1200	560	1.77	1.52
55	2.89	1.57	.338E 01	1300	560	1.73	1.45
56	2.98	1.54	.119E 01	1500	560	1.73	1.37
57	3.01	1.52	.664E 00	1600	560	1.75	1.35
58	3.05	1.48	.163E 00	1800	560	1.82	1.32
59	3.09	1.44	.203E-01	2000	560	1.90	1.29
60	3.14	1.40	.148E-03	2200	560	1.99	1.27
61	2.70	1.67	.257E 02	750	470	2.12	1.96
62	2.98	1.78	.165E 02	820	470	1.77	1.61
63	3.21	1.85	.964E 01	910	470	1.58	1.40
64	3.35	1.87	.573E 01	1000	470	1.49	1.28
65	3.45	1.87	.320E 01	1100	470	1.45	1.21
66	3.52	1.85	.174E 01	1200	470	1.45	1.17
67	3.57	1.83	.901E 00	1300	470	1.46	1.14
68	3.63	1.77	.181E 00	1500	470	1.52	1.11
69	3.66	1.74	.614E-01	1600	470	1.56	1.10
70	3.72	1.68	.124E-02	1800	470	1.65	1.07
71	3.24	2.01	.262E 02	620	390	1.78	1.65
72	3.59	2.15	.165E 02	680	390	1.47	1.34
73	3.85	2.23	.999E 01	750	390	1.32	1.17
74	4.01	2.26	.614E 01	820	390	1.24	1.07
75	4.15	2.25	.327E 01	910	390	1.21	1.01
76	4.24	2.23	.169E 01	1000	390	1.20	.970
77	4.31	2.19	.752E 00	1100	390	1.22	.944
78	4.36	2.15	.294E 00	1200	390	1.25	.926
79	4.40	2.10	.908E-01	1300	390	1.28	.913
80	4.49	2.02	.938E-03	1500	390	1.37	.889
81	4.14	2.50	.189E 02	560	330	1.30	1.19
82	4.49	2.62	.113E 02	620	330	1.14	1.01
83	4.71	2.66	.687E 01	680	330	1.06	.924
84	4.87	2.67	.386E 01	750	330	1.03	.865
85	4.98	2.65	.213E 01	820	330	1.02	.830
86	5.08	2.60	.926E 00	910	330	1.03	.803
87	5.14	2.55	.353E 00	1000	330	1.05	.786
88	5.20	2.49	.908E-01	1100	330	1.09	.772
89	5.26	2.43	.120E-01	1200	330	1.13	.761
90	5.33	2.37	.106E-03	1300	330	1.17	.748
91	4.69	2.90	.260E 02	430	270	1.22	1.13
92	5.18	3.10	.166E 02	470	270	1.02	.930
93	5.50	3.20	.110E 02	510	270	.927	.825
94	5.77	3.25	.663E 01	560	270	.867	.752
95	5.97	3.26	.362E 01	620	270	.838	.704
96	6.10	3.23	.193E 01	680	270	.832	.676
97	6.21	3.18	.867E 00	750	270	.840	.656
98	6.29	3.11	.344E 00	820	270	.859	.643
99	6.37	3.03	.744E-01	910	270	.892	.631
100	6.45	2.95	.628E-02	1000	270	.931	.620
101	5.96	3.65	.227E 02	360	220	.934	.861
102	6.45	3.84	.152E 02	390	220	.812	.734
103	6.88	3.96	.917E 01	430	220	.733	.647
104	7.16	4.00	.560E 01	470	220	.697	.599
105	7.35	4.00	.341E 01	510	220	.681	.571
106	7.51	3.96	.178E 01	560	220	.678	.548
107	7.64	3.89	.758E 00	620	220	.687	.532
108	7.73	3.80	.278E 00	680	220	.704	.522
109	7.83	3.71	.598E-01	750	220	.730	.513
110	7.92	3.61	.487E-02	820	220	.761	.505
111	7.44	4.53	.207E 02	300	180	.736	.675
112	8.09	4.76	.128E 02	330	180	.637	.572
113	8.51	4.86	.810E 01	360	180	.590	.517
114	8.80	4.89	.516E 01	390	180	.567	.486
115	9.05	4.87	.280E 01	430	180	.555	.460
116	9.22	4.82	.147E 01	470	180	.555	.445
117	9.34	4.74	.720E 00	510	180	.562	.435
118	9.46	4.64	.255E 00	560	180	.577	.427
119	9.58	4.52	.484E-01	620	180	.600	.419
120	9.70	4.40	.264E-02	680	180	.627	.412

LOGIC

Dynamic logic probe displays five states

by Mihai Antonescu
Federal Institute of Technology, Lausanne, Switzerland

Providing the convenience of the logic probe proposed by Prasad and Muralidharan[1], which utilizes a seven-segment display readout rather than discrete LEDs or lamps, this five-state detector also senses the presence of pulses and differentiates between the logic 0 and open-circuit conditions. Furthermore, provision has been made to bias the probe via its external-reference inputs, permitting it to check logic levels in circuits built with either TTL or complimentary-MOS devices.

As shown in the figure, the test signal, V_{in}, is compared with reference voltages V_{ref1} to V_{ref4} at comparators A_1 to A_3. Voltages V_{ref1} to V_{ref2} are derived from the supply that powers the circuit under test, with V_{ref3} (developed from the probe's power source) and V_{ref4} at approximately 0.05 volt and 0.1 v below ground, respectively. Switches S_{1a} and S_{1b} at the voltage divider are used to set the required logic-level references at A_1 and A_2 in order to check either TTL or C-MOS circuits.

Gates G_1–G_{13}, comprising the combinational-logic detector, determine V_{in}'s relation to V_{ref1}–V_{ref4} and activate the appropriate segments of the display (see table). A_1 and A_2 are used to check for the logic 1, 0, and guard-band conditions. A_3 is used to detect the no-connection, or open-circuit, condition, which can be differentiated from the logic 0 state because V_{ref4} is maintained at 0.1 v below ground. Note that the logic 0 state for TTL will typically be 0.4 v and is hardly ever below 0.2 v, whereas the logic 0 state for C-MOS will be typically 0.01 v.

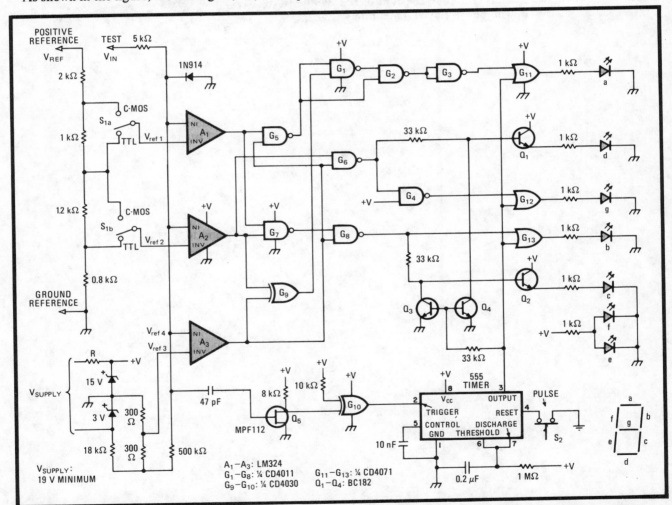

All-state. Logic probe having seven-segment display detects logic 1 and guard-band conditions, can differentiate between logic 0 state and open circuit, and senses a pulse train. Unit can check logic levels in circuits built with the two most popular families, C-MOS and TTL.

Test voltage		Display	Comparator			Display segments						
C-MOS*	TTL	Letter	A_1	A_2	A_3	a	b	c	d	g	e	f
$V_{in} < 40\%$	$V_{in} < 0.8$	L	L	L	H				on		on permanently	
$40\% < V_{in} < 60\%$	$0.8 < V_{in} < 2$	F	L	H	H	on				on		
$V_{in} > 60\%$	$V_{in} > 2$	H	H	H	H		on	on		on		
NC	NC	O	L	L	L	on	on	on	on			
pulse	pulse	P	—	—	—	on	on			on	*% of V_{ref}	

Switch S_2 must be depressed to catch any expected input pulses having a width down to 15 nanoseconds. This action resets the 555 one-shot, enabling it to override the displayed symbol with the letter P when the pulse arrives. If a train of pulses having a repetition rate greater than about 0.2 seconds (the time constant of the 555) is detected, the P will be displayed indefinitely.

With faster one-shots, pulses of 5 ns can be snared.

The probe can be powered by any dc source having a minimum voltage of 19 v. Resistor R should be selected to pass about 30 mA to the probe circuit. ☐

References
1. S. Jayasimha Prasad and M. R. Muralidharan, "Logic tester has unambiguous display," *Electronics*, March 3, 1977, p. 117.

Digital comparator saves demultiplexing hardware

by V. L. Patil and Rahul Varma
Central Electronics Engineering Research Institute, Pilani, India

Comparing two m-digit numbers, where each digit comprises n bits, by conventional means requires the services of a demultiplexer for separating the data into two corresponding sets, $2mn$ storage elements that convert the data into bit-parallel, digit-parallel form, and m magnitude comparators for performing the actual comparison. The demultiplexing can be simplified, however, and the number of storage elements reduced to $3m$ with this technique, which utilizes strobed memory elements in the form of D flip-flops and combinational logic to ascertain the relationship of the two numbers.

The method is illustrated for an example where two 4-bit, 3-digit numbers are compared. As seen, the corresponding digits of both numbers are simultaneously introduced to the 7485 4-bit comparator, A_0, with the least significant bits being introduced first. The result of the comparison is then strobed into the 7475 quad latch, A_1, by digit strobe D_1.

Similarly, the second-most significant bits (SSB) and the most significant bits are then strobed into A_2 and A_3, respectively, by strobes D_2 and D_3. The combinational logic that follows then evaluates the three-digit (MSD, SSD, and LSD) comparison from:

$$OL = L_3 + E_3L_2 + E_3E_2L_1$$
$$OG = G_3 + E_3G_2 + E_3E_2G_1$$
$$OE = E_3E_2E_1$$

where $OL = 1$, $OE = 1$, and $OG = 1$ signify that $A < B$, $A = B$ and $A > B$, respectively, and L_i, E_i, and G_i are the individual corresponding outputs of flip-flops A_i.

The truth table outlines circuit operation. ☐

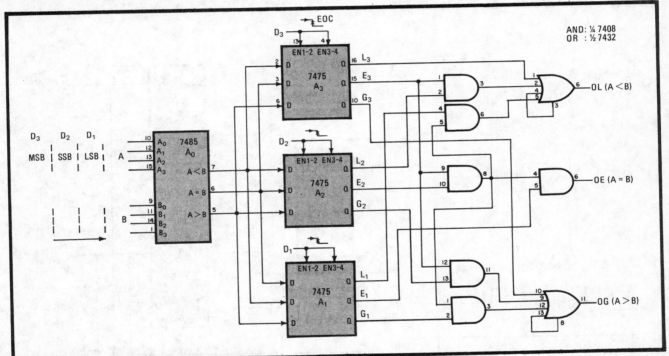

Reduction. Circuit performs n-bit, m-digit comparison of two numbers without a conventional IC demultiplexer, reduces number of memory elements normally required. Simplified decoding technique utilizes combinational logic. Truth table outlines circuit operation in comparing most, second-most, and least significant digits.

MSD			SSD			LSD			OUTPUT		
G_3	E_3	L_3	G_2	E_2	L_2	G_1	E_1	L_1	OG	OE	OL
>	=	<	>	=	<	>	=	<	>	=	<
0	0	1	X	X	X	X	X	X	0	0	1
0	1	0	0	0	1	X	X	X	0	0	1
0	1	0	0	1	0	0	0	1	0	0	1
1	0	0	X	X	X	X	X	X	1	0	0
0	1	0	1	0	0	X	X	X	1	0	0
0	1	0	0	1	0	1	0	0	1	0	0
0	1	0	0	1	0	0	1	0	0	1	0

Digital comparator minimizes serial decoding circuitry

by Harland Harrison
Memorex Inc., Communications Division, Cupertino, Calif.

Using significantly fewer chips than the comparator proposed by Patil and Varma[1], this two-word, 4-bit comparator offers other advantages as well—it accommodates any word length and is more easily modified to handle any bit width. The control signals needed to facilitate the comparison can also be more conveniently applied.

The circuit outputs are first cleared with a negative-going pulse from the start signal. This sets outputs O_{LESS} and $O_{GREATER}$ low. O_{EQUAL}, derived from O_{LESS} and $O_{GREATER}$, goes temporarily high. At this time, the num-bers can be presented to data buses A and B for comparison, with the least significant bit pair introduced first. As a consequence of the configuration, any number of bit pairs per word can be compared without modifying the circuit at all. The data buses each accept up to 4 bits, but this number may be expanded simply by cascading 7485 comparators.

The result of each bit-pair comparison is then latched into the 7474 flip-flops by the D_i clock pulse, with the results of each bit-test being fed to the cascade inputs of the 7485. As a result, the comparator keeps track of the previous bit-pair check while continuing to update its results as each succeeding bit pair is introduced. Thus, the need for additional memory and logic elements is eliminated. The final result becomes valid after the D_m clock pulse, where m is the word length in bits, and remains valid until the next start pulse. □

References
1. V. L. Patil and R. Varma, "Digital comparator saves demultiplexing hardware," *Electronics*, Aug. 14, 1980, p. 129.

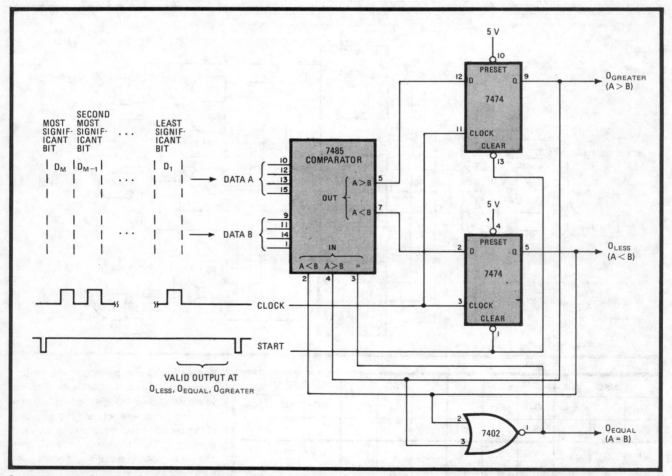

Less memory. Circuit performs 4-bit comparison of two numbers with minimal circuitry. 7485 comparator replaces large numbers of flip-flop–type memories and logic elements by keeping track of previous bit-pair checks in real time as each pair is introduced. Circuit accommodates any word length; bit width is expandable simply by cascading 7485 comparators.

Dual one-shot keeps firmware on track

by Patrick L. McLaughlin
Teletech LaGuardia Inc., R&D Labs, Lafayette, Colo.

By noting the absence of pulses generated by status-reporting statements inserted in a running program, this missing-pulse detector reinitializes a microprocessor-based system when glitches on the power line or peripheral circuitry occur. The circuit provides more efficient system performance than a periodic reset timer and is much less expensive than installing line filters or isolators. Only one chip is required—a dual retriggerable monostable multivibrator.

Problems created by a power glitch—such as shuffling of information in the data registers and program jumps to undefined locations or to a location that gives rise to

infinite loops—are conventionally solved by placing a timer in the system's reset line to initialize the system every 15 minutes or by using a brute-force power-line filter or even a dynamotor power isolator. A timer probably offers the best low-cost solution, but system speed is degraded by the unnecessary periodic interruptions.

A better solution is to provide a way for the program to report to the system hardware that it is running and on track. Using the 74123 dual one-shot, as shown in the figure, to monitor so-called report statements that are entered in the program's housekeeping loop automatically resets the microprocessor if and when the reports stop for longer than a specified period.

In general operation, both one-shots (one serving as the missing-pulse detector, the other as the output timer) trigger each other alternately in an astable, free-running mode, with R_1C_1 setting the report window, t_w, and R_2 setting the reset time, t_s. On power up, pin 12 of the 74123 is low and the processor is kept at rest until both one-shots time out. Then pin 12 is brought high, enabling the processor. If no report is made before time t_w,

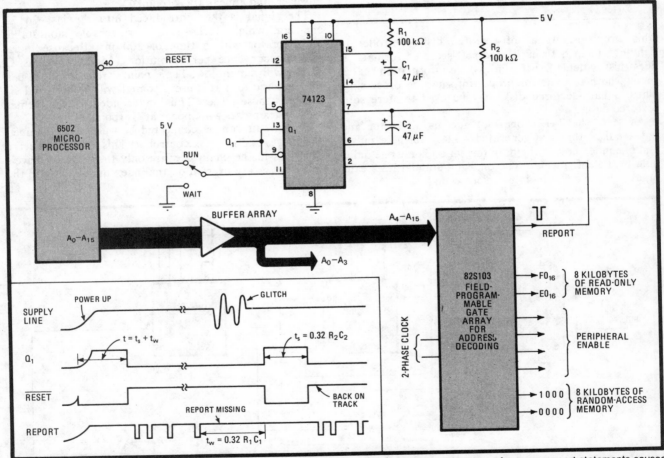

Restart. 74123 dual one-shot, configured as missing-pulse detector and output timer, detects absence of program report statements caused by power-line glitches in order to efficiently reinitialize microprocessor. Reports are entered as often as required in wait-for-data–type systems to ensure pulse rate falls within t_w window. Circuit accommodates static-type stop typical 8080/8085 wait instructions.

the cycle is repeated. An active-low series of report pulses made any time before t_w resets the missing-pulse detector (the output is Q_1), keeping pin 12 high and the processor running.

Usually, report statements are routinely entered before, after, or at both ends of the program's housekeeping loop and in most cases will be called frequently enough to fall within the t_w time window. In loops that may delay normal reporting, however, such as wait-for-data types, inclusion of additional report statements is advisable.

Note that if pin 11 is brought to ground, the one-shot at the output will be inhibited without resetting the processor. Thus, this circuit can accommodate static-type stops typical of the 8080/8085 wait instruction and is usable with slow-running programs and single-stepping arrangements.

The 74123 can be rewired to accept positive-going report pulses simply by introducing the report line to pin 1 of the chip and making pin 5 the output reset line. Pin 3 is then connected to 5 volts and pin 10 disconnected from the positive supply and connected to pin 4 instead. Finally, pin 2 is connected to pin 12. □

Index separator extracts all disk formats

by David L. Jaffe
Veterans Administration Medical Center, Palo Alto, Calif.

This circuit allows a soft-sectored disk controller to handle data in both hard- and soft-sectored formats. It does this by detecting the index-hole information that is sent in both formats for proper information processing. Thus, a hard-sectored disk may be used to store soft-sectored data.

As seen, the 74121 one-shot accepts all sector and index pulses that are generated—32 sector-hole pulses and one index hole in the hard format and only one index hole in the soft format. The one-shot standardizes each input pulse to a width of 480 microseconds.

The 74122 one-shot that follows is configured to pass pulses whose falling edges are displaced more than 3.56 milliseconds apart. No index pulse from a hard-sectored disk appears at this output because the time between the last sector pulse and the index pulse is only 2.55 ms. Missing index pulses are restored by the NAND gate, however, and appear at G_1 (point 1).

The signal is then introduced into the last 74122 one-shot, which works as a retriggerable monostable multivibrator with a time of 200 ms. Because index pulses occur once per revolution (166.66 ms), its Q output will remain low. Then, point 2 remains high. If a soft-sectored format is used, point 1 will be high and G_2 will pass those pulses. Thus, independent of the format used, index pulses will appear at G_3 (point 3).

The circuit can be connected between daisy-chained disk drives and the disk controller. This circuit can serve all drives in the chain because only the selected drive's index pulses are exerted on the index line leading to the controller. □

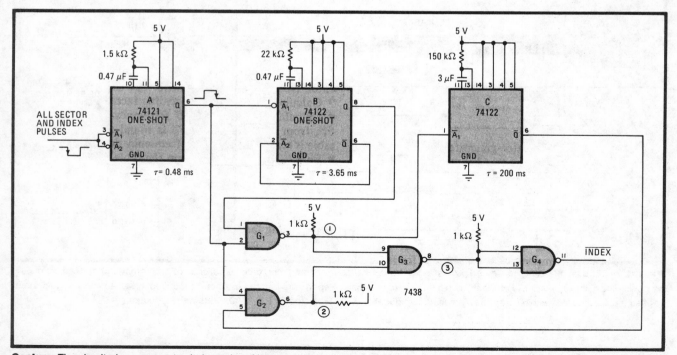

Capture. The circuit above separates index pulses from sector-hole output of hard-disk format and detects single index pulse for soft disks, so that both formats can be handled by one disk controller. As a result, a hard-sectored disk can store soft-sectored data.

Dual-feedback amplifier zeros comparator hysteresis

by Svein Olsen
Royal Institute of Technology, Stockholm, Sweden

Amplifiers with positive feedback may be combined to create voltage comparators and zero-crossing detectors devoid of hysteresis. Alternatively, the amount of hysteresis, either positive or negative, may be selected. In both cases, feedback ensures that true bistable (switching) operation is achieved without undue sacrifice of noise immunity—a necessary condition for optimum comparator and zero-detector performance.

The ideal voltage comparator cannot be realized with a single amplifier because bistable operation does not occur until hysteresis starts. Witness today's typical comparator—a fast differential amp and a transistor-switch output stage that actually operates as a linear amplifier within a small region about the transition level. Achieving a step transition for slowly varying input signals is difficult with these high-gain, wideband devices, too, because of the radio-frequency oscillations and multiple transitions that occur in association with very small noise signals.

Introducing positive feedback to increase loop gain and thus ensure bistable operation, as some have tried, will yield clean switching independent of input slope. But hysteresis also is introduced, and, worst of all, Δt, a varying input/output delay—which depends on the slope of the input signal and the instantaneous value of hysteresis—comes into play.

The block diagram (a) shows how to achieve bistable operation while eliminating all of these problems. Amplifiers 1 and 2, each having positive feedback (α, β, respectively), are applied to their individual summing junctions, where they are combined with the input signal. Amplifier 1 also drives the second summing junction with a dc-level shift signal ($\pm k$) that is a function of the amp's hysteresis. Note that this feedback signal can be derived by either a switching or a linear stage.

Depending upon its polarity, the signal may add to or subtract from the amount of hysteresis inherent in amplifier 2. In the special case, total circuit hysteresis may be eliminated with little loss of noise immunity. At the same time, the circuit will retain high gain for true bistable operation. (The lengthy mathematical analysis of the circuit may be found elsewhere.[1])

A practical circuit having TTL-compatible outputs is shown in (b). Feedback in both amplifiers is determined by resistors r and R. In this application, r is 150 ohms and R is 15 kilohms, so that V_{H1} = 40 millivolts ($V_{in\ min}$ = 15 mV root mean square) and V_x = 20 mV, where V_{H1} is the hysteresis for amplifier 1 and V_x is the noise immunity.

Amplifier Q_1–Q_2 provides an inverted feedback signal to the second summing junction, with the magnitude of

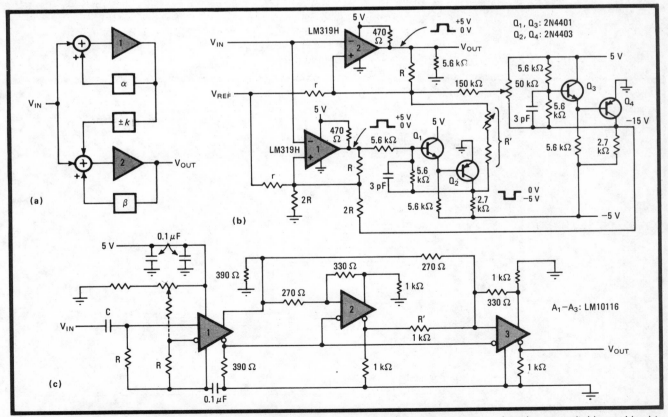

Ideal. Amplifiers with high loop gain work as nearly perfect comparators and zero-crossing detectors when they are suitably combined to cancel hysteresis (a). The implementation of a practical comparator (b) and a zero-crossing element (c) are relatively simple.

the signal set by potentiometer R'. The negative voltage at the junction of amplifier 1 required to establish a level-shift voltage at amplifier 2 is provided by Q_3–Q_4. The output hysteresis is adjustable to zero.

A fast (3-nanosecond) zero-crossing detector with zero hysteresis is shown in (c). This application requires an LM10116 emitter-coupled-logic receiver to be used, and although its low amplification factor makes it a little more difficult to achieve high loop gain, three sections are used to make up for the shortcoming.

Amplifier 1 is the input stage biased for Class A amplification. The input RC values are selected according to the impedance-matching requirements and to provide the required low-frequency response. Amplifiers 2 and 3 serve the functions previously mentioned. □

References
1. Svein Olsen, "The Zero Hysteresis Comparator," RVK-78 Conference Notes, Stockholm, March 29, 1978.

Decoder logs signals' order of arrival

by Claude Haridge
Ottawa, Ontario, Canada

This decoder indicates the sequence of arrival of up to four digital input signals and therefore serves as an excellent priority encoder. Alternatively, it can aid the technician in troubleshooting high-speed circuits. Using Schottky TTL devices to minimize propagation delays, the decoder can resolve two signals only 30 nanoseconds apart.

As shown, one flip-flop, three NAND gates, and four light-emitting diodes per input are needed to capture the corresponding signals and compare their arrival times. There are four such sections. In order to perform the time-difference checks accurately, the gates of each section are cross-coupled as shown in the figure, so that they provide an effective signal-lockout function. Polarity switches at each input enable the user to designate either the rising or falling edge of a signal as a valid gating stimulus.

A system reset brings the Q output of each flip-flop low. At this time, all the LED indicators are off. A valid trigger input sets its corresponding flip-flop, which then turns on its indicator—LED A, B, C, or D. Simultaneously, the gates leading to the remaining three LEDs of the activated section are enabled. These three LEDs are used to indicate the relative arrival of succeeding pulses.

Thus, the lighting of LED A, followed by the LED associated with the A > C output, indicates that a signal at input A arrived before a pulse at input C. In this case, note that the LEDs connected to the C > A, B > A, and D > A ports are inhibited from turning on until the next system reset. Succeeding pulses reaching the B, C, and D inputs in any order enable the corresponding outputs and lock out the appropriate LEDs until all four inputs have been detected. □

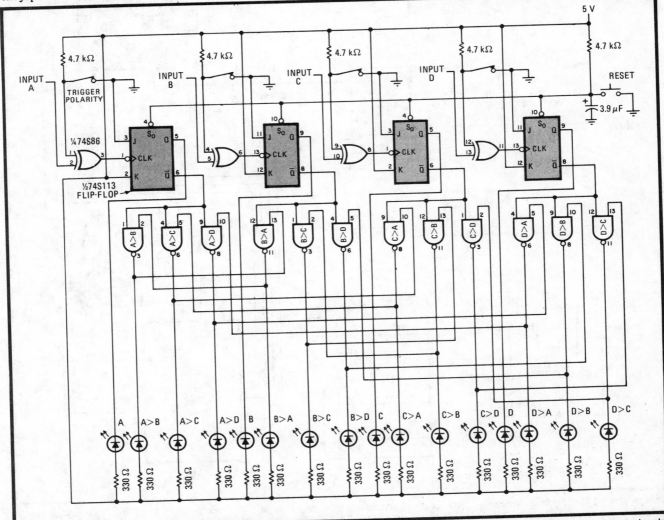

Signal sequence. Circuit indicates relative arrival times of four digital signal inputs. Using Schottky TTL, unit resolves any two signals separated by as little as 30 ns. Polarity switches at each input enable detection of signal's rising or falling edges.

Four-chip meter measures capacitance to within 1%

by Peter Henry
Seattle, Wash.

Measuring capacitance over the range of 1,000 picofarads to 1,000 microfarads, this four-chip meter has an overall accuracy of 1%. Costing less than $20, the unit has a digital readout and is built from parts that are readily available.

Engaging switch S_1 momentarily fires timer A_1, whose pulse width is determined by capacitor C_1 and one of four timing resistors, R_1 through R_4. The timer enables an astable multivibrator, A_2, and resets a three-digit decimal counter, which then counts the number of pulses from A_2 until the timer runs out or a count of 999 (overflow) is reached. The number is then displayed.

A seven-decade range (see table) is achieved by switching in R_1–R_4, and R_5–R_6, which sets the frequency of A_2 to approximately 1 or 1,000 hertz. For best performance, R_1–R_4 should be hand-picked to achieve the desired 1:10, 1:100 or 1:1,000 ratios if an accuracy to within 1% is required.

Calibration is achieved with a known capacitance of

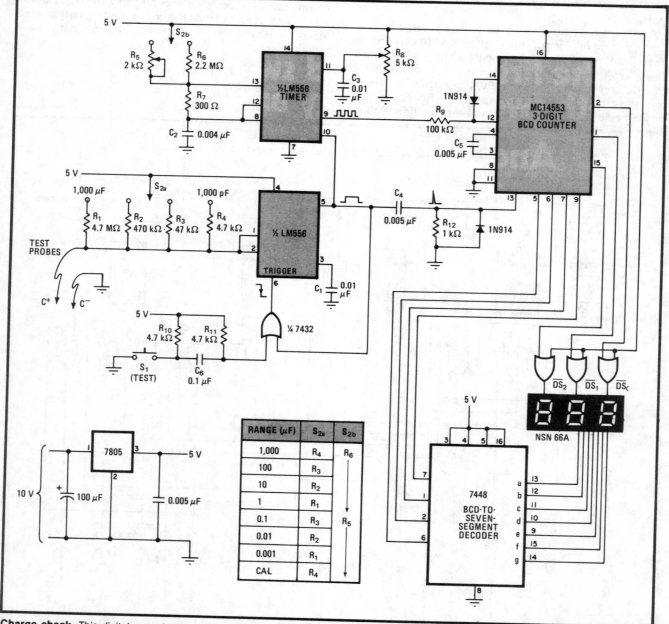

RANGE (µF)	S_{2a}	S_{2b}
1,000	R_4	R_6
100	R_3	
10	R_2	
1	R_1	
0.1	R_3	R_5
0.01	R_2	
0.001	R_1	
CAL	R_4	

Charge check. This digital capacitance meter measures accurately over the range of 1,000 picofarads to 1,000 microfarads. The circuit displays the number of pulses from astable multivibrator A_2 in the measurement count period during which 555 timer A_1 is active. The measurements are repeatable to within a few counts on all but the lowest scale, giving an overall accuracy to within 1%.

approximately 0.3 μF. Potentiometer R_5 is adjusted for identical readings on the calibrating and 1-μF scale. Then potentiometer R_8 is adjusted for the same readings on both scales. This procedure is repeated as often as necessary for perfect agreement.

The circuit is very reliable and will yield repeatable measurements to within a few counts on all but the lowest scale. Differences in capacitance of 10 pF can be detected. Leaky capacitors may be difficult to measure because of their series resistance. □

Time-slot assigner chip cuts multiplexer parts count

by Henry Wurzburg
Motorola Inc., Semiconductor Group, Phoenix, Ariz.

In some communications systems, particularly digital telephony equipment, it is hard to examine the data from a given source after it has been time-division–multiplexed with other data for serial transmission over a common data line. Capturing the data from its time slot

and converting it into parallel form for examination usually requires many integrated circuits, since the slot must be programmable.

A special-purpose IC, the MC14417 time-slot assigner carries out this serial-to-parallel function with the aid of only a few inverters and one other IC. What's more, the cost of implementing the circuit is only a few dollars.

The timing of a simple three-slot TDM system is shown in (a). In digital telephone systems, a data frame may consist of anywhere from 24 to 40 time slots, each containing 8 bits of data transmitted at rates of up to 2.56 megabits per second.

In the all–complementary-MOS capture circuit of (b), the MC14094 shift register acts as a serial-to-parallel

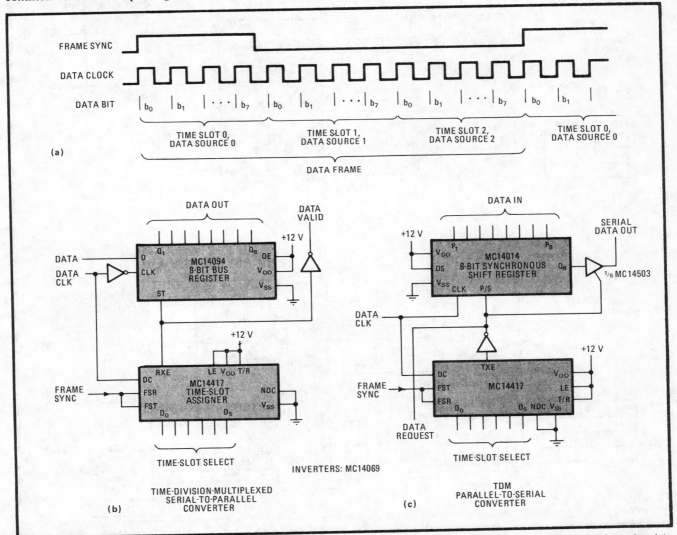

The right slot. Time-domain multiplexing (a) assigns to data from several sources specific time slots in a serial data stream. Capturing data from a specific slot is made easy with the MC14417 time-slot assigner (b), which works with the MC14094 shift register to provide data from the source dictated by the select inputs of the 14417. The versatile chip can also provide parallel-to-serial multiplexing (c).

converter, while the 14417 computes when the data is to be captured and converted. Just which time slot it captures is determined by the binary data present at inputs D_0–D_5 of the 14417. The circuit also provides a valid-data output signal. As for speed, the circuit works for clock rates of up to 2.56 MHz with systems having up to 40 time slots.

Implementing a parallel-to-serial converter for multiplexing data onto the TDM data line is equally simple if the 14417 is used as shown in (c). Here, a three-state buffer prevents the serial data bus from being loaded during idle time-slot periods. The frequency limitations of this second circuit are the same as for the capture circuit. □

Enhanced multiplier cuts parts count

by Guy Ciancaglini
Fellows Corp., Springfield, Vt.

The encoder-pulse–feedback multiplier circuit proposed by Frank Amthor [*Electronics*, Sept. 11, 1980, p. 139] and later simplified by Michael M. Butler [*Electronics*, Nov. 20, 1980, p. 128] may be implemented in a higher-speed TTL version that costs less and has fewer parts.

Butler's circuit reduced the original four-latch outputs to three lines so an eight-channel analog-multiplexer can be used. But the price paid was a space-consuming

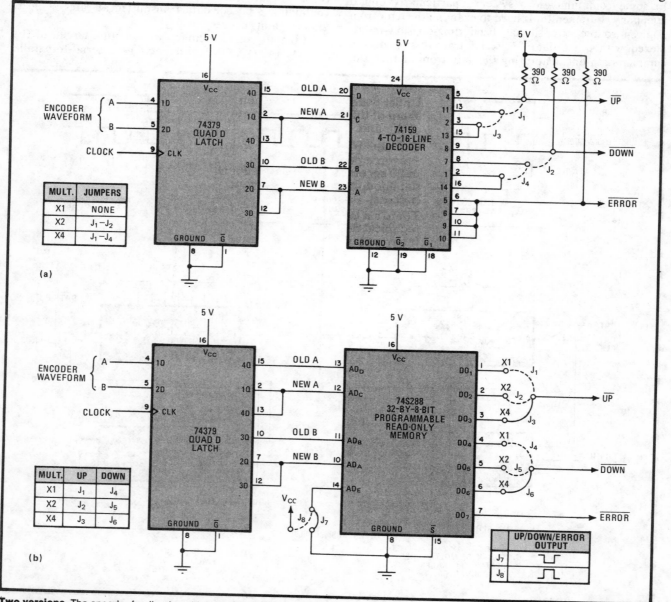

Two versions. The encoder feedback multiplier (a) uses transistor-transistor logic to save printed-circuit board space. The TTL PROM version (b) costs a bit more, handles positive or negative true logic, and needs even less board space. Both circuits are programmable.

exclusive-OR package.

The TTL design implements the multiplier's common edge detector with a 74379 quad D-latch connected as shown in Fig. 1a. Furthermore, the 74159 4-to-16-line decoder enables it to use all four latch outputs, eliminating the exclusive-OR package.

Another plus for the TTL design is its versatility, which it owes to the fact that the collector outputs of the decoder are now open and may be hooked together in a wired-OR configuration. By including four jumpers or a dual–in-line–packaged switch, these outputs may be selected for one, two, or four times the original encoder feedback (see table). Since the decoder has a slower propagation delay than the latch frequency, the latch clock rate is limited to at most 25 megahertz.

Use of a PROM programmer can save even more space, but at a slightly higher cost. By replacing the decoder with a 32-by-8-bit TTL programmable read-only memory, the package is reduced in size and in pin count from 24 to 16 pins. The output pull-up resistors are also eliminated because of the PROM's three-state outputs. In this design variation, the $\times 1$, $\times 2$ and $\times 4$ outputs are on individual lines. By making use of the fifth address input to the PROM, the output polarity may be set to positive or negative true logic using jumpers (Fig. 1b). □

TRUTH TABLE FOR ENCODER MULTIPLIER														
A	B	Latch output				NO.	Up*			Down*			Error*
		Old A	New A	Old B	New B		X1	X2	X4	X1	X2	X4	
0	0	0	0	0	0	0	1	1	1	1	1	1	1
0	↑	0	0	0	1	1	1	1	1	1	1	0	1
0	↓	0	0	1	0	2	1	1	0	1	1	1	1
0	1	0	0	1	1	3	1	1	1	1	1	1	1
↑	0	0	1	0	0	4	0	0	0	1	1	1	1
↑	↑	0	1	0	1	5	1	1	1	1	1	1	0
↑	↓	0	1	1	0	6	1	1	1	1	1	1	0
↑	1	0	1	1	1	7	1	1	1	1	0	0	1
↓	0	1	0	0	0	8	1	1	1	0	0	0	1
↓	↑	1	0	0	1	9	1	1	1	1	1	1	0
↓	↓	1	0	1	0	10	1	1	1	1	1	1	0
↓	1	1	0	1	1	11	1	0	0	1	1	1	1
1	0	1	1	0	0	12	1	1	1	1	1	1	1
1	↑	1	1	0	1	13	1	1	0	1	1	1	1
1	↓	1	1	1	0	14	1	1	1	1	1	0	1
1	1	1	1	1	1	15	1	1	1	1	1	1	1

*For PROM version: when address E is tied high, all output states are inverted.

Pulse-width monitor flags poor timing

by T. G. Barnett and J. K. Stothers, *Neonatal Research Group, London Hospital Medical College, London, England*

Pulse intervals can be monitored to ensure they fall within a specified range by using two complementary-MOS 4098 dual monostable multivibrators. The original application of this circuit was to monitor biologically produced pulse trains. However, the principle can be applied to any case where it is necessary to know if the limits of a pulse interval have been exceeded.

The 4098 is two independent one-shots in a single package and each one-shot has leading- and trailing-edge triggering, retriggerable and nonretriggerable modes as well as a reset and complementary outputs. These facilities have been incorporated within a monitor that senses whether a pulse train has intervals longer or shorter than those of a chosen range.

The period of each one-shot may be obtained from its data sheet or approximated by:

$$T(time) = 0.5 \times RC$$

for values of $C \geq 0.01$ microfarad.

The value of the capacitor should be as small as possible and the resistor should not be more than 10 megohms. All unused inputs must be connected to either the drain- or source-supply voltage in accordance with the data-sheet instructions.

As the circuit in the figure shows, monostable A_1, operated in the retriggerable mode, is triggered on the leading edge of an input pulse. The $\overline{Q}$ output is normally low unless the input-pulse interval is greater than the duration of the monostable's pulse-width value, set by resistor R_1 and capacitor C_1. If the pulse interval exceeds this value, then $\overline{Q}$ will go high, resulting in the output of the 4071 OR gate going high. Thus the maximum interval time is set by this monostable.

The leading edge of the input pulse also triggers monostables A_2 and A_3, both of which are operated in the retriggerable mode. Output Q of A_2 acts as a delay and is fed into the trailing-edge–trigger input of A_4, whose Q output drives the reset pin of A_3. The delay that is caused by A_2 is a few microseconds from being triggered on receipt of the leading edge of the input pulse, as its reset pin is low until A_4 is triggered. A_4 is operated in the nonretriggerable mode and sets the minimum-pulse–interval time.

The Q output of A_3 will go high only if its reset pin is set high by A_4, whose Q output will go high only a short time after A_3 has received a trigger pulse. However, if a further input pulse is received within the time the Q output of monostable A_4 is high, then monostable A_3 will be triggered, its Q output will go high, and the 4071 OR gate will go high. The actual pulse width of A_3, set by R_3 and C_3, can be chosen to suit any application. □

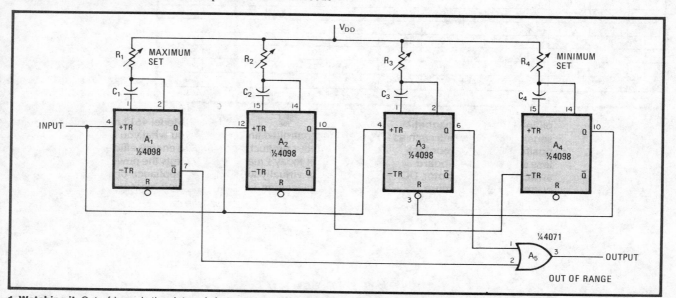

1. Watching it. Out-of-bounds time intervals between a train of pulses are detected at OR gate A_5 because one-shot A_1 stays triggered unless the time between pulses is too great. Meanwhile one-shot A_3 triggers if it receives successive pulses too soon. It also drives the OR gate

Improving the LM395 for low-level switching

by Yehuda Gabay
Israel Atomic Energy Commission, Beersheba, Israel

The most significant drawback of a power transistor like National Semiconductor's LM395 is its relatively high quiescent current (10 milliamperes or so), which makes it impossible to use as a reliable switching device for small loads or loads that require dynamic currents ranging from zero to some high value. Adding a transistor-diode network and an optocoupler to the circuit, however, adapts the LM395 as a low-level (down to 0-mA) switch without sacrificing the current-handling capabilities of the power transistor and provides input-to-output isolation as well.

This circuit is configured as a normally-off switch whose quiescent load voltage is a maximum of 0,6 volt. Placing a logic 1 at the input of optocoupler U_1 causes transistor Q_1 to turn off. Thus the power transistor, Q_2, conducts and the desired current flows through the load, R_L.

If the input to the optocoupler goes to a logic 0, Q_2 cuts off and no current flows through the load. In this state, Q_1 conducts and the quiescent current of Q_2 that must flow is shunted through diode D_1 and through Q_1 to ground. It should be noted that D_2 bypasses transients to ground that are caused by an inductive load.

In the case where the user desires to implement a normally closed switch, it is only necessary to remove the circuitry centered around Q_1. Then, U_1's output transistor will serve to bypass Q_2's quiescent current to ground when necessary. ☐

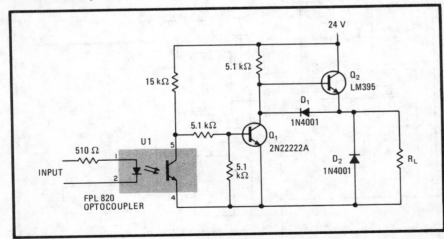

Bypass. A floating switch in the form of an optocoupler adapts power transistor Q_2 for handling small load currents, directing transistor Q_1 to bypass Q_2's high quiescent current (10 mA) when a logic 0 is applied to the circuit input. If a normally on switch is desired, Q_1 and its associated circuitry need only be removed. U_1's output transistor then will take Q_2's quiescent current to ground.

Contact tester quantifies open-, short-circuit tendencies

by Steven Nirenburg and Wunnava V. Subbarao
Florida International.University, Miami, Fla.

Many present-day electronic systems, being modular in nature, rely heavily on connector blocks to hook the various functional units together. As such, it is becoming increasingly important to detect any momentary open-circuit or short-circuit tendencies of the system at the connector—especially in high-vibration environments—both in production-line testing and during actual operation. This tester detects both, while indicating if either condition persists beyond a given time preset by the user.

Consider the detection of an open-circuit tendency of contact S_1, as shown in the figure. For the purposes of discussion, the open-circuit condition is arbitrarily chosen to be one in which the resistance across S_1 is greater than 10 ohms for a period equal to or greater than 100 microseconds.

On system reset, the 74192 counters and 7476 flip-flops are brought to logic 0. If S_1 is closed, voltage V_1 will be near zero and the outputs of comparators G_1 and G_2 will be high. Light-emitting diode D_0 then glows, indicating the contact is closed.

If S_1 is momentarily opened or shows any contact deterioration, V_1 rises slightly above ground potential, forcing G_1 low and gating the output of the 1-megahertz clock through to the counters. Thus should the contact deterioration last for 100 μs, 100 clock pulses will be counted and the resulting carry pulse generated from the second 74192 will set flip-flop F_1. And if the ohmic resistance across S_1 goes above 10 Ω, V_1 will rise above 50 millivolts, forcing G_2 low and flip-flop F_2 high.

Thus D_1 will glow if F_1 is set and F_2 is clear. D_2 will glow if F_1 is clear and F_2 is set. D_3 will light if both F_1 and F_2 are set, so that the predetermined open-circuit time and resistance of S_1 may be readily recorded.

Short circuits are readily detected by connecting points A and B across the normally opened contact under test. When the contact is open, V_1 is near zero and the system remains in the reset position, lighting up D_0. If shorted momentarily, S_1 will cause either D_1, D_2 or D_3 to light. For the values shown in the figure, D_1 will glow if the short circuit exceeds 100 μs or more; D_2 indicates if S_1's resistance is less than 1 $M\Omega$; D_3 illuminates if both of the aforementioned conditions exist.

By changing the clock frequency or the counting limit, any time interval can be preset. Similarly, the impedance at which the circuit responds may be selected by adjusting the threshold voltage at G_2. □

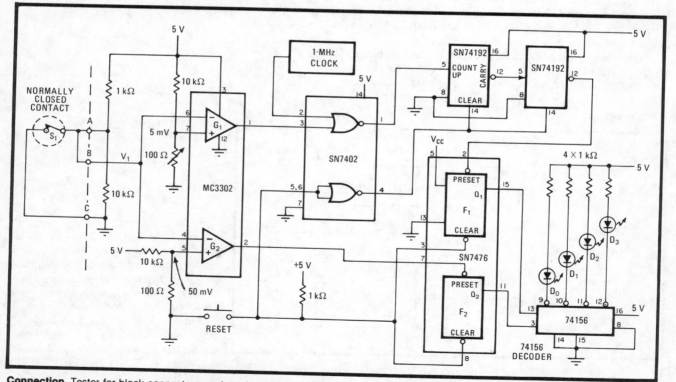

Connection. Tester for block connectors, pc boards, and cable assemblies indicates if duration of open or short circuit in circuit pin or lead exceeds preset time and checks relative magnitude of resistance across switch or broken wire. Four LEDs indicate state of affairs.

PLL performs accurate phase measurements

by N. H. Sabah

Engineering and Architecture Faculty, American University of Beirut, Lebanon

The excellent tracking ability inherent in a phase-locked loop is utilized in this meter to measure phase differences accurate to 0.1°. Although intended for use in the dc-to-1-kilohertz audio-frequency range, the upper limit of the unit can be extended by suitable selection of a high-frequency PLL and appropriate circuitry to reduce phase jitter.

The reference and the signal to be measured, f_a and f_b respectively, are applied to the LM208 operational amplifiers, which form the isolating stages. The LM211 comparators that follow provide a rise time of less than 100 nanoseconds and a phase-shift equivalent time between points $A'(f)$ and $B'(f)$ of less than 20 ns. A

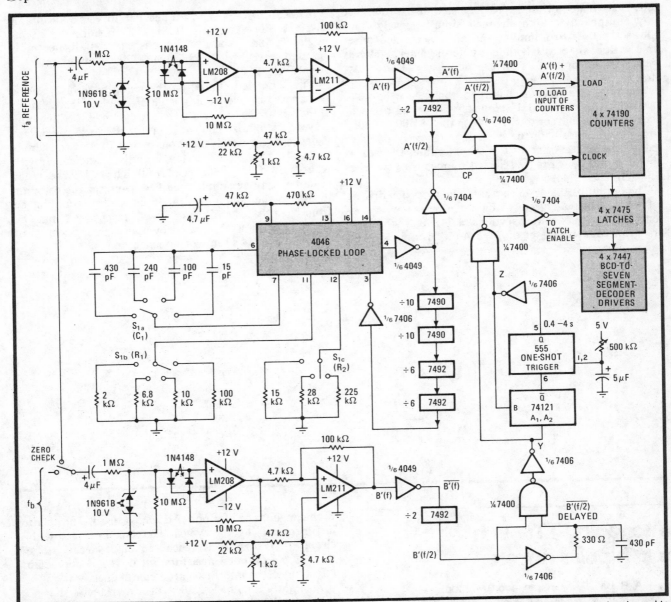

Angular accuracy. Meter utilizes tracking ability of PLL to perform phase measurements accurate to 0.1°. 4046 delivers clock signal equal to 3,600 f_a to conventional display (not shown), where count time is determined by f_b. Thus phase angle of f_b with respect to f_a is displayed.

PHASE METER'S RANGING COMPONENTS				
Frequency (Hz)	C_1 (pF)	R_1 (kΩ)	R_2 (kΩ)	Jitter (ppm)
1 — 10	430	100	∞	15,000
10 — 100	240	10	225	10,000
100 — 300	100	6.8	28	8,000
300 — 1,000	15	2	15	5,000

zero-phase check switch is provided so that the reference may be applied to both channels simultaneously. This allows the user to minimize the aforementioned offset time with channel B's 1-kilohm potentiometer, which is located at the input of its corresponding LM211 comparator.

The reference waveform is then applied to the 4046 PLL, which has a 3,600:1 frequency divider in its feedback loop. The output of the 4046 is thus 3,600 f_a and is virtually in phase with the incoming signal. In order to reduce the phase jitter to a minimal value, the PLL is operated over four ranges selected by means of switches S_{1a} to S_{1c} (see table).

The output of the 4046 serves as the clock for driving a four-digit display circuit, which can be made up conventionally with cascaded sections of 74190 synchronous up/down counters, a set of 7475 4-bit bistable latches,

7447 BCD-to-seven-segment decoder/drivers and suitable displays. (The one-chip ICM7217 provides the counter, latch, and decoding functions and could conceivably be used to reduce the chip count, but requires multiple supply voltages.)

The count is initiated on the rising edge of f_a and is terminated by the leading edge of a pulse from channel B. Pulses are counted on alternate cycles of the incoming wave, to minimize control circuitry. Because the circuit is designed for steady-state phase measurements, there is no loss in accuracy. The (lagging) phase angle of f_b with respect to f_a is then displayed. The 74190 counter circuitry may be simply modified to preset the counters to 360 in the countdown mode, instead of counting up from 0, so that the phase of f_a with respect to f_b may be shown. Flicker is eliminated by appropriate selection of the 555 one-shot's timing components. □

Interfacing TTL with fast bipolar drivers

by J. A. R. Ball, P. J. Grehan, and P. Welton
Darling Downs Institute, School of Engineering, Queensland, Australia

Surprisingly, there are as yet no suitable integrated circuits for translating the 0-to-5-volt output swing of TTL into arbitrary bipolar levels. But even the discrete interfacing circuits that have appeared over the years will fall short in performance, especially if the requirement calls for a high-speed switch to drive the relatively high capacitance of a power device or load. The solution lies in modifying the typical textbook interface with a circuit that acts to decrease the input-circuit storage time of the output transistors but does not appreciably affect any other interface parameter or specification.

A slightly modified ±10-v TTL interface is shown in (a), which will be suitable for relatively high-speed switching at low to medium current (below 100 milliamperes). In this circuit, Q_1 turns on and remains in the active region when the TTL output exceeds 1.5 v. Providing the current drawn out of the base is sufficient, Q_3 will saturate and the voltage applied to the load will be almost 10 v. When the TTL output falls sufficiently, Q_1 and Q_3 turn off, and charge stored in the base of Q_3 escapes via resistor R_3. Transistors Q_2 and Q_4 comprising the other half of the circuit act in a complementary fashion, conducting when the TTL output falls below 1.5 V and applying −10 v to the load.

One disadvantage of this circuit is that it is possible for Q₃ and Q₄ to be conducting at the same instant during a change of state to cause a supply current spike whose magnitude may exceed the nominal load current by more than three times. Also, most of the power lost in the output transistor will be dissipated during a change of state when both are in the active region. Thus, the average dissipation will be proportional to the switching frequency. These problems may be minimized by increasing the zener voltage, V_Z, so as to increase the dead zone between the input threshold levels of the circuit. Switching speed may be increased by optimizing the value of the speed-up capacitors C_1 and C_2, operating Q_3 and Q_4 at very large base currents, and reducing R_3 and R_4 to minimize storage time.

This basic circuit can also be used to control far larger currents than 100 mA, providing appropriate output transistors are used. However, the storage time of these devices then becomes a major problem, and so speed is sacrificed. The circuit in (b) shows how to reduce the delay time by adding two transistors for supplying reverse base current to whichever output transistor is in the act of turning off.

Here, when the TTL output goes high, Q_1 conducts and Q_3 saturates as before, while Q_2 turns off and Q_4 begins to come out of saturation. In addition, the emitter current of Q_1 turns on Q_6, which provides a path for the escape of charge stored in the base of Q_4. This effectively shortens Q_4's turn-off delay.

When the TTL output goes low, then Q_1 and Q_6 turn off, Q_2 and Q_5 conduct, Q_4 saturates because of the base current supplied by Q_2, and Q_3 is rapidly turned off because of the action of Q_5. Discharge transistors Q_5 and Q_6 should be selected for high-speed saturated switching, so that they will not delay the turn-off of their associated output transistors.

Adding Q_5 and Q_6 will reduce the storage delay of the output transistors by a factor of from 2 to 4. The circuit in (b) provides a rise and fall time of about 80 nanoseconds for a load of 11 ohms (2-ampere load). The active pull-up output ensures the interface's low output impedance in either the logic 0 or logic 1 state. A further advantage is that the output voltage is specified within narrow limits in both states, unlike the case with totem-pole–type circuits. □

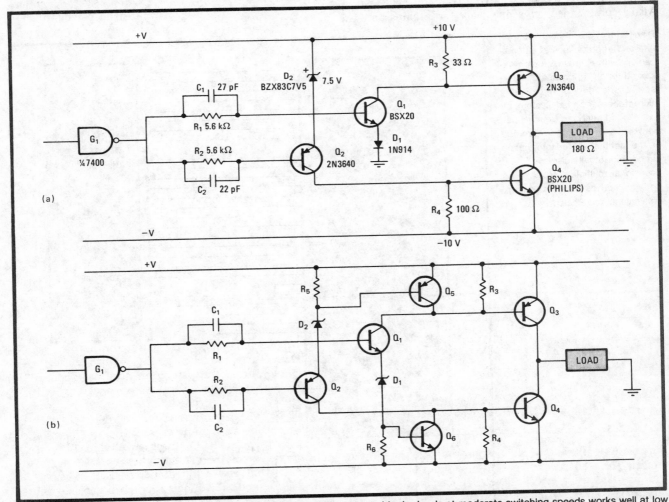

Conversion. Interface (a) for translating the 0-to-5-V TTL swing into arbitrary bipolar levels at moderate switching speeds works well at low load currents. For increased loads, circuit (b) offsets the large storage delay of the output transistors and reduces crossover switching.

Adapter equips HP analyzer for general ROM tracing

by Israel Gal
Liad Electronics, Moshav Yaad, Israel

A two-socket adapter turns the popular Hewlett-Packard family of HP1611A logic analyzers—which can normally be configured for debugging one specific microcomputer—into a general-purpose read-only-memory tracer. Thus, as this example shows, it can be used with the Z-80 Personality Module as a developmental tool for Intel machines, without the need for Intel's ICE series of in-circuit emulators.

Tracing is simply achieved by placing the microprocessor's address and data lines directly in parallel with those of the external program memory and disabling all other input lines to the Z-80. Placing a low-insertion-force socket, such as those produced by Textool Inc., at the Z-80 end enables fast connection to the conversion circuit. At the memory end, use of a hardwired 24-pin spring clip adds increased flexibility for in-field testing. Also recommended is a scope probe for latching onto the appropriate circuit point of the desired clock signal. The clock and its inverse signal are available, so that the user can synchronize the timing to each particular processor.

In operation, the logic analyzer will be synchronized as usual to accept address, data, and external information in every possible combination. Thus, most of the additional options of the analyzer, such as pretriggering, post-triggering, trace and count triggering, and trigger enable and disable can be utilized. The single-step and trace-then-halt options of the Intel 8031-8051 machines cannot be used here, although they will be functional on every other processor that has a wait line.

Using the HP1611A this way has several drawbacks, among them the fact that there is no disassembly—information is displayed in hexadecimal or octal format. And the information shifted onto available on-chip RAM or registers is not itself displayed, only the representation of the transfer as an operating code. Also, as a result of the clocking arrangement, there can be situations where the directive will be displayed twice (although the address is always correct). However, where low cost, convenience, and efficiency are important, this circuit is satisfactory. □

Translator. Parallel connection of data and address lines of external memory with HP1611A logic analyzer through appropriate interface eases debugging of any microprocessor-based system by a dedicated analyzer. Scheme has drawbacks—lack of disassembler, the fact that shifted information cannot be actually displayed, and occasional multiple display of op code directives—but is cheap, convenient, and efficient.

LED indicates timing error in emitter-coupled-logic one-shot

by M. U. Khan
Systronics, Naroda, Ahmedabad, India

Rather than scrutinize waveforms on an oscilloscope, it is possible to employ a simple circuit to monitor the output of a one-shot to determine if it is being triggered at the right time or if the output pulse width is correct.

If the clock pulse arrives while the normally low output $\overline{Q}_1$ or set line S_1 of the one-shot is at a logic 1 level, the $\overline{Q}_2$ output of the indicator flip-flop goes to a logic 0 level, turning on the light-emitting diode. Q_1 of the one-shot remains at the logic 1 level only in its quasi-stable state, whereas S_1 goes to the logic 1 level only in its recovery state. Thus whenever the one-shot is triggered too early—in other words, before recovering—the LED turns on. When the mistriggering is corrected, by reducing either the clock rate or the width of the one-shot, it automatically turns off.

Besides the LED, the indicator circuit consists of an MC 10103 OR gate and an MC 10231 D-type flip-flop, both emitter-coupled-logic devices. The circuit works satisfactorily up to 75 megahertz. For higher speeds—up to 100 MHz—propagation-delay compensation through an additional OR gate (dotted line) is needed. In the latter case, both the OR gates should be replaced by an MC 1660 dual four-input OR-NOR gate. □

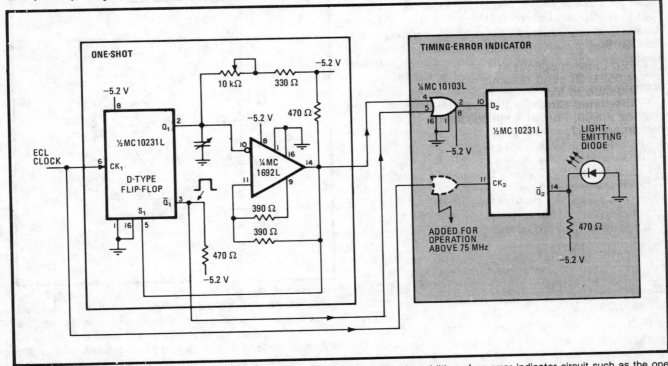

Hot shot. Spotting timing errors in a fast one-shot multivibrator is simplified with the addition of an error indicator circuit such as the one shown in the shaded area. If the clock rate is too high or the output pulse width is too small, the LED will indicate it.

Wired-OR ECL one-shot has near-zero propagation time

by Jozef Kalisz
Warsaw, Poland

Because of their output configurations and current-handling capabilities, emitter-coupled-logic and TTL circuits can easily yield the wired-OR function simply by having the outputs of two gates tied together. This trait may be employed to build a pulse-stretching circuit in either logic family that is equivalent to a monostable multivibrator having virtually zero propagation time.

Such a circuit, shown in (a) for ECL, relies on the positive-feedback loop created by gates G_1 and G_2. In the steady state, the input voltage of G_2 is maintained at the V_{IH} level of about -1 volt by resistors R_1 and R_2. The positive input trigger pulse, derived from a typical ECL gate, brings the driving-point potential to -1.8 v, permitting capacitor C to charge.

As long as the input voltage to G_2 remains below about -1.3 v, the gate's output voltage will be high, thus stretching the input pulse. If the propagation time of the gates is not taken into account, the output pulse width is approximately equal to $T = 0.98\ CR_1\|R_2$. With the gates in the 10000 logic family, the minimum pulse width of the driving pulse can be made 4 nanoseconds, which is equal to the propagation time in the loop. The circuit may directly drive a coaxial cable or a microstrip line, provided they are correctly terminated. In such a case, pull-down resistor R_4 is not required.

A similar circuit is shown in (b), with open-collector TTL gates used to implement the wired-AND function. The output pulse width is approximately $T = 0.28 \times CR_1\|R_{IL}$, where R_{IL} is the input resistance of G_2 when its input voltage remains below the 1.4-v threshold. Typically, $R_{IL} = 4$ kilohms. The shortest input pulse required is about 20 ns, and this value again is equal to the circuit's propagation time. □

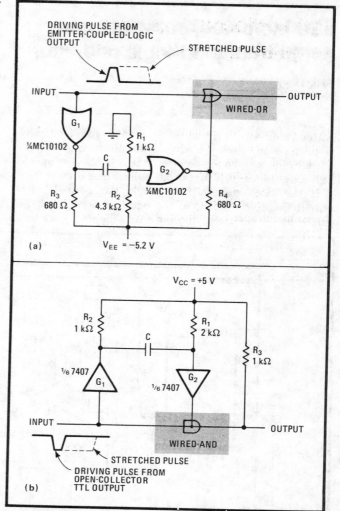

(a)

(b)

Infinitesimal. Wired-OR connection of emitter-coupled-logic gates (a) permits the building of a pulse-stretching circuit that is equivalent to a one-shot having virtually zero propagation time. In this case, it is 4 nanoseconds, equal to that of the minimum pulse needed to excite the circuit. Similar results are derived from wired-AND gates of TTL (b), although the propagation time is a bit longer—20 ns.

Twin optocouplers raise serial transmission speed

by Luis E. Murguis
Autotrol SA, Buenos Aires, Argentina

In a balanced 20-milliampere current loop for long-distance serial data transmission, optical couplers are a convenient way of connecting both receiver and transmitter to the transmission line, and provide isolation as well. However, an active pullup scheme employing an additional optical coupler at the receiver can improve transmission speed by an order of magnitude.

In the setup shown in (a), the fall time of the output voltage depends on the saturation current, I_i, of the coupler's input. However, the rise time of the output voltage, which determines the maximum transmission frequency, corresponds to the turn-off time of the coupler's output and is a function of load resistor R_L. Lowering the value of R_L raises the transmission rate, but only up to a limit set by the amount of current the optical coupler can handle.

Instead of trading off transmission speed and coupler loading, a second optical coupler produces a faster rise time and improves the transmission frequency almost 10 times over systems configured in the conventional way. The two optical couplers are connected as shown in (b) to produce an active pull-up and pull-down circuit at the output and thus speed up the output-voltage rise time. Both the rise and fall times are now a function of I_i, as the couplers alternate between their on and off states. Resistors R_1 and R_2 are optional and provide a fixed bias in case a circuit failure causes I_i to fall to zero. Another advantage of this circuit is that it improves fanout since a load resistor is no longer needed. □

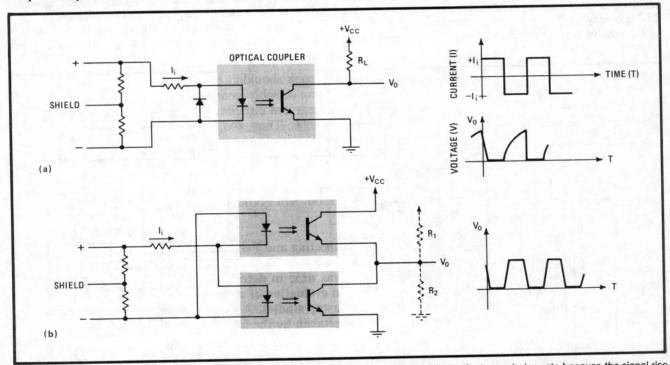

Active output. A conventional, single-coupler design for a 20-milliampere current loop (a) limits the transmission rate because the signal rise time is a function of resistor R_L. Using two couplers in an active pull-up output (b) forces faster rise times and hence higher transmission rates.

Digital phase meter updates measurement each cycle

by R. E. S. Abdel-Aal
Department of Electronic Science, University of Strathclyde, Glasgow, Scotland

Because this meter measures the phase delay between two low-frequency square waves once every cycle, it is useful in applications where instantaneous readings of this delay are continuously required. The circuit resolution is within 1% for signal frequencies of up to 250 kilohertz.

Generally, the meter counts the number of pulses of a 25-megahertz clock for a time equal to the phase delay between the two incoming waveforms. Then it strobes the measured value into output latches once a cycle. The result is a continuously updated value expressed as a 15-bit binary number plus a sign bit.

To achieve this, the cycle is viewed as one that varies from plus to minus 180°. By using only one half of the cycle for measurement, the circuit is free during the other half to store the results in the output latches and to clear the phase counters for the next measurement.

The circuit automatically determines which of the signals is to be the reference, with the phase delay measured from the rising edge of the leading signal to the rising edge of the lagging waveform. The falling edge of the reference serves as the latching signal and to set up the counters for the next cycle.

In operation, the two incoming signals, A and B, are applied to two gates of A_1. Here, the complemented signals $\overline{A}$ and $\overline{B}$ are obtained with negligible differential delay. The other two gates in the chip generate gating signals corresponding to $A\overline{B}$ and $\overline{A}B$. Flip-flop A_2 determines which input signal is the reference.

If A leads B, then the Q output of A_2 goes low and gating signal $A\overline{B}$, together with input signal A, drives the 74LS157 selector chip, A_3. Otherwise, gating signal $\overline{A}B$ together with input signal B will be selected.

The selected phase-gating signal is used to enable a chain of synchronous counters, A_4–A_7, which are driven

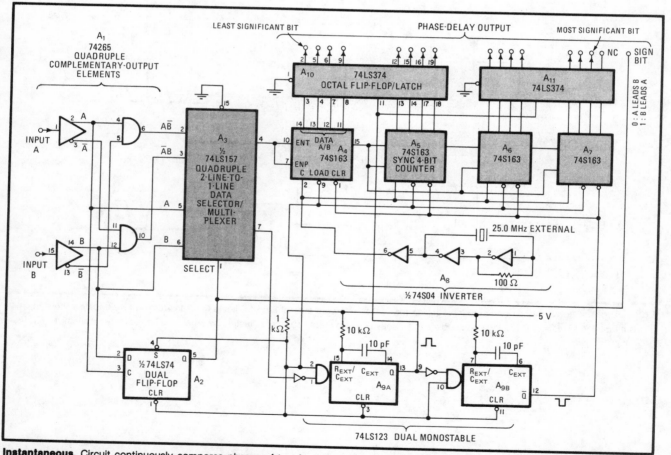

Instantaneous. Circuit continuously compares phases of two incoming square waves, providing a 15-bit and plus-sign output that has a resolution of $(f_{kHz}/250)\%$. With a 25-MHz clock, the practical upper frequency limits that can be handled for incoming signals is 250 kHz, with lowest-frequency boundaries being about 400 Hz. Lower limits can be reduced further by decreasing the clock frequency.

from a crystal-controlled 25-MHz clock built around three inverters in A_8. When the phase-gating signal drops, A_4–A_7 stop counting, holding their final result, which indicates the phase delay, at their parallel outputs. Following this, a short pulse from one-shot A_{9A} latches the results of the count in A_{10} and A_{11}. Then the pulse-counter chain is cleared by a second pulse from A_{9B}. To ensure a proper count and store cycle, the sum of the widths of the two short pulses should be less than half the period of the highest-frequency input signal. Also, the short pulse used to clear the counters should be greater than the clock period.

The upper limit on the frequency of the input signals is set by the resolution of the phase measurement that can be tolerated. With this circuit, the resolution is given by $(f/250)\%$, where f is the frequency in kilohertz.

The lower limit of the signal frequency is set by the overflow of the phase counters before the end of half a cycle of the input signal (that is, the maximum phase delay measured). With a 25-MHz clock and a 15-bit binary number representing the magnitude of the phase (excluding the sign bit), the minimum input frequency will be $25(10^6)/(2(2^{15}-1)) = 381$ hertz. At low input frequencies, however, a lower-frequency clock can be used while maintaining good resolution, and thus the frequency limit can be brought down even further.   □

POWER SUPPLIES

One-chip voltage splitter conserves battery power

by David Bingham
Intersil Inc., Cupertino, Calif.

Positive and negative supply voltages of equal magnitude are usually secured in a battery or other low-power floating-source arrangements by establishing system ground at half the source potential by means of a simple voltage divider. But this scheme more often than not consumes excessive power. Modifying Intersil's ICL7660 positive-to-negative voltage converter to work as a voltage divider, however, will increase the power-conversion efficiency to as high as 98% at an output current of 10 milliamperes.

The conventional voltage divider circuit shown in (a) uses two resistors and a unity-gain operational-amplifier buffer. While this circuit can function at relatively low power, depending upon the op amp used and the value of R, it will suffer from an inherently low power efficiency if the load should be connected between system ground and either V^+ or V^-. In such cases, the current flowing through the load will always be the same as that drawn from the battery, and thus the maximum efficiency can never be greater than 50%.

The ICL7660 can be made to simulate a divide-by-2 voltage converter by simply grounding pin 5 (normally the V^- lead) and using the normally grounded lead at pin 3 as the output, as shown in (b). The voltage distribution on the chip will be unchanged, since pin 3 is midway between V^+ and V^-, as before. And no power is lost in heating up any resistance, as the ICL7660 operates in the switched-capacitor (charge-transfer) mode to derive the output voltage.

With this configuration, an open-circuit output voltage equal to $V/2 \pm 0.1\%$ is achieved. The output impedance is 13 ohms for a supply voltage of 9 v and 0.1 mA $< I_{out} < 80$ mA, or 17 ohms for $V = 6$ v and an output current in the same general range.

Because the ICL7660 can source only an output current reliably, difficulty may be encountered if the load is connected between pins 3 and 8 of the device. To ensure startup for current-sinking applications, a 1-MΩ resistor is placed between pin 6 and ground. This step guarantees that there will always be some voltage across the on-chip oscillator and the control circuitry.

As for circuit performance (c), conversion efficiency will be no lower than 80% for $V = 6$ v and 0.5 mA $< I_{out} < 80$ mA. In equation form:

$$\eta = (V_{out}I_{out}/V^+I^+)100$$

where I_{out} is the magnitude of the output current, regardless of sign.

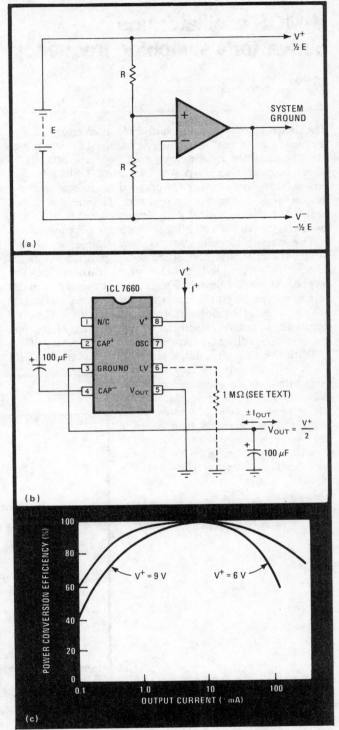

Efficient. Simple resistive voltage divider (a) dissipates excessive power and thus is ordinarily not suited to providing positive and negative supply voltages from floating source. Suitably wired ICL7660 converter (b) provides the function without power loss, yielding conversion efficiencies (c) approaching 98%.

125

V-MOS oscillator ups converter's switching frequency

by Bill Roehr
Siliconix Inc., Santa Clara, Calif.

The benefits of switching a flyback converter at high frequency to increase its efficiency and minimize its size may be realized by employing a V-groove MOS field-effect transistor as its power oscillator. Unlike bipolar power transistors, where storage-time effects hamper device turn-off, the turn-on and turn-off times for V-MOS units are fast—typically a few nanoseconds. Thus, switching speeds of 250 kilohertz can easily be achieved.

The circuit configuration is very simple, as shown. When the circuit is first energized, a positive voltage is capacitively coupled to the gate, turning on the VN10KM V-MOS device. Enhancement voltage is maintained by the potential across the transformer's primary, which is reflected onto its feedback winding. The FET continues to conduct until the core saturates, whereupon the feedback voltage collapses and turns the device off.

With the FET off, energy stored in the magnetic field surrounding the primary winding is transferred to the secondary winding. Zener diode D_1 clamps the primary winding voltage to the desired potential and limits the voltage across the V-MOS gate to some value below its 60-volt breakdown rating. The energy transferred to the feedback winding has the proper polarity to hold the FET in cutoff. When the transformer comes out of saturation, the operating cycle repeats. Diode D_2 prevents negative spikes from damaging the gate of the FET. Resistor R_1 suppresses any parasitic oscillations caused by switching.

Energy transferred to the secondary winding delivers power to filter capacitor C_2 via rectifying diode D_3. A single 4.7-μF capacitor provides sufficient filtering at the 250-kHz operating frequency. The dc output voltage may be made positive with respect to the main rail by grounding terminal 1 and negative with respect to the main rail by grounding terminal 2.

A dc output of up to 60 V can be developed by simply selecting a zener diode of that same value, although practically any voltage can be obtained by altering the transformer's turn ratio. The supply voltage should be set between 3 and 5 v dc.

Note that the physical size required for this flyback converter will be minimal, since the reactive components will be small and light because of the high operating frequency. ☐

High-flying. V-MOS power-FET converter easily operates at switching frequencies of 250 kHz and can work up to several megacycles, thereby increasing the efficiency of the flyback converter and also minimizing its size. Dc output potentials of up to 60 V may be ordered by appropriate selection of zener diode D_1.

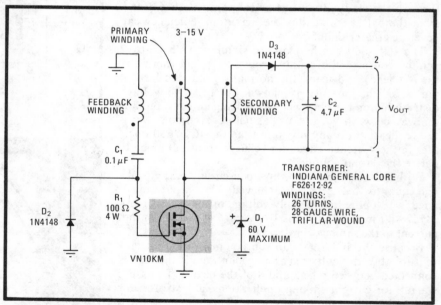

Low-loss shunt protects
high-current supplies

by Roy Hartkopf and Ron Kilgour
Alphington, Victoria, Australia

The usual method for providing short-circuit protection in low-voltage, high-current power supplies is to employ a current-sensing resistor in series with the load. Unfortunately, this scheme develops an appreciable voltage drop across the resistor when large currents flow and may consequently reduce the available output voltage to a great degree. The voltage drop can be virtually eliminated with an alternative method, shown here, which uses an audio transformer and a single-turn winding to sense the overcurrent condition at the secondary of the supply's power input transformer. Besides being inexpensive, the current sensor will react faster to overloads than some of the more conventional circuits.

As shown in the figure, current protection may be

secured for a typical 27-volt, 20-ampere supply by winding a single turn of 10-gauge wire, which is placed in series with the power transformer's secondary and the supply's rectifier bridge, onto a small audio transformer connected in the control section of the supply. During normal operation, transistor Q_1 will be saturated because current is delivered to its base from the 27-v supply line. Note that the secondary of the audio transformer, in conjunction with diode D_1, will contribute a relatively small negative voltage at the summing junction of P_1.

Should the current demands increase, however, the magnitude of the negative voltage developed at the audio transformer's secondary will increase and, consistent with the setting of potentiometer P_1, pull the base-to-emitter voltage down to cut off Q_1. The 2N2646 unijunction transistor will then turn on and trigger the silicon controlled rectifier, and the control signal will be brought low. Thus this signal can be used to cut off the supply. This action will be instantaneous, occurring on the first overload cycle. □

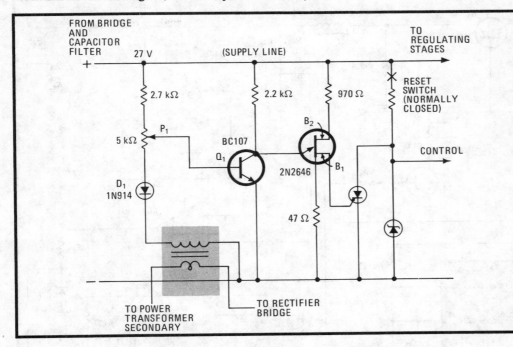

Current gauge. An audio transformer and a single turn of heavy-gauge wire, placed between input transformer's secondary and rectifier, give high-current supplies overload protection without introducing input-to-output voltage drop that occurs with units employing current-sensing resistors. Potentiometer P_1 sets the overload point. Overload detection is instantaneous, occurring on the first positive cycle of input voltage.

FROM BRIDGE AND CAPACITOR FILTER
27 V
(SUPPLY LINE)
TO REGULATING STAGES
2.7 kΩ
2.2 kΩ
970 Ω
RESET SWITCH (NORMALLY CLOSED)
P_1
5 kΩ
BC107
Q_1
B_2
2N2646
B_1
CONTROL
D_1
1N914
47 Ω
TO POWER TRANSFORMER SECONDARY
TO RECTIFIER BRIDGE

Low-cost timers govern switched-mode regulator

by Luces M. Faulkenberry
Texas State Technical Institute, Waco, Texas

This step-down switching power supply, which uses 555 timers for pulse-width modulation, combines good performance with very reasonable cost. Providing an output of 12 volts at 1 ampere for an 18-v input, the unit offers input-current limiting, 0.1%/v line regulation, 0.5% load regulation, and an output ripple of only 20 mV. However, the design equations given here enable the user to specify his own requirements. The supply can be built for less than $15.

Operating as an astable multivibrator at 20 kilohertz, timer A_1 generates the trigger pulses needed to switch the output of monostable multivibrator A_2 to logic 1 during each cycle. Modulating the control pin of one-shot A_2 with the output of the 741 operational amplifier controls the width.

The op amp compares a preset fraction of the supply voltage, V_{out}', with the 6.8-v reference, V_{ref}. When $V_{ref} > V_{out}'$, the control pin of the one-shot moves high and each pulse from the output of A_2 is lengthened accordingly until the reference and supply voltages are virtually equal. Similarly, if $V_{ref} < V_{out}'$, the output pulses are shortened.

As seen, transistors Q_1 and Q_2 in the simple feedback loop perform the switching function. Monitoring transistors Q_3 and Q_4 limit the current by bringing A_2's reset pin low when the design-maximum peak current through the inductor is reached, thereby shortening the width of the output pulses until the cause of the trouble is removed. Q_3 can also serve in a dual capacity as a switch to turn off the supply during overload conditions. For example, should automatic shutdown of the supply be necessary, Q_3 could be used to fire a silicon controlled rectifier in order to hold the reset pin of oscillator A_1 low permanently. In these cases, a simple circuit would also be needed to reset the supply manually. □

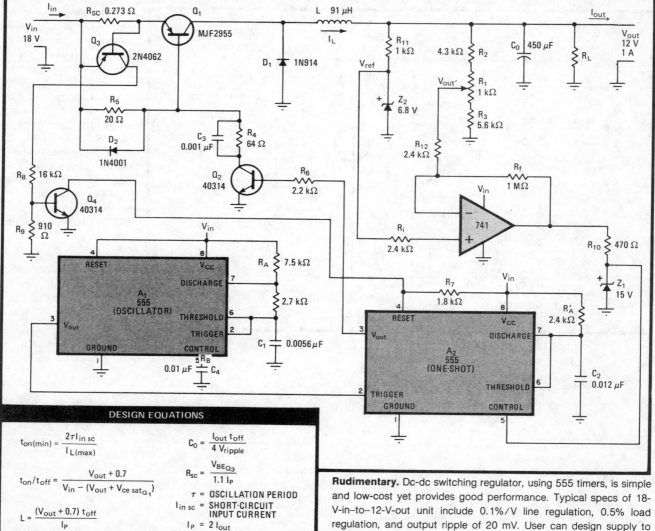

DESIGN EQUATIONS

$$t_{on(min)} = \frac{2\tau I_{in\,sc}}{I_{L(max)}}$$

$$t_{on}/t_{off} = \frac{V_{out} + 0.7}{V_{in} - (V_{out} + V_{ce\,sat_{Q_1}})}$$

$$L = \frac{(V_{out} + 0.7)\, t_{off}}{I_P}$$

$$C_0 = \frac{I_{out}\, t_{off}}{4\, V_{ripple}}$$

$$R_{SC} = \frac{V_{BEQ_3}}{1.1\, I_P}$$

τ = OSCILLATION PERIOD
$I_{in\,sc}$ = SHORT-CIRCUIT INPUT CURRENT
$I_P = 2\, I_{out}$

Rudimentary. Dc-dc switching regulator, using 555 timers, is simple and low-cost yet provides good performance. Typical specs of 18-V-in-to-12-V-out unit include 0.1%/V line regulation, 0.5% load regulation, and output ripple of 20 mV. User can design supply to meet his own requirements with aid of given equation set.

Low-power inverter ignites gas-discharge lamps

by Akavia Kaniel
Measurex Corp., Cupertino, Calif.

This inexpensive low-power inverter generates the high voltage required to ignite gas-discharge lamps of the mercury-vapor type and supplies the small current needed to maintain conduction. It also prevents the deposition of ions on the lamp's cathode that tends to shorten its operating lifetime. Using one integrated circuit, an operational amplifier, and two field-effect transistors, the inverter can be built for less than $30, including the cost of the unit's pulse transformer.

As shown, the SG3524 pulse-width modulator and transformer T_1 convert a 24-volt dc input into the 1,500-v potential required for turning on the Ultra Violet Products 11SC2 lamp. When switch S_1 is closed, the chip's E_a output goes high, thus inducing a high-voltage square wave across T_1's secondary.

As current begins to flow in the primary, feedback amplifier A_1 comes into play. Detecting the relative magnitude of the current through the 0.2-ohm sense resistor, A_1 automatically sets the width of the 20-kilohertz modulating pulses so that a constant ac current of 5 milliamperes is delivered to the lamp. Use of a push-pull output and the balanced transformer connection ensure that the switched square wave is symmetrical about the zero axis. This ac driving signal thus prevents the migration and subsequent buildup of ions around the lamp's cathode. □

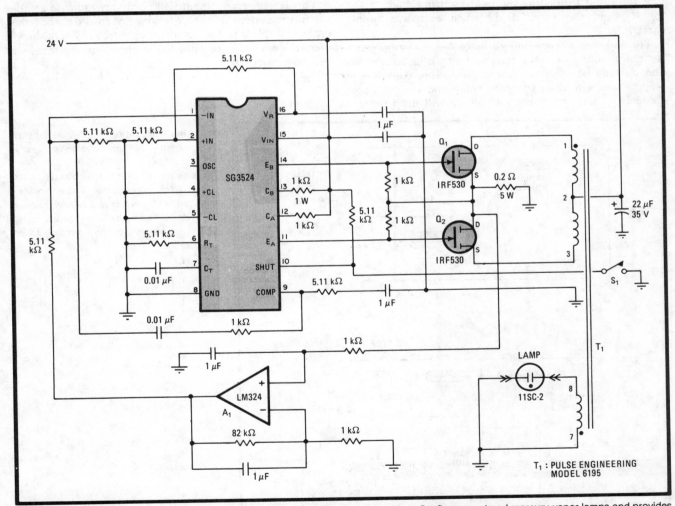

Arc-over. Low-power transistor-driven inverter generates high-voltage square wave to fire fluorescent and mercury-vapor lamps and provides low current to maintain ionization. Symmetry of inverter's output prohibits build-up of ions at lamp's cathode, thus increasing operating life.

Reed-coil relay is behind flexible fault detection

by Daniel Appiolaza
Mendoza, Argentina

Mechanically providing such functions as undercurrent and overcurrent protection for power supplies and fault indication for an automobile's turn signals or stoplights is easier to achieve inexpensively with relays having a separate reed and coil. Using the coil as a remote current-sensing device also makes the relay flexible enough to do a myriad of other jobs not possible with self-contained units.

Consider the example of current-overload monitoring (a). Here, the normally open reed switch serves to activate the shunt formed by the light-emitting diode, resistor R_1, and the zener diode when excessive supply current flows.

The coil, made from four turns of No. 12 gauge wire, is tightly wound over the reed so that an instantaneous line current equal to or larger than approximately 5 amperes dc will close the reed relay and trigger zener diode D_1. Thus the reference voltage will drop to zero until the line current is reduced and the reset switch is depressed.

A second example is the fault detector of an automobile's brake signals (b), where it is important to know when a stop or turn lamp has failed (a feature not supplied by auto makers). Here, two reed/coil assemblies are required, with the reed contacts being normally closed.

If for any reason either of the stoplights does not turn on when the brake is applied, no current can flow through either coil. Consequently, the reed switches will not open and the panel LED will indicate trouble with the signalling system.

With normally closed relay contacts, however, the stoplights may still turn on despite a failure in the reed circuit or even the LED/resistor itself. Alternatively, it might be better if the reeds are of the normally open type. Then the circuit can be wired to switch on the panel LED only when the car's stoplights become active.

This latter arrangement will positively indicate a failure in the system. If the LED does not turn on when the brake is applied in the normally open reed system, however, it does indicate difficulty with either the lamp or the monitor circuit. □

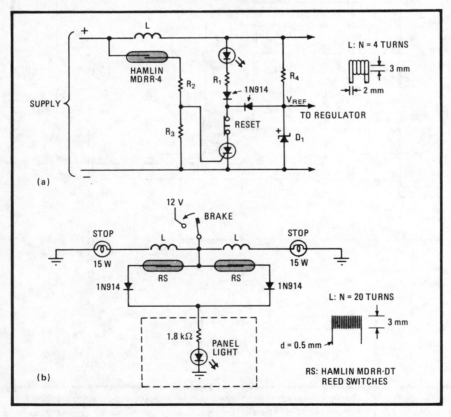

(a)

(b)

L: N = 4 TURNS

L: N = 20 TURNS

RS: HAMLIN MDRR-DT REED SWITCHES

Switching separates. Two-element relay having remote four-turn current-sensing coil and normally open reed switch (a) provides inexpensive overcurrent protection for power supply. When implemented in car's brake-signal system, relay detects faulty turn or stoplights. A normally open relay circuit might be preferable to the normally closed configuration shown.

Milliampere current source is voltage-controlled

by William J. Mundl
Concordia University, Department of Psychology, Montreal, Canada

The constant small positive or negative current produced by this voltage-controlled source is useful for a variety of low-level measurements. As the current also has a virtually linear relationship with the input voltage, it may be modulated as desired by a given input waveform or, still more usefully, be put under microprocessor control to create an automated test system.

As seen in (a), incoming signals in the range of 0 to 10 volts are buffered by the LM358 micropower operational amplifier A_1 and then introduced to A_2, which with transistor Q_1 makes the current-monitoring feedback circuit. For a given input voltage, A_2 amplifies and inverts Q_1's emitter-to-base voltage variations, so that any increase or decrease in current due to temperature or load variations is counteracted. As a result, the current will rise linearly from zero to I_{max}, where I_{max} is determined by resistor R, with the variation of I for a given V_{in} being about 2%. In this circuit, the maximum attainable value of I_{max} is approximately 4 milliamperes, obtained with a 1.5-kilohm load impedance.

Calibration of the circuit is simple. Potentiometer R_1 need only be adjusted to null the output current for V_{in} = 0. For convenience in setting the output current, an oscilloscope can be placed across a 1-kΩ resistor.

The layout for this circuit's counterpart, a negative current sink, is similar, as shown in (b). Q_1 becomes an npn transistor, the supply potential on the circuit is reversed, and an inverting stage is added at the input.

Although the circuit is relatively insensitive to variations in the supply voltage, use of a regulated power supply of the simple series type is recommended. □

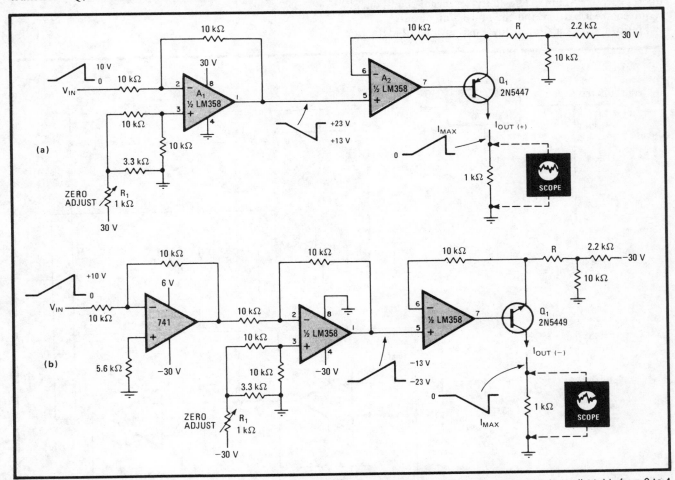

Milliampere magnitudes. The circuit's input voltage sets its constant output current to within 5% of the desired value, adjustable from 0 to 4 mA if R = 1.5 kΩ. Its linear response makes it attractive for microprocessor-based (automated) tests and measurements. The positive source in (a) or negative sink in (b) is simply calibrated by means of resistor R_1 and an oscilloscope monitor.

Power-fail detector uses chip's standby mode

by Jerry Winfield
Mostek Corp., Carrollton, Texas

As microprocessors are used more frequently for consumer and industrial applications, the need to preserve data and program status during power outages has become increasingly important. Until now, this function has been implemented with a small, outboard complementary-MOS random-access–memory battery-charging circuitry, power-fail circuitry, and a battery.

The MK3875, one of the MK387X family of single-chip microcomputers, simplifies the job of providing a battery backup system by incorporating 64 bytes of standby RAM and the battery-charging circuit onto the microprocessor chip. The only external components required are a battery and the power-fail circuit.

Figure 1 shows a simple, low-cost power-fail–detection

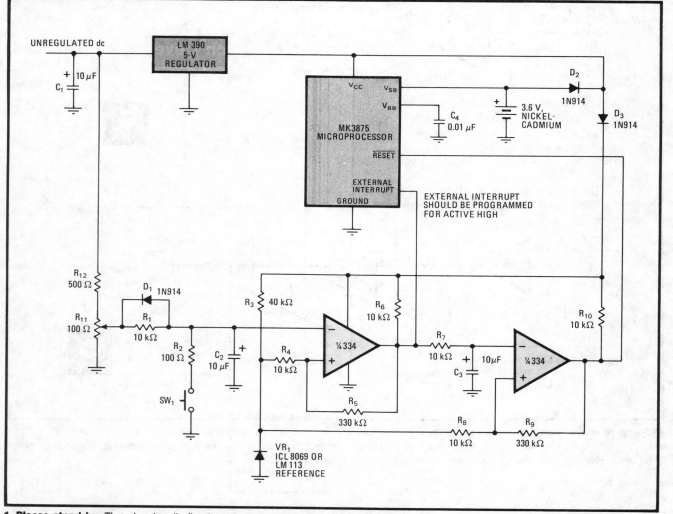

1. Please stand by. Though primarily for detecting power failures, this circuit also adds power-on and push-button reset functions to the MK3875 microcomputer, which has 64 bytes of standby RAM and a battery-charging circuit for implementing a standby power mode.

circuit that can be designed with readily available parts. Figure 2 details the timing relationship between $\overline{\text{RESET}}$ and V_{cc} for enabling and disabling the standby RAM function. Simply stated, $\overline{\text{RESET}}$ must be low when V_{cc} is below its specified voltage, which is 4.75 volts for a 5% part and 4.5 v for a 10% part.

The circuit shown in Fig. 1 detects power failures and resets the device automatically at power-on and manually during operation. The circuit monitors the unregulated voltage that feeds the V_{cc} regulator and compares this voltage against a voltage reference. When the voltage drops below the reference, the $\overline{\text{RESET}}$ line is pulled low. Hysteresis is designed into the comparator to prevent the oscillation caused by slow rise and fall times.

The trimming potentiometer, R_{11}, should be adjusted so the negative threshold voltage V_{th-} is greater than the minimum input voltage of the V_{cc} regulator. Adjusting the threshold voltage above the minimum will yield additional time before the $\overline{\text{RESET}}$ line goes low should the external interrupt be used for saving variables.

As mentioned earlier, the circuit also functions as a power-on or manual reset. The power-on reset is created by the addition of C_2 and D_1, and the manual reset is created by the addition of R_2 and SW_1.

The power-fail circuit can also be configured to generate an external interrupt to the MK3875 to save variables before the $\overline{\text{RESET}}$ line is activated. Adding capacitor C_3 allows time for executing the save routine before the $\overline{\text{RESET}}$ line is pulled low; the external interrupt should also be programmed as an active-high input.

The MK3875 was designed primarily for use with a small 3.6-v nickel-cadmium battery and will automatically supply a maximum charging current of 19 mA at 3.2 v and a minimum trickle charge of 0.8 mA at 3.8 v. The size of the battery will depend on the length of required standby time. (With a V_{cc} variation of 4.75 to 5.25 v, the standby current for the RAM will vary between 3.7 mA to 6 mA.)

Among those battery manufacturers whose small nickel-cadmium batteries could be used with the MK3875 are Varta, Yuasa, General Electric, Gould, Sanyo, and Panasonic. □

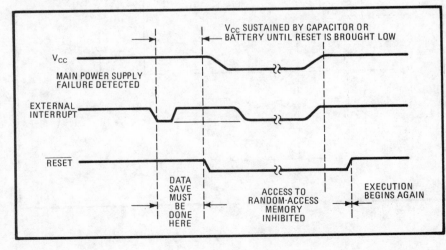

2. Wave goodbye. Where a save routine is needed to preserve critical data before power is lost, the external interrupt must be toggled before the reset line, during which time the routine is executed. The time allowed to save the data is determined by the value of C_3.

High-current voltage regulator works with negative supplies

by Robert A. Pease
National Semiconductor Corp., Santa Clara, Calif.

Monolithic voltage regulators combine the voltage-stabilizing and power-protection circuitry of discrete component designs into a single package. As a result, current-limiting, voltage-limiting, and even thermal limiting features are built into the regulating function and therefore require no further consideration by the designer. Unfortunately, most high-power monolithic voltage regulators are intended for positive-supply voltages.

Currently, the only negative-voltage monolithic regulators that are available are those with 1.5 or 3 amperes of rated output current. The LM337 adjustable and LM345 fixed −5-volt regulators are two such devices. New high-current monolithic regulators, such as the LM338, rated at 5 A, and the LM396, rated at 10 A, are normally characterized as positive regulators. Yet they can also be used in applications calling for negative regulators, such as in an emitter-coupled-logic computer where several amperes at −2 V are often required.

The figure shows an LM396 that is controlled by an LF351 operational amplifier that holds the LM396's adjust pin at 1.25 V below the −5.2-V bus.

The accuracy of the output voltage depends on the −5.2-V supply, which is used as a reference. Short-circuit limiting to 15 A and thermal-limit protection to 170°C are provided by the LM396. Although the −12 V dc need not be closely regulated, it must be present or else the −2-V supply will fall toward −3 or −4 v, which is excessively negative.

Similarly, a positive regulator such as an LM338 or one or more LM396s have been used to regulate 5, 10, 20 A, or more of −5.2 V dc when a 9-v dc power and a −15-V dc bias supply are used. ☐

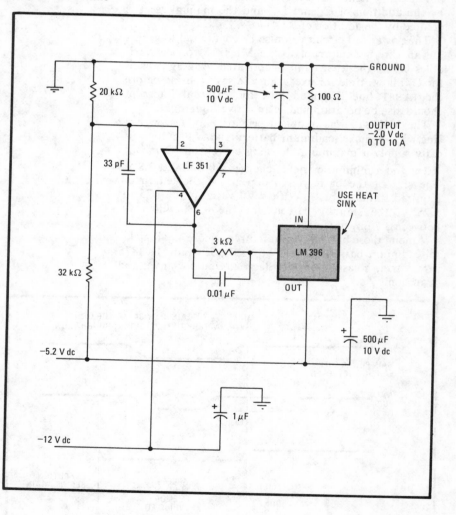

Both ways. An LM396 monolithic positive-voltage regulator can be used, as shown here, to regulate a 10-ampere negative supply. Feedback to the regulator chip is furnished by an LF351 operational amplifier. The LM396 regulator provides full short-circuit protection to 15 A, as well as temperature protection to 170°C.

Regulator boosts supply voltage for programming EE-PROMs

by Henry Fung and John Rizzo
Intel Corp., Special Products Division, Santa Clara, Calif.

The 2816 is a new electrically erasable programmable read-only memory in which writing and erasing can be accomplished on board by feeding a 21-volt dc pulse to the chip's V_{PP} pin. But generating the pulse requires a power supply with an output voltage of $+24$ v dc, which is then clamped by a zener diode to about $+21$ v dc. When that is not available, a switching regulator can be used to convert the commonly available $+5$ v dc into $+24$ v dc. The advent of large-scale integration technology simplifies the design of such a dc-to-dc converter. Figure 1 shows the circuit diagram for a voltage convert-er using a TL497 switching voltage regulator that is very inexpensive to build.

The circuit operates as follows: the frequency at which transistor Q_1 is switching is determined by capacitor C_1. The converter's output voltage is fed back to an internal comparator that controls the on and off time of Q_1. When Q_1 is turned off, the voltage across the inductor inverts, and the blocking diode, D_1, is forward-biased to provide a current path for the discharge of the inductor into the load and filter capacitors (C_2 and C_3). While Q_1 is turned on, the current into the inductor increases linearly. D_1 will then become reverse-biased and the output load current will be provided by the filter capacitors. But current output above 80 milliamperes will cause the output-voltage regulation to degrade.

The switching-regulator efficiency may be calculated as a ratio of output power to input power (including a 50% duty cycle). Therefore:

$$\text{efficiency } (\%) = \frac{\text{output power}}{\text{input power}} \times 100\%$$

1. Big boost. A dc-to-dc converter based on a TL497 switching regulator boosts a 5-V supply voltage to 24 V dc for programming electrically alterable read-only memories. Q_1 is switched at a rate determined by C_1, and the induced voltage in L_1 is the output.

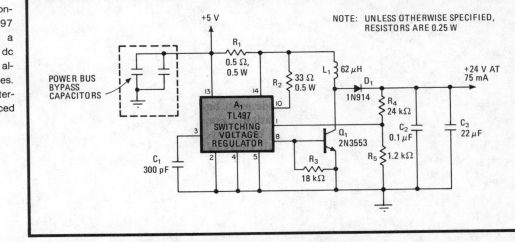

2. Sensing switch. The programming voltage, V_{PP}, is applied when the output of A_2, an open collector gate, is high for 10 ms during a write cycle. C_1 charges up and ultimately turns on Q_1, which provides up to 75 mA of drive to erase or write into a memory.

$$= \frac{24\text{ v} \times 80\text{ mA}}{5\text{ v} \times 1{,}160\text{ mA} \times 0.5} \times 100\%$$
$$= 66\%$$

The output voltage from the switching regulator may now generate the V_{PP} pulse required to program the 2816 EE-PROM. The next requirement is a circuit that switches the 24 v on during write and erase cycles (Fig. 2)

D_1 suppresses any noise on the 24-v line and clamps the line at about 21 v. A_2 is an open-collector gate and when its output is low, C_1 and pin 5 of A_3 will be shorted to ground. Therefore, Q_1 will be turned off and the V_{PP} pulse will stay at a level equal to the 5-v supply voltage less one diode drop. When a write cycle is initiated, the output of gate A_2 will be high for 10 milliseconds,

allowing C_1 to charge. The time constant, determined by R_2 and C_1, is 600 microseconds. As soon as the capacitor is charged up to the zener diode voltage, the feedback amplifier will force this voltage to remain constant. The final output voltage is adjusted by R_3. Q_1 provides the additional current-drive capability up to 75 mA. Diode D_2 across pins 5 and 6 of A_3 ensures a V_{PP} pulse that will be glitchless.

The 2816 has an inhibit mode that allows the device to be deselected during programming. Consequently, only one switch is needed for many devices in a system. However, the V_{PP} switch must still supply the I_{PP} standby current for the unselected devices.

The circuit has been tested over the 2816's full operating temperature range. □

Stacked voltage references improve supply's regulation

by Wes Freeman and George Erdi
Precision Monolithics Inc., Santa Clara, Calif.

By combining low-cost precision voltage references, inexpensive yet accurate power supplies that work over a wide range of voltages may be built. When suitably stacked, these voltage references even improve the regulating performance of the supply.

Consider the circuit in Fig. 1, which can be built for approximately $10. It uses two 10-volt references so combined that the supply will work over a range of 0 to 20 v, with switch S_1 selecting the 0-to-10- and 10-to-20-v ranges.

An operational amplifier isolates potentiometer R_1, which sets the output voltage to within 300 microvolts of the desired value. The op amp's short-circuit current, approximately 22 milliamperes, limits the maximum base current available to the power transistor. As a result, the maximum available output current is nearly 1 ampere.

The supply's line regulation is within 0.005% of scale reading per volt in the 10-to-20-v range. In the 0-to-10-v range, line regulation is significantly improved to within 0.0001%/v and is mainly limited by the op amp's supply rejection ratio because the output of the second reference regulates the line voltage of the first.

Load regulation is determined by the change in the op amp's open-loop gain versus load current. In this circuit, measured values were ±0.001%/A in the 0-to-800-mA range. Output voltage drift due to temperature is ±0.002% of scale reading per °C.

At an increase in component count and hence also in cost, the performance of the supply may be improved appreciably, as seen in Fig. 2. The addition of a third reference regulates both the 0-to-10- and 10-to-20-v ranges. A Darlington power-output transistor permits a 4-A load current.

As a result, the total change in output voltage is less than ±0.001% for a change in load current of 0 to 2 A and a change in line voltage ranging from 33 to 59 v. Potentiometers R_2 and R_3 adjust the output voltage for the 10-v and 20-v ranges, respectively, while R_4 nulls the op amp's offset voltage.

The substitution of a highly linear precision potentiometer and turn-counting dial for R_1 permits a dial accuracy of ±2 mv from 0 to 20 v, with a resolution of 200 μv. Moreover, if a better grade of reference (REF-01) is employed, the temperature coefficient is ±0.001% of scale reading per °C. □

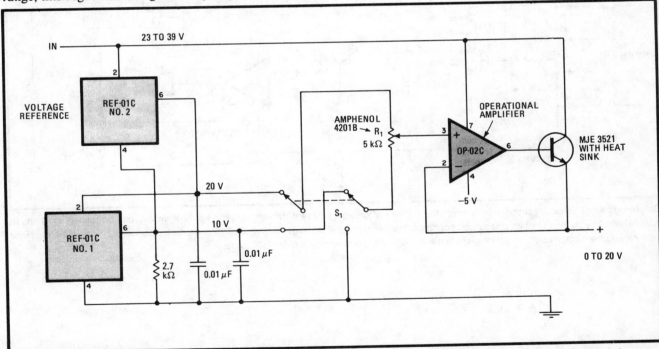

1. Piggyback. Two series-connected voltage references may be united to yield an extended supply output range with significantly improved line regulation at the lower range. The circuit's output can be set to within 300 μV of the desired value. Maximum output current is 1 A.

Comparator circuit regulates battery's charging current

by Ajit Pal
Indian Statistical Institute, Calcutta, India

As charge builds up in a battery, its effective plate-charging area gradually decreases. To prevent damage, a good battery charger should continuously limit the charging current from the power line as a function of time. This completely solid-state charger performs the required regulation for a 12-volt automobile battery using a simple circuit built around the μA710 comparator. Although designed for 220-v operation, the charger is easily adapted for 110-v service, making it suitable for application in the U.S.

The comparator automatically adjusts the charging current by sensing the battery voltage, which increases as charge accumulates. The 710 also regulates the current by controlling the on-off switching times of a thyristor that is placed in series with the battery.

As shown in the figure, a dc voltage proportional to the battery voltage is applied to pin 3 of the comparator, with potentiometer R_1 determining the actual value. Simultaneously, a ramp signal that is derived from the power line is fed to pin 2 of the 710, with R_2 setting the slope of the ramp.

When the battery is being discharged, the voltage at pin 3 of the 710 is nearly equal to the lowest instantaneous ramp voltage, and so the output of the 710 is virtually always high. Thus, the thyristor is on for almost the entire 180° switching cycle.

At the other extreme, when the battery is almost fully charged, the voltage at pin 3 is practically equal to the highest instantaneous ramp voltage, and so the thyristor is on for only a small portion of the cycle. For intermediate conditions, the thyristor will be on from between 0° and 180° of the cycle. The maximum charging current is limited by the resistor R_3. □

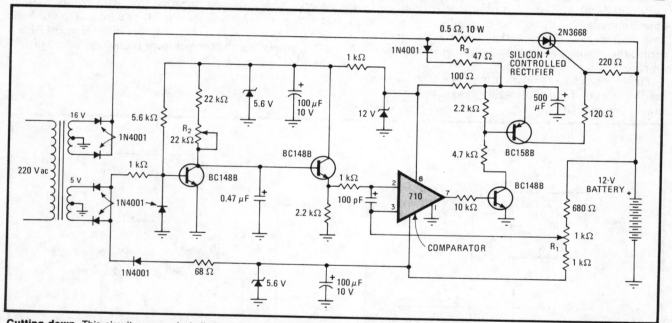

Cutting down. This circuit progressively limits the amount of charging current through a standard 12-V automobile battery as it attains its nominal terminal voltage from its discharged condition, thus avoiding cell damage. The single 710 comparator performs comparison regulation functions. Other circuitry sets conditions where the thyristor can be fired over a 0° to 180° cycle.

SIGNAL CONVERSION

One-chip DVM displays two-input logarithmic ratio

by David Watson
Intersil Inc., Reading, Berks., England

The popular ICL7106 series of analog-to-digital converters that serve so widely nowadays as one-chip digital voltmeters can be easily converted to display the logarithm of the ratio between two input voltages, making them useful for chemical densitometry, colorimetry, and audio-level measurements. Only slight wiring modifications at the device's input and integrating ports are required.

Shown in (a) is the new configuration. The modifications from the standard a-d converter connection include the addition of a resistive divider, R_1–R_2, at the reference inputs, and the placing of resistor R_p in parallel with the device's integrating capacitor.

As shown with the aid of the timing diagram in (b), the time constant of the integrating network is given by $\tau = C_{int}R_p$, with the asymptotic endpoint voltage of the integration voltage being $V_{as} = R_p (V_1 - V_2)/R_{int}$, where V_1 and V_2 are the input voltages to be measured. The final integrator voltage therefore becomes $V_{int} = R_p (V_1 - V_2)(1 - e^{-T/\tau})/R_{int}$, where T is the fixed integration period.

During the deintegration portion of the cycle, the exponential decay moves toward the total voltage, V_{tot}, which equals $V_{int} + V_{ref} (R_p/R_{int})$. But $V_{ref} = kV_2$, where k is set by the resistive divider, so that $V_{tot} = R_p (V_1 - V_2)(1 - e^{-T/\tau})/R_{int} + R_p kV_2/R_{int}$. The integrator voltage actually crosses zero when the exponential waveform reaches $V_{final} = V_{ref}R_p/R_{int} = R_p kV_2/R_{int}$.

As seen, the time needed to reach the zero crossing is given by $T_{DEINT} = \tau \ln(V_{tot}/V_{final})$. Making $k = (1 - e^{-T/\tau})$ and $\tau = T/2.3$, it is realized that $T_{DEINT} = T \log_{10}(V_1/V_2)$. For this condition, k = 0.9, which is achieved by making $R_1 = 1$ MΩ and $R_2 = 9$ MΩ.

Theoretically, the system's full-scale output voltage is reached when $\log_{10}(V_1/V_2) = 2$, but noise will probably limit the range of the converter. Note also that the accuracy of the system is no longer independent of passive component variations. The simplest way to ensure that k = 0.9 is to use a pretrimmed divider. The system is calibrated by making $V_1 = 10V_2$ and by adjusting R_p until the display reads 1.000. □

Log converter. ICL7106 analog-to-digital converter may be used to measure the logarithmic ratio of two input voltages. Modifying converter's input circuit (a) and integrating network and selecting suitable time constants ensure that its output is proportional to $\log_{10}(V_1/V_2)$. Timing diagram (b) clarifies circuit operation.

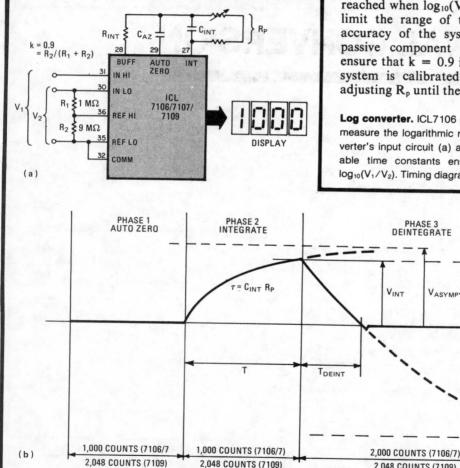

Serial-to-parallel converter decodes width-modulated BCD

by William D. Kraengel Jr.
Valley Stream, N. Y.

Converting a binary-coded-decimal pulse train into its parallel equivalent is normally straightforward, unless of course, the signal assumes the form of a pulse-width–, pulse-code–, or pulse-position–modulated data stream. In data-processing cases where the stream is encoded by means of pulse-width modulation, however, this simple 4-bit decoder will serve well in performing the serial-to-parallel transformation.

The MC14538 one-shot, A_1, and the CD4015 4-bit shift register, A_4, form the central part of the decoder, serving as the timing and storage elements. As can be seen from the schematic and the timing diagram, the BCD input data is grouped into 5-bit cycles, with bit 5 being the framing pulse. A_1 must generate a pulse width of $t_{pw} = RC = \frac{1}{2}(t_1 + t_2)$ when triggered, and one-shot A_2 has a very small triggering time of $t_s = R_1C_1 = 10$ microseconds, where both times are defined as shown in the timing diagram.

The firing time for A_1 must be selected to correspond to the input frequency of the serial BCD data. Under this condition, the one-shot is triggered by the negative edge of each serial input data bit, and if the serial input data line is low at the time the one-shot times out, a logic 0 is introduced into the shift register. On the other hand, a logic 1 will be read into the shift register if the input data goes high by the time A_1 times out.

Shift register A_3 serves as a counter, acting to disable A_4 and enable quad latch A_5 and one-shot A_2 during the framing pulse. The valid data from A_4 (which is inverted) is latched into A_5 as A_1 times out during the framing pulse. Simultaneously, A_2 is triggered so as to generate a data available/reset strobe signal for any peripheral control circuitry. The parallel equivalent BCD data and its inverse are available at the outputs of quad latch A_5. ☐

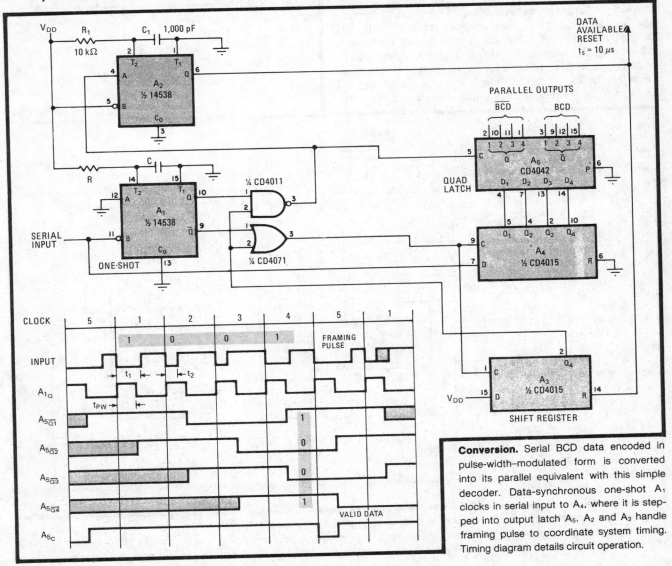

Conversion. Serial BCD data encoded in pulse-width–modulated form is converted into its parallel equivalent with this simple decoder. Data-synchronous one-shot A_1 clocks in serial input to A_4, where it is stepped into output latch A_5. A_2 and A_3 handle framing pulse to coordinate system timing. Timing diagram details circuit operation.

141

Switched V-f converter linearizes analog multiplier

by Kamil Kraus
Rokycany, Czechoslovakia

This analog voltage multiplier provides a degree of linearity not attainable with circuits that use rudimentary voltage-to-frequency converters. And when modified, it is a more versatile analog divider than the circuit proposed by Kumar[1], which finds the quotient for only one fixed reference voltage because of the way its current source is configured. The much improved performance is achieved with a one-chip unit designed specifically for V-f conversion duties, and a simple but accurate switched-capacitor arrangement to do the actual multiplication.

The product of two voltages is found by utilizing the TL604 single-pole, double-throw switches, thereby sampling input voltage V_2 periodically and placing a corresponding charge on capacitor C_u. The average current that flows to charge C_u during these intervals will thus be proportional to V_2, C_u, and the sampling frequency, which is a function of input V_1. The equivalent resistance corresponding to the average current that flows will therefore be $R_{eq} = k/C_u f$, where k is a constant and f is the sampling frequency. Assuming a high sampling frequency, a pure resistance equal to R_{eq} may be considered to be in series between the output of the switch and the inverting input of the TL071 operational amplifier, as shown.

Thus the output voltage V_{out} may be expressed as some function of V_2 multiplied by the switching function, or, more clearly, as $V_{out} = -V_2(R_2/R_{eq}) = -V_2 R_2 C_u f/k$, where the sampling frequency, on the order of 50 to 500 kHz for $0 < V_1 < 25$ v, is generated by the V-f converter. But the sampling frequency is given by $f = V_1/2R_1 C k_1$, and so $V_{out} = V_1 V_2 R_2 C_u/R_1 C k k_1$, which is proportional to $-V_1 V_2$ (constant k_1 is introduced by the VCO).

If the output circuit is modified slightly (see inset), the circuit will function as a divider. Then, $V_{out} = V_2(R_{eq}/R_2) = R_2 V_2 k/C_u R_1 C_1 k_1 \sim -V_2/V_1$. □

References
1. Umesh Kumar, "Improved analog divider finds large-signal quotients," *Electronics*, Dec. 6, 1979, p. 135.

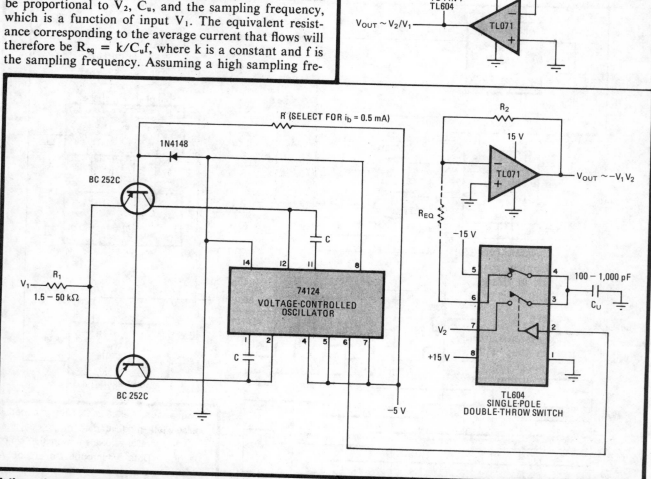

Mathematics. One-chip V-f converter and switched capacitor arrangement provided by solid-state switches yield excellent linearity and wide-range voltage-handling performance in an analog multiplier. Interchanging R_{eq} and R_2 by modifying output circuit slightly (see inset), where R_{eq} represents the average current flowing in capacitor C_u during sampling period, converts unit into two-input analog divider.

Voltage-detector chip simplifies V-f converter

by Lloyd Powell
David Taylor Naval Ship Research and Development Center, Annapolis, Md.

One-chip voltage detectors such as Intersil's ICL8212 contain all the necessary reference, discharge, and hysteresis circuitry needed to build a simple voltage-to-frequency converter. Providing a 0-to-1-kilohertz output for a 0-to-2-volt input in its basic range, the low-cost circuit requires only a few additional passive components, including an operational amplifier.

As shown, A_1 integrates incoming signals until its output voltage, and hence also the voltage across capacitor C_1, becomes $V'_{ref} = V_{ref}(R_2 + R_4)/R_2$, where V_{ref} is the internal reference voltage of the ICL8212. At that instant, A_2's comparator goes high and switches its out-

put transistor. While transistor Q_1 provides a positive-going output pulse, C_2 holds A_2's comparator high, so that C_1 is discharged quickly, in just 5 microseconds. Thus the process of integration and discharge occurs at a rate given by output frequency $f = V'_{in}/V_{ref}R_1C_1$.

Linearity and offset are better than 0.2% over the 0-to-1 kHz voltage-to-frequency range, assuming the operational amplifier used has low offset voltage and bias current. Suggested capacitance values for other frequency segments are given in the box in the figure. The input-voltage range can also be selected by means of R_1. For greatest accuracy, capacitors having the highest stability should be selected, and thus those of the silver-mica and polycarbonate type should be used where practical. For less stringent applications, those of the ceramic and disk type will suffice.

Supply voltages may range from ±2 to ±18 v without loss of circuit linearity. ☐

Cost-effective conversion. Micropower voltage detector chip and op amp form integrating V-f converter. Simple, low-cost circuit has 0.2% linearity over 0-to-2-volt input range. Frequency range, nominally 0 to 1 kilohertz, is chosen by appropriate selection of C_1 and C_2 (see box).

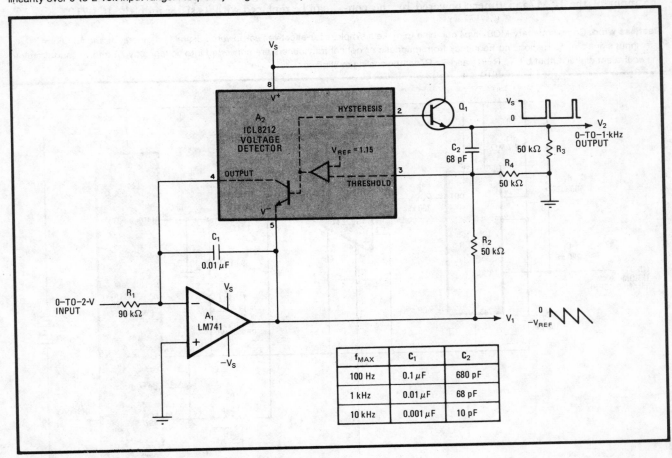

f_{MAX}	C_1	C_2
100 Hz	0.1 μF	680 pF
1 kHz	0.01 μF	68 pF
10 kHz	0.001 μF	10 pF

Low-power f-V converter turns portable tachometer

by Dan Watson
Intersil Inc., Cupertino, Calif.

Placing a frequency-to-voltage converter in the form of a complementary-MOS timer and operational amplifier at the front end of an analog-to-digital converter reduces the power, wiring complexity, and costs associated with designing an efficient digital tachometer or anemometer for field use. When combined with the multifunctional capability of such a-d converters as Intersil's ICL7106, a direct or scaled reading of the input parameter expressed in revolutions per minute can be readily determined with few additional parts.

The ICL7106 contains not only all of the required clock and display-driving circuitry, but also a reference, so that the external reference voltage normally required in circuits of this type can be omitted.

Signals applied by a magnetic or optical transducer to the input of the ICM7555 timer (powered by the con- verter's reference voltage) are converted into fixed-width pulses of corresponding frequencies. The ICL7611 micropower op amp integrates these pulses, and conse- quently the smoothed signal introduced to the a-d con- verter is a direct function of the input frequency. Thus, the signal will have an amplitude of

$$V_{in} = (RPM/60)(t_{pw})(V_r)(E)(R_4/R_3)$$

where

t_{pw} = pulse width of timer = $1.1\ R_2 C_2$
V_r = reference voltage of ICL7106 = 2.8 volts
E = number of events per revolution from the mag- netic or optical sensor, the number of fan or propeller blades, or the number of point closures per revolution in an automotive application.

The converter's full-scale output is 200 millivolts. Note that the V^- timer port is powered by the internal low-reference voltage of the converter, precluding the need for a second reference because of the rail-to-rail output swing of the ICM7555.

The output of the converter is given by n = (V_{in}/V_r) $(R_7 + R_8)/R_{8a}$. The a-d converter contains on-chip dis- play circuitry for driving a liquid-crystal display. If a light-emitting-diode display is desired, the a-d converter can be replaced with its sister unit, the ICL7107. □

Restless wind. Complementary-MOS chips combine to make a simple, cost-effective flea-powered digital tachometer or anemometer for field use. Input signals of corresponding frequency from magnetic or optical transducers are converted into voltages by A₁ and A₂, and then into the equivalent digital output by A₃. R₃–R₄ and R₇–R₈ set the scaling multipliers.

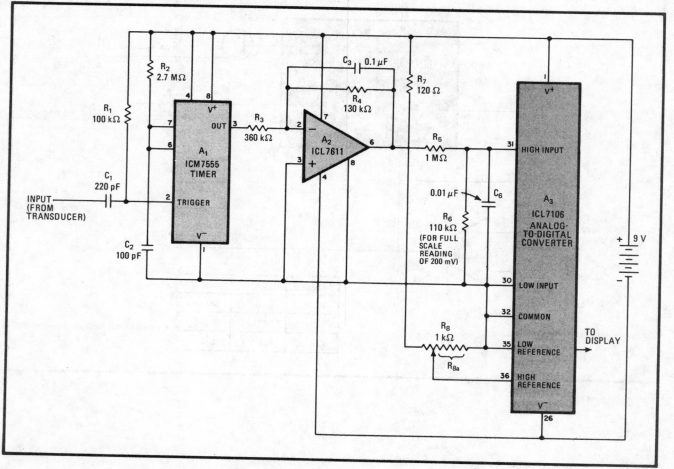

Integrator improves
555 pulse-width modulator

by Larry Korba
Ottawa, Ont., Canada

In one method of providing linear pulse-width modulation with the 555 timer, a current source charges a timing capacitor, creating a ramp signal that drives the modulation input of the 555. Unfortunately, the circuit offers only a limited dynamic range of pulse widths and is highly sensitive to temperature. A better way is to use a resettable integrator as the timing element.

Charging with a constant current source (a) at best yields a 2:1 dynamic range for a supply of 5 volts—the linear operating range for voltage–to–pulse-width conversion is approximately 2.1 to 4.1 v, and the timing capacitor is totally discharged every timing cycle. Furthermore, the circuit requires temperature compensation to eliminate any timing fluctuation due to the temperature sensitivity of Q_1, since the base-emitter voltage varies at the relatively high rate of -5 millivolts per °C. And, to add to the circuit's woes, I_{cbo} varies with temperature as well.

The resettable integrator (b) made up of A_2, Q_1, C, and R applies a trigger pulse to the 555, causing Q_1 to turn off. Integrator A_2 then ramps up until the voltage level at the modulation input of the timer equals that at pin 5. When that happens, Q_1 is turned on again, resetting the integrator and turning off the 555.

The voltage applied to the integrator, V_c, is set to 2.1 v. This makes the shortest linearly modulated pulse width equal to the trigger pulse width—2 microseconds. With the timing values shown, the maximum pulse width is 6 milliseconds, producing a dynamic range of more than 3,000:1 over the linear operating region.

The active components affecting the timing circuit are A_2, Q_1, A_1, and V_{cc}. Since the average temperature coefficient for the offset voltage of A_2 is a very low 5 microvolts/°C (affecting the timing by only 2.5 parts per million/°C), the circuit's almost negligible adverse temperature effects are largely due to the variation with temperature of the off current of Q_1, I_{dss}. I_{dss} doubles every 10°C; for the 2N4360, it is about 10 nanoamperes at room temperature.

It is important to note that for both circuits, the effects of V_{cc} and the 555 on timing stability are the same. As a bonus, however, the new circuit provides a linear ramp output that can be loaded fairly heavily without seriously affecting circuit timing. □

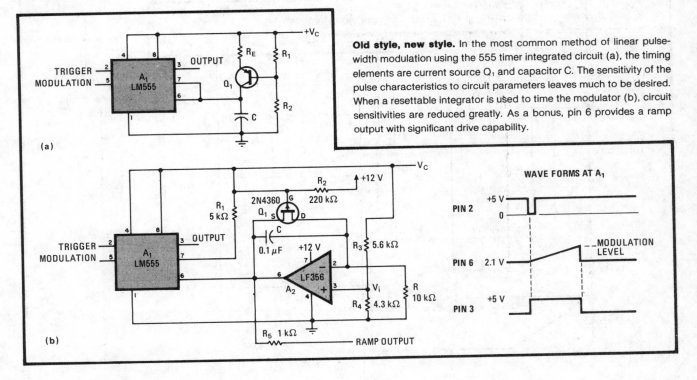

Old style, new style. In the most common method of linear pulse-width modulation using the 555 timer integrated circuit (a), the timing elements are current source Q_1 and capacitor C. The sensitivity of the pulse characteristics to circuit parameters leaves much to be desired. When a resettable integrator is used to time the modulator (b), circuit sensitivities are reduced greatly. As a bonus, pin 6 provides a ramp output with significant drive capability.

'Dithering' display expands bar graph's resolution

by Robert A. Pease
National Semiconductor Corp., Santa Clara, Calif.

Commercially available bar-graph chips such as National's LM3914 offer an inexpensive and generally attractive way of discerning 10 levels of signal. If 20, 30 or more steps of resolution are required, however, bargraph displays must be stacked, and with that, the circuit's power drain, cost and complexity all rise. But the techniques used here for creating a scanning-type "dithering" or modulated display will expand the resolution to 20 levels with only one 3914 or, alternatively, make it possible to implement fine-tuning control so that

performance approaching infinite resolution can be achieved.

The light-emitting-diode display arrangement for simply distinguishing 20 levels is achieved with a rudimentary square-wave oscillator, as shown in Fig. 1. Here, the LM324 oscillator, running at 1 kilohertz, drives a 60-millivolt peak-to-peak signal into pin 8 of the 3914.

Now, the internal reference circuitry of the 3914 acts to force pin 7 to be 1.26 v above pin 8, so that pins 4 and 8 are at an instantaneous potential of 4.0 mv plus a 60-mv p-p square wave, while pins 6 and 7 will be at 1.264 v plus a 60-mv p-p square wave. Normally, the first LED at pin 1 would turn on when V_{in} exceeded 130 mv, but because of the dither caused by the ac component of the oscillator's output, the first LED now turns on at half intensity when V_{in} rises above the aforementioned value. Full intensity is achieved when $V_{in} = 190$ mv.

When V_{in} rises another 70 mv or so, the first LED will fall off to half brightness and the second one will begin

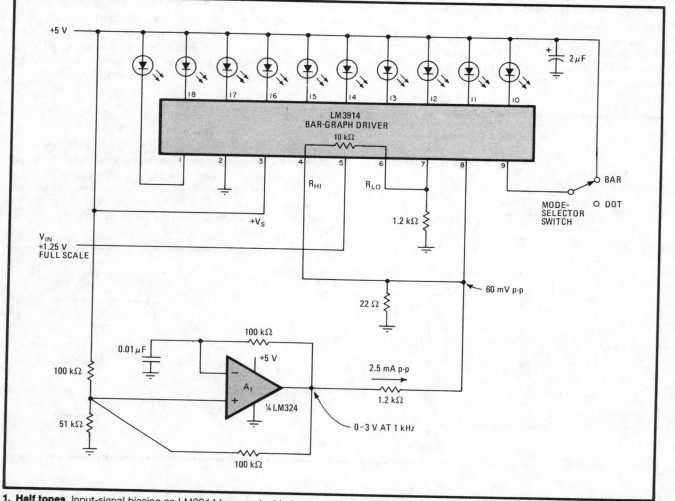

1. Half tones. Input-signal biasing on LM3914 bar-graph chip is set by the instantaneous output of a low-amplitude square-wave oscillator so that bar-graph resolution can be doubled. Each of 10 LEDs now has a fully-on and a partially-on mode, making 20 states discernible.

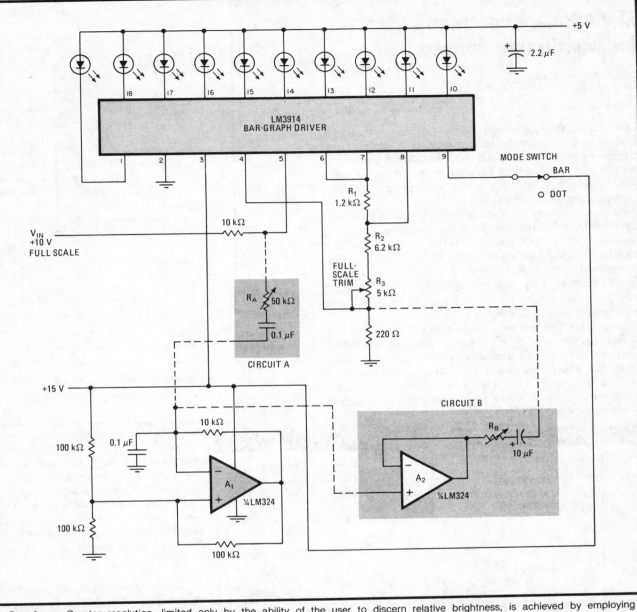

2. Spectrum. Greater resolution, limited only by the ability of the user to discern relative brightness, is achieved by employing a triangular-wave oscillator and more sensitive control circuitry to set the voltage levels and thus light levels of corresponding LEDs. Two RC networks, circuits A and B, provide required oscillator coupling and attenuation. B replaces A if oscillator cannot suffer heavy loading.

to glow. When V_{in} reaches 320 mv, the first LED will go off, and the second will turn on fully, and so on. Thus 20 levels of brightness are easily obtained.

Similarly, greater resolution can be achieved by employing a triangular-wave oscillator and two simple RC networks as seen in Fig. 2. Here, by means of circuit A, this voltage is capacitively coupled, attenuated, and superimposed on the input voltage at pin 5 of the LM3914. With appropriate setting of the 50-kilohm potentiometer, each incremental change in V_{in} can be detected because the glow from each LED can be made to spread gradually from one device to the next.

Of course, if the signal-source impedance is not low or linear, the ac signals coupled into the input circuit can cause false readings at the output. In this case, the

circuit in block B should be used to buffer the output of the triangular-wave oscillator.

The display is most effective in the dot mode, where supply voltages can be brought up to 15 v. If the circuit's bar mode is used, the potentials applied to the LEDs should be made no greater than 5 v to avoid overheating.

To trim the circuit, set the LM3914's output to full scale with R_3. R_A or R_B should then be trimmed so that when one LED is lit, any small measured change of V_{in} will cause one of the adjacent LEDs in the chain to turn on. $\square$

Multiplexers compress data for logarithmic conversion

by Andrzej Piasecki
Warsaw, Poland

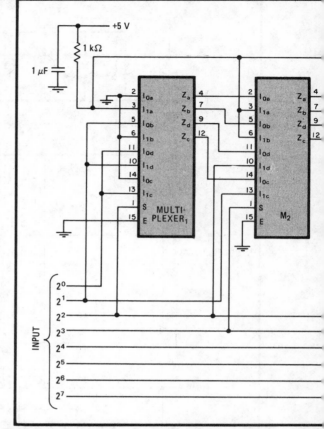

Cascaded multiplexers and a few gates are all that is needed to build this digital log converter, which compresses an 8-bit signal into a 5-bit number according to the transformation $2^n \rightarrow 4n$. Conversion to higher numbers is achieved by cascading additional multiplexers and appropriate gating circuitry.

As seen in the figure and the truth table for n extending from 0 to 28, the design of the circuit is simplified because each of the circuit's 74157 multiplexers can transfer without alteration 4 bits of the signal formed by a preceding multiplexer.

Alternatively, following multiplexing it can transport input bits that extend the second and third digits to the two least significant bits at the output.

As a result, the two most significant output bits of any multiplexer are fixed within a given input-number range. They are encoded by transferring the given 0 and 1 logic states into successive multiplexer inputs, with the most significant input bit (at logic 1) switching on whichever multiplexer is appropriate for transferring the desired number to the output.

Multiplexer manipulation. Using digital multiplexers, this circuit converts 8-bit input numbers into their corresponding 5-bit logarithmic equivalents, performing the operation in 100 ns. The truth table illustrates the simplicity of the design technique that performs the conversion. Multiplexers may be cascaded for extending the range over which n may be transformed into its log value.

As the input number decreases, the number of multiplexers required to transfer the desired data increases. NAND gates G_1 through G_5 derive the logic value of the most significant bit of the 5-bit number at the output. Note that the algorithm used will necessitate that the designer observe considerable care in wiring up the additional multiplexers that would be required to process larger numbers.

The propagation time of a digital logarithmic conversion is about 100 nanoseconds. The circuit draws no more than 120 milliamperes. ☐

Number n	Input					Number n	Input				
	2^4	2^3	2^2	2^1	2^0		2^4	2^3	2^2	2^1	2^0
0	0	0	0	0	0	0	0	0	0	0	0
1	0	0	0	0	1	2	0	0	0	1	0
2	0	0	0	1	0	4	0	0	1	0	0
3	0	0	0	1	1	6	0	0	1	1	0
4	0	0	1	0	0	8	0	1	0	0	0
5	0	0	1	0	1	9	0	1	0	0	1
6	0	0	1	1	0	10	0	1	0	1	0
7	0	0	1	1	1	11	0	1	0	1	1
8	0	1	0	0		12	0	1	1	0	0
10	0	1	0	1		13	0	1	1	0	1
12	0	1	1	0		14	0	1	1	1	0
14	0	1	1	1		15	0	1	1	1	1
16	1	0	0			16	1	0	0	0	0
20	1	0	1			17	1	0	0	0	1
24	1	1	0			18	1	0	0	1	0
28	1	1	1			19	1	0	0	1	1

TRUTH TABLE: DIGITAL LOG CONVERTER

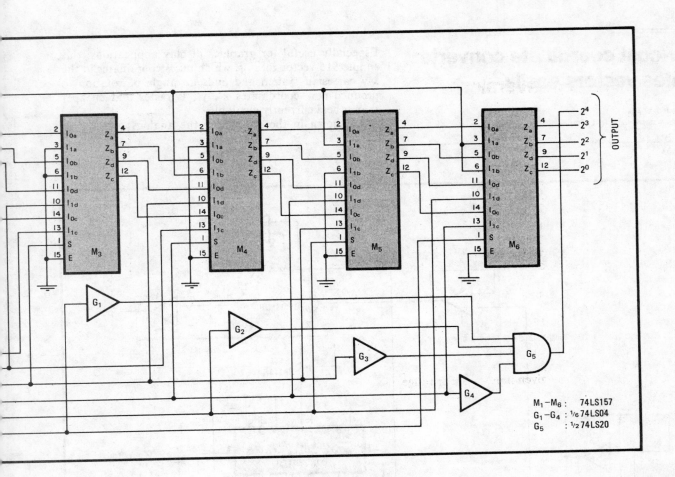

M₁–M₆ : 74LS157
G₁–G₄ : ⅙ 74LS04
G₅ : ½ 74LS20

Low-cost coordinate converter rotates vectors easily

by Arthur Mayer
Sperry Systems Management, Great Neck, N. Y.

Especially useful for graphics display applications, this simple $15 vector rotator, which takes coordinates in the x-y cartesian system and adds an angle of rotation to produce new coordinates x', y', is faster and cheaper than others currently available.

As shown in the schematic, the analog voltage pair

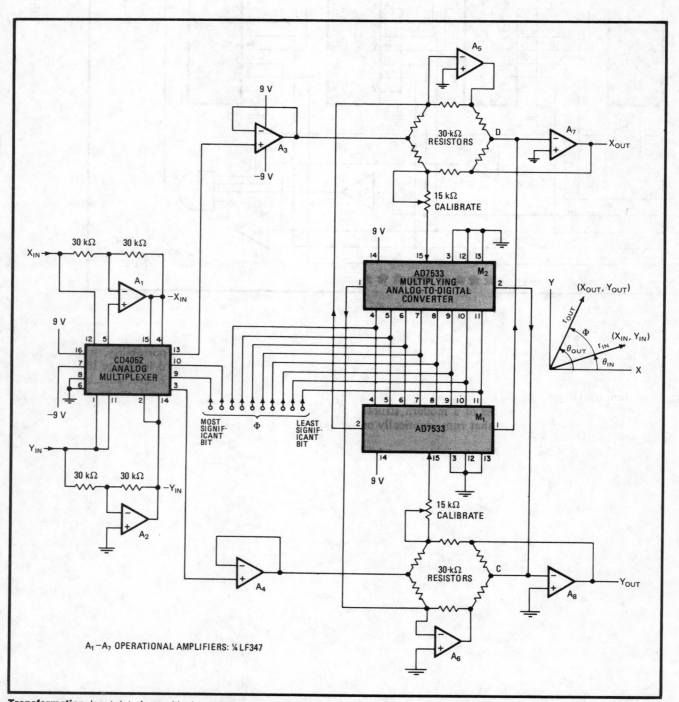

Transformation. Input data for positioning a cursor in graphic displays, often presented in x-y (cartesian) coordinates, may be rotated by Φ in steps of 0.35° to new location x', y'. One analog multiplexer, two multiplying d-a converters and eight op amps in a unique cross-fed summing network perform the operation. Alternatively, the circuit will transform a vector from polar (r,θ) into rectangular (x,y) form.

(x,y) represents the vector $r\angle\theta$, where $r^2 = x^2 + y^2$ and tangent $\theta = y/x$. The two inputs x_{IN}, y_{IN}—together with $-x_{IN}$, $-y_{IN}$ obtained from inverting amplifiers A_1 and A_2—are applied to the CD4052 dual analog multiplexer, which is controlled by the two most significant bits of the binary-coded rotation angle Φ. Each dual multiplexer output signal passes through a unity-gain amplifier, A_3 or A_4, and then through a tandem of inverting amplifiers (A_5, A_7 or A_6, A_8) to the final output.

Each tandem of inverting amplifiers is coupled with an AD7533 multiplying digital-to-analog converter to make a four-quadrant multiplier: A_5 and A_7 are coupled with M_1, and A_6 and A_8 are coupled with M_2. The digital input to both converters is provided by the remaining bits of Φ.

The analog input to M_1 is the average of the signals from A_4 and A_8, and the analog input to M_2 is the average of the signals from A_3 and A_7. The output currents from the cross-fed d-a converters feed the summing junctions of A_5 through A_8, where they add to the inputs that have been selected by the multiplexer, thus producing the output voltages x_{OUT}, y_{OUT}.

All resistances in the circuit are 30 kilohms so it is convenient to use dual in-line packages, like Beckman's 698-3, with eight resistors per DIP. Another DIP, Bourns's 7102, could replace the two 15-kΩ trimmers needed to raise the effective input impedance of each AD7533 to $15(2)^{1/2}$ kΩ, the value required in this design.

Regardless of the value of Φ, $x^2_{OUT} + y^2_{OUT} = x^2_{IN} + y^2_{IN}$. In other words, the output vector's magnitude is always equal to that of the input vector. However, the relationship between the input and output vectors is given by $\theta_{OUT} = \theta_{IN} + \Phi'$, where $\tan(\Phi'/2)$ is equal to $(2^{1/2} - 1)(\Phi - 45°)/45°$ and Φ is between 0° and 90°. The difference between Φ' and $\Phi - 45°$ vanishes for $\Phi = 0°$, 45°, and 90° and is always less than 1° for other values of Φ in the first quadrant. Note that the error and its variation with angle recur in the other three quadrants.

The 45° offset in Φ' is due to the bipolar operation of the AD7533 converter. The offset may be corrected by simply adding 45° to the digital equivalent number at the Φ input lines. The remaining error will be small enough to go unnoticed on most graphical displays.

To calibrate the vector rotator, x_{IN} is set to some constant voltage and set $y_{IN} = 0$. Then the trimmers are adjusted to make $x_{OUT} + y_{OUT} = 0$ when $\Phi = 0°$ and $x_{OUT} - y_{OUT} = 0$ when $\Phi = 90°$.

With the addition of a clock and a counter to make $\Phi = \omega t$, the vector rotator becomes a sine-cosine generator. For example, for a 5-volt root-mean-square output, x_{IN} and y_{IN} is set to 5 V dc; then $x_{OUT} = 5(2)^{1/2} \cos\omega t$ and $y_{OUT} = 5(2)^{1/2} \sin\omega t$.

Because of the functional error in the angle as given by the formula for $\tan(\Phi'/2)$, either output will contain third and fifth harmonics each having a magnitude 0.8% that of the fundamental. Total harmonic distortion, therefore, is 1.1%. □

Adapting a home computer for data acquisition

by Peter Bradshaw
Intersil Inc., Cupertino, Calif.

A personal computer, of the kind made by Apple and Atari, can be easily interfaced with an instrumentation module if a machine interrupt is used to overcome their inherent incompatibility—a condition attributable to the different clock speeds at which module and machine run. The interrupt scheme shown here facilitates the transfer of data by exploiting the data-ready signal available on most modules that generate a multiplexed binary-coded decimal output. Thus, the computer can be freed for other tasks, as in any timeshared system.

As an example, consider the arrangement in the figure whereby the Intersil 7226 multipurpose counter is interfaced with the popular MC6800 or MCS6502 microprocessors, which are at the heart of many personal computing systems. After the counter measures a designated interval, its store output moves low, signaling the MC6820 peripheral interface adapter with an interrupt request. This interrupt should be serviced within 100 milliseconds and control register CRA and the ports PA_0–PA_7 set to the required bits (see table).

Thereafter, an interrupt is generated through the PIA's CA_2 port and the 74LS02 open-collector NAND gates each time the multiplexed display-digit outputs of the counter match that of the bits on the PA_0–PA_7 lines. The BCD output data corresponding to each display digit D_1–D_8 is thus successively applied to the PB_0–PB_3 inputs (at a 4-kilohertz rate) and then to the processor.

The second through ninth interrupts should each be typically serviced in less than 244 microseconds. This task can be easily accomplished if proper priority is assigned to the interrupts. Thus the data will be read in

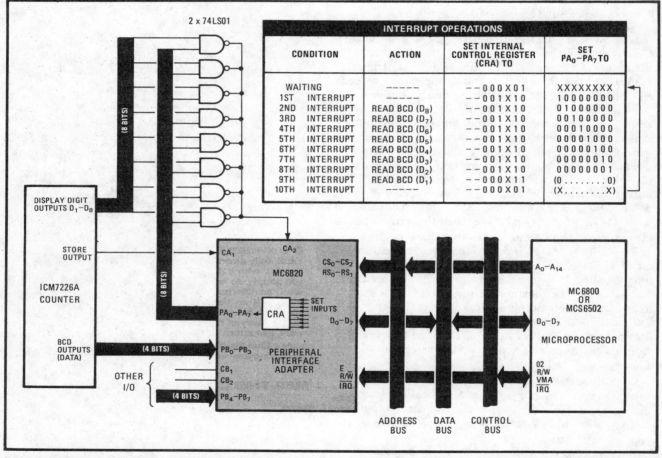

2 x 74LS01

INTERRUPT OPERATIONS			
CONDITION	ACTION	SET INTERNAL CONTROL REGISTER (CRA) TO	SET PA_0–PA_7 TO
WAITING	-----	--000X01	XXXXXXXX
1ST INTERRUPT	-----	--001X10	10000000
2ND INTERRUPT	READ BCD (D_8)	--001X10	01000000
3RD INTERRUPT	READ BCD (D_7)	--001X10	00100000
4TH INTERRUPT	READ BCD (D_6)	--001X10	00010000
5TH INTERRUPT	READ BCD (D_5)	--001X10	00001000
6TH INTERRUPT	READ BCD (D_4)	--001X10	00000100
7TH INTERRUPT	READ BCD (D_3)	--001X10	00000010
8TH INTERRUPT	READ BCD (D_2)	--001X10	00000001
9TH INTERRUPT	READ BCD (D_1)	--000X11	(0........0)
10TH INTERRUPT	-----	--000X01	(X........X)

DISPLAY DIGIT OUTPUTS D_1–D_8
(8 BITS)
STORE OUTPUT
ICM7226A COUNTER
BCD OUTPUTS (DATA)
(4 BITS)
OTHER I/O
(4 BITS)

CA_1 CA_2
MC6820
CS_0–CS_2
RS_0–RS_1
CRA SET INPUTS
PA_0–PA_7
PB_0–PB_3
D_0–D_7
CB_1
CB_2
PB_4–PB_7
PERIPHERAL INTERFACE ADAPTER
E
R/W
IRQ

A_0–A_{14}
MC6800 OR MCS6502 MICROPROCESSOR
D_0–D_7
02
R/W
VMA
IRQ

ADDRESS BUS   DATA BUS   CONTROL BUS

Prompt servicing. Using an interrupt scheme, instrumentation modules and other data-gathering processors with BCD multiplexed outputs can be readily interfaced with home computers such as the Apple and the Atari. Interrupts for reading the data corresponding to each display digit of counter in succession are generated by the microprocessor system itself, which produces a pulse at CA_2 each time the contents of its updated PA_0–PA_7 output register equal that of the scanned display digit outputs D_1–D_8.

less than 4 ms, so there will be no problem with data overruns (200 ms between measurements).

Ideally, the first interrupt should either include a check to ensure that digit D_8 is not high and the input is correct or else be followed by a statement that creates an interrupt when line D_1 is high. In addition, the computer bus will usually require some form of bidirectional buffering to the peripheral interface adapter.

The same system can be used with any processor in the MC6800 series; with other processors, a more complex interrupt-handling scheme is required. ☐

SIGNAL SOURCES

FSK transmitter uses
two gated oscillators

by Akavia Kaniel
Measurex Corp., Cupertino, Calif.

The 4528B complementary-MOS dual monostable multivibrator can operate as a frequency-shift–keyed (FSK) transmitter. Each half of the chip, shown in Fig. 1, is used here as a gated oscillator and is activated either when a mark or a space frequency is to be transmitted.

As long as the input signal to the clear input (CLR pin 3) is present, transistor Q_1 is turned on and the oscillator will not oscillate. Once the CLR pin is pulled high, however, Q_1 turns off and the outputs of flip-flops No. 1 and 2 turn low. Transistor Q_2 turns on for an instant, triggering the self-starting oscillator. At the same time flip-flop No. 1 senses that point A, shown in Fig. 1, has gone low and turns Q_2 off.

With Q_1 and Q_2 off, the oscillator runs at a frequency determined by resistor R_T and capacitor C_T and is given by the expression: $F = 1/(2.3 \times R_T \times C_T)$ for 1 kilohertz $\leq F \leq 100$ kHz, where $R_S \approx 2 \times R_T$.

When the CLR input is pulled low, Q_1 turns on and the oscillation stops. The complete FSK transmitter circuit is

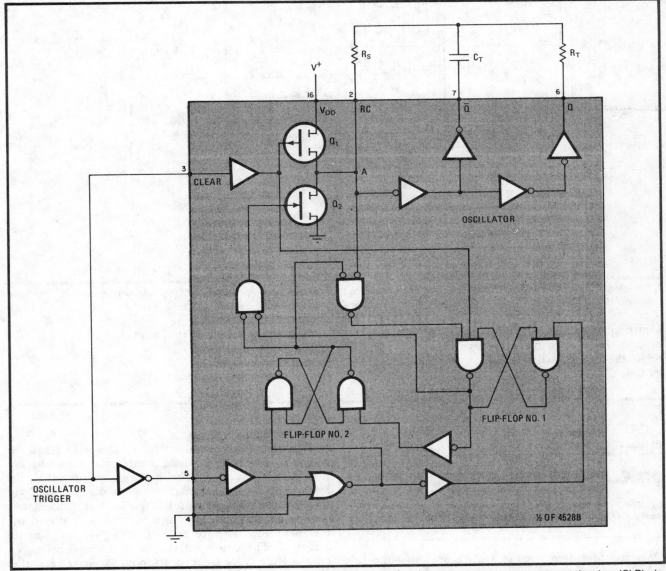

1. Shifty. The core of the frequency-shift–keyed transmitter is a gated oscillator, which is controlled by a signal present at the clear (CLR) pin. The full circuit uses two such oscillators—one for a mark and another for a space—contained in a 4528 dual one-shot package.

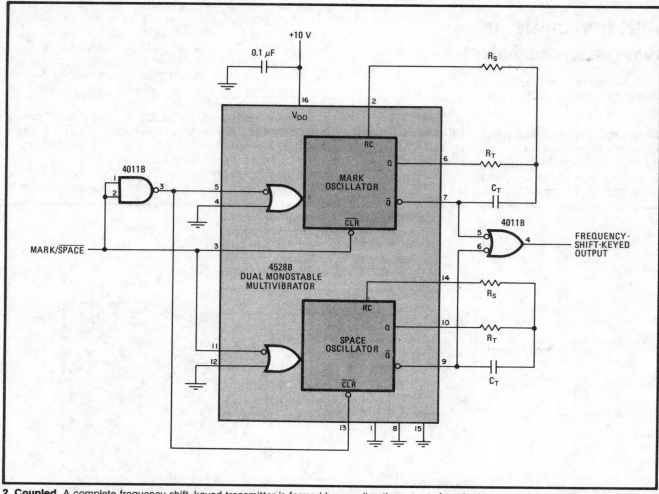

2. Coupled. A complete frequency-shift–keyed transmitter is formed by coupling the outputs from both monostable multivibrators through a dual-input NAND gate, as shown here. Mark and space frequencies are fixed by R_T and C_T, where $R_S = 2R_T$.

shown in Fig. 2. It is formed by coupling both oscillator outputs. When the mark-to-space control input goes high, the mark oscillator signal appears at the FSK output, and when the same line is low, the space oscilla- tor signal appears at the FSK output. □

Simple sound generator takes orders from microcomputer

by Joseph Huijts
Waalre, the Netherlands

Only six integrated circuits are required to build this low-cost programmable sound generator. The circuit, as shown in the figure, permits a choice of 8 different levels of loudness, 16 time durations, and 8 frequencies (they are not related to musical intervals).

In operation, 2 bytes of data are sent from a microcomputer to this circuit, which produces a tone. The duration is programmable; thus no action from the microcomputer is required to end the tone.

The first byte is sent to a 40174 hex D-type flip-flop, to control frequency and loudness. The second byte is sent to a 4029 binary/decade counter with the ability to load data in parallel. The least significant nibble is loaded into the counter enabling an oscillator circuit—a NAND Schmitt trigger with RC feedback. This oscillator causes the counter to decrement until it is inhibited by the final count indicated by the CARRY OUT pin going to a logic 0. The time span that is produced depends on both the oscillator frequency (about 10 hertz) and the nibble that is loaded into the counter. In this way 16 different time spans can be selected from 0 to 1.5 seconds in 0.1 second steps.

The final count output also controls a second oscillator, producing the output tone. The frequency is controlled by the R and C values of the feedback circuit. The capacitor can be paralleled by a programmable combination of other capacitors with three bilateral analog switches like those used in a 4066, set by the most significant nibble of the 40174 hex dual flip-flop. The frequency can be adjusted between 700 and 2,300 Hz. The least significant nibble controls the loudness in eight 5-dB steps with a 74LS145 binary-coded-decimal–to-decimal decoder-driver. The sound-producing frequency is connected to the D input of the 74LS145, selecting outputs 0–7 when low or outputs 8 and 9 (not connected) when high. The A, B and C inputs—controlled by the least significant nibble—select a resistor to feed the loudspeaker. A 2-microfarad tantalum capacitor rounds the edges of the generated square wave. ☐

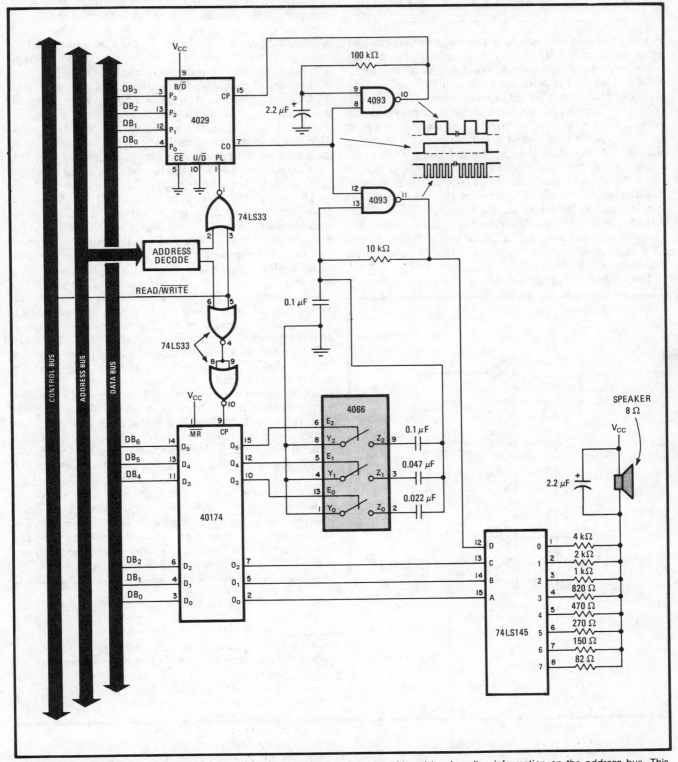

Sound off. Programmable sound generation under microcomputer control is achieved by decoding information on the address bus. This decoding directs frequency and loudness information bytes to the 40174 hex flip-flop and duration information bytes into the 4029 counter.

Op-amp summer forms simple high-speed phase generator

by Dieter R. Lohrmann
Department of the Army, Harry Diamond Laboratories, Adelphi, Md.

A simple operational-amplifier summing circuit can generate an output voltage that is a rectangular- or sine-wave function of a dc source potential. For analog applications such as the direct phase modulation of a radio-frequency carrier, this circuit combines fast response with low throughput delay, making it superior to the often-used method of digitizing and reconverting an input signal with the aid of a microprocessor. In digital uses it can generate a pulse train having almost any pulse voltage–versus–dc input voltage characteristic.

In the circuit's general configuration, which for simplicity omits the stabilizing circuitry like bypass resistors and capacitors, resistors R_1–R_7 form a voltage divider whose taps are alternately connected to the inverting and noninverting inputs of the adjacent comparators A_1–A_6. The outputs of the comparators are simply summed via resistors R_8–R_{13}.

For a digital application (a), the incoming ramp is used to generate a variable pulse-width train. When the ramp voltage is below the node voltage at point 1, comparators A_1, A_3, and A_5 are low (-7 volts), whereas A_2, A_4, and A_6 are high ($+7$ V). Thus, the output voltage will be midway between the two supply voltages, or at zero.

As the ramp rises above the node voltage at point 1, comparator A_1 switches, activating a fourth comparator, while two remain off. The output voltage thus jumps to 2 V, assuming resistances R_8 to R_{13} are of equal value. This voltage remains constant while the ramp voltage increases, until it exceeds the potential at the divider's second node, causing comparator A_2 to switch off. At this time, A_2, A_3, and A_5 are low, and A_1, A_4, and A_6 are high, returning the output voltage to zero.

As the ramp voltage climbs past the potential at the third node, a similar operation moves the output to 2 V, because four comparators will be on and two will be off. The output drops to zero again when the ramp moves to a potential higher than at node 4.

The duration of each transition will be dependent upon the node and dc input voltages, which may be appropriately selected by the user. Consequently, a pulse train having almost any set of variable-width characteristics can be ordered.

In analog applications, a good approximation of a sine-wave function can also be generated if the voltage divider's switching intervals are made equal to ΔV, the voltage increment required to switch the output of each comparator from negative to positive saturation. Because the comparator's transitions are nonlinear, the steep sides of each comparator's rectangular transfer function are rounded off, and therefore a sine wave can be very nearly approximated.

Such a scheme is useful in phase or frequency modulators, as shown in (b), because it enables direct modulation at any arbitrarily large modulation index without introducing additional frequency offset. The function generator's output is simply introduced at the intermediate-frequency port of a single-sideband modulator. At

Speedy switching. Op-amp summing stage (a), wired in an inverting-to-noninverting input arrangement, provides sine- or rectangular-wave phase generation for fast response and low throughput delay. If the comparators' thresholds are selected so that the summer's switching profile approximates a sine wave, the circuit may be used to phase- or frequency-modulate an rf carrier directly (b).

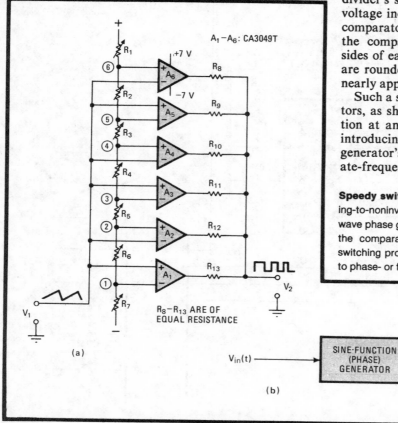

(a)

A_1–A_6: CA3049T

R_8–R_{13} ARE OF EQUAL RESISTANCE

(b)

$V_{in}(t)$ → SINE-FUNCTION (PHASE) GENERATOR → $a \sin [2\pi(V_{in}/V_{ref})]$ → ⊗ → $V_c \cos (\Omega t + 2\pi V_{in}(t)/V_o)$

rf CARRIER
$V_c \cos \Omega t$

the output of the modulator will appear the sum of the i-f and rf frequency, which is a cosine function applied to the modulator's rf port.

In this case, the function generator performs a phase modulation, because the phases of the generator and the rf carrier are added in the modulator. Thus, V_{in} causes a phase modulation of the rf carrier. The maximum modulation index is determined by the number of amplifiers in the phase generator. For a maximum modulation index of M, $2M/\pi$ amplifiers are necessary.

If the SSB modulator is of the phasing type (which cancels the lower sideband by phase-shift mixing), orthogonal signals will be required at its i-f and rf ports. This function generator can be easily modified to generate a cosine-function signal, instead of a sine-wave output. Thus, a sine- and cosine-function generator may be combined to provide the orthogonal signals required for the SSB mixer. □

Adjustable e^x generator colors synthesizer's sounds

by Randall K. Kirschman
Mountain View, Calif.

Providing the control signals for voltage-controlled amplifiers, oscillators and filters in order to modulate sound parameters such as loudness, pitch and timbre, this adjustable e^x generator is the indispensable ingredient required to attain superior performance in a music synthesizer. Only four integrated circuits and a few passive components are needed in the inexpensive unit, which costs under $6.

When gated or triggered, the generator produces a waveform that passes through four states:
- An exponential attack.
- An initial decay, or fallback.
- A sustain, or steady dc level.
- A final decay, or release.

Each of these four parameters is continuously variable, so that waveforms having a large variety of shapes can be generated.

The waveforms are generated by the sequential charging and discharging of capacitor C_1 (see figure). In general operation, C_1 is connected to a current source or sink as required, through the 4016 complementary-MOS

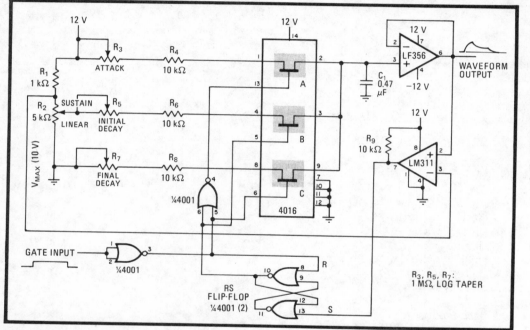

Musical tint. Four-state generator provides myriad control waveforms for modulating voltage-controlled amplifiers, oscillators, and filters in a music synthesizer, and thus is useful for coloring loudness, pitch, and timbre. Attack and decay times are variable from 5 to 500 milliseconds; sustain level is adjustable from 0 to 10 volts.

analog switches. These switches are controlled by simple logic set into action by the gate-input pulse. Triggered operation is made possible by adding a monostable multivibrator to the circuit.

In the dormant state (gate input low), analog switch C is on, switches A and B are off and the RS flip-flop formed by two 4001 NOR gates is reset. The onset of a gate pulse turns on switch A and turns C off. Consequently, C_1 charges through R_3 and R_4, producing the attack segment of the waveform. Note that the LM356 buffer protects C_1 from excessive loading.

When the voltage across C_1 reaches V_{max} (determined by voltage divider R_1–R_2), the LM311 comparator sets the RS flip-flop. This action in turn switches B on and A off. Thus the initial decay segment is generated as C_1 discharges through R_5 and R_6 to reach the sustain voltage, the level of which is determined by the setting of potentiometer R_2.

Concurrently, the comparator's output has gone low, but the RS flip-flop remains set until the gate pulse moves to logic 0, at which time switch C turns on. Thus C_1 discharges through R_7 and R_8 to produce the final-decay portion of the wave, after which the circuit reverts to its dormant state. □

Two-chip generator shapes synthesizer's sounds

by Jonathan Jacky
Seattle, Wash.

Generating the same adjustable modulating waveforms for a music synthesizer as the circuit proposed by Kirschman[1], but using only two integrated circuits, this generator also works from a single supply. It has, in addition, separate gate and trigger inputs for providing a more realistic keyboard response.

When gated or triggered, the generator, which is built around Intersil Inc.'s C-MOS 7555 timer, produces a waveform that passes through four states:

- An exponential attack.
- An initial decay, or fallback.
- A sustain, or steady dc level.
- A final decay, or release.

Each of these four parameters is continuously variable, so that waveforms having a wide variety of shapes can be generated.

The waveforms are generated by the sequential charging and discharging of capacitor C_1. Here, the 7555 controls the sequencing while diodes switch the currents, unlike Kirschman's circuit where comparators and flip-flops control the stepping and analog switches steer the currents. Furthermore, the 7555 is well suited for handling the two logic signals provided by most synthesizer keyboards—the gate, which is high as long as any key is depressed, and the trigger, which provides a negative pulse as each key is struck. The gate and trigger features eliminate the need to release each key before striking the next to initiate an attack phase.

In the dormant state (the gate input at pin 4 of the 7555 is low), capacitor C_2 is discharged. When the gate goes high and a trigger pulse appears at pin 2, the 7555 output (pin 3) goes high and charges C_1 through R_3, R_4, and D_1, producing the attack segment of the waveform. Note that diode D_2 is reverse-biased because pin 7 of the 7555 is high and that diode D_3 is back-biased by logic 1 signal applied to the gate input.

When the voltage across C_1 reaches 10 volts, pin 3 of the 7555 goes low and pin 7 is grounded, terminating the attack phase. D_1 and D_3 are now reverse-biased and C_1 discharges through D_2, R_5, and R_6 to produce the initial decay. The sustain level reached is determined by the voltage divider formed by resistor R_1 and potentiometer R_2. During this phase, a second attack can be obtained by striking another key (see timing diagram). When the last key is released, the gate goes low and C_1 will discharge through D_3, R_7, and R_8 to produce the final decay. The CA3130 operational amplifier serves as a buffer to protect C_1 from excessive loading. □

References
1. Randall K. Kirschman, "Adjustable e* generator colors synthesizer's sounds," Electronics, July 17, 1980, p. 123.

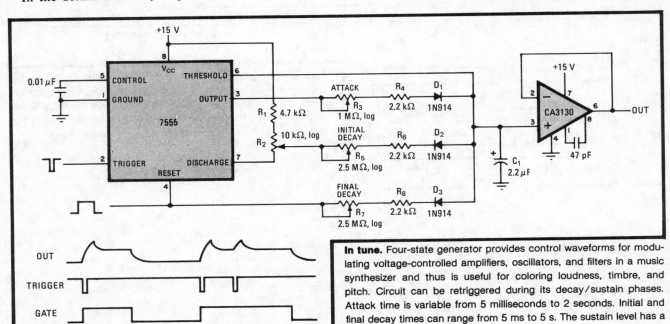

In tune. Four-state generator provides control waveforms for modulating voltage-controlled amplifiers, oscillators, and filters in a music synthesizer and thus is useful for coloring loudness, timbre, and pitch. Circuit can be retriggered during its decay/sustain phases. Attack time is variable from 5 milliseconds to 2 seconds. Initial and final decay times can range from 5 ms to 5 s. The sustain level has a dynamic range of 0 to 10 V.

Sync clock, counter improve programmable-width generator

by M. V. Subba Rao and V. L. Patil
Central Electronics Engineering Research Institute, Pilani, India

The typical programmable pulse-width generator either has limited programming capability or creates an initial timing error because of the asynchronism between an input trigger and the system's internal clock. Employing a binary-coded-decimal–programmable divide-by-n counter and a synchronous-start oscillator in a basic circuit overcomes these drawbacks, as shown here.

A trigger to the B_0 input of the 74121 monostable multivibrator generates a pulse that presets the 7476 flip-flop and also loads a preset number into the 74192 divide-by-n counter. The flip-flop then initiates pulse generation in the 74123 oscillator, whose output is counted down by the 74192 until zero is reached.

At this time, its borrow output, B_3, clears the flip-flop and the oscillator is disabled. The pulse width of the waveform at Q_3 is thus proportional to the number of clock pulses counted.

For the component values specified in the figure, the clock period is 1 microsecond. Thus, the circuit will generate pulses of from 1 to 9 μs, in steps of 1 μs. The 74192s can be cascaded to yield larger pulse widths. □

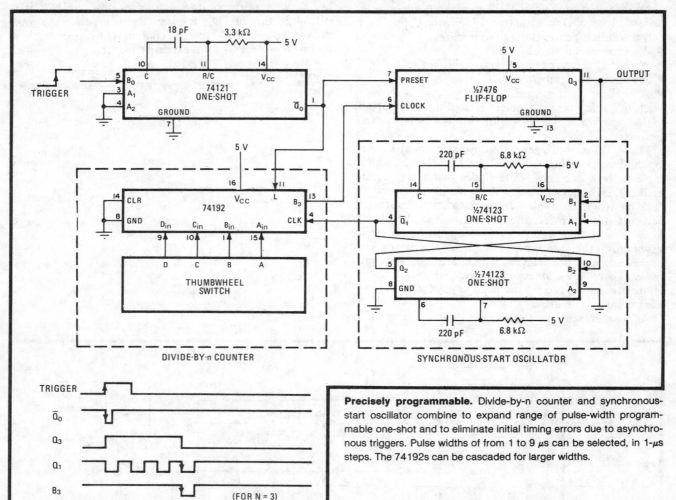

Precisely programmable. Divide-by-n counter and synchronous-start oscillator combine to expand range of pulse-width programmable one-shot and to eliminate initial timing errors due to asynchronous triggers. Pulse widths of from 1 to 9 μs can be selected, in 1-μs steps. The 74192s can be cascaded for larger widths.

Four chips generate pseudorandom test data

by Wayne Sward
Sperry Univac Division, Salt Lake City, Utah

The inexpensive pseudorandom–bit-sequence generator shown here requires only four integrated circuits and will serve well in testing digital data links. Joined through a minimum of interconnections, it will furnish a recurring 511-bit string suitable for a variety of other applications as well.

The octal D-type latches in A_1, along with flip-flop A_2, form a 9-bit serial shift register that drives binary counter A_3, which detects the register's illegal all-zero state; exclusive-OR gate G_1 provides the required feedback connection. On power-up, the outputs of A_1 assume arbitrary logic values, and the 11-megahertz system clock steps the bits to the load input of A_3. When the first logic-1 bit cycles through to A_3, the counter presets to 6. As long as at least 1 bit in the shift register thereafter contains a logic 1, A_3 can never reach a count of 15. Consequently, its terminal-count output will always remain low.

If only zeros should appear in the shift register after power-up or during the course of operation, however, A_3 will eventually reach a count of 15, and its terminal-count output will go high. This action forces the three-state outputs of A_1 to become inactive, or an open circuit, and a logic 1 will be introduced (through resistor R_1) into the data stream, at the D input of A_2. This bit is detected by A_3 on the following clock cycle and normal operation is restored. Note that the circuit configuration eliminates the nine-input gate that is usually required at the input of the counter in order to detect the existence of an all-zero state.

The test code generated by this circuit is shown in the table, its format being compatible with the popular HP3780 bit-checking data unit. Of course, if the format of the test code must be altered, it may be changed simply by connecting the load input of A_3 to the appropriate stage of the shift register.

If the low-power Schottky chips used in this generator are all replaced by their standard Schottky equivalents, the bit rate can be extended to 26 MHz, though with a slight penalty in power dissipation. No additional wiring changes will be required. □

Self-correcting code. Simple generator provides a serial string of 511 pseudorandom bits suitable for testing digital data links at up to 11 MHz. The code, in a format compatible with the popular HP3780 test generator or data-bit checker, is easily changed by connecting the counter to the appropriate stage of shift register A_1–A_2. Bit rates to 26 MHz are achieved by replacing ICs with their Schottky counterparts.

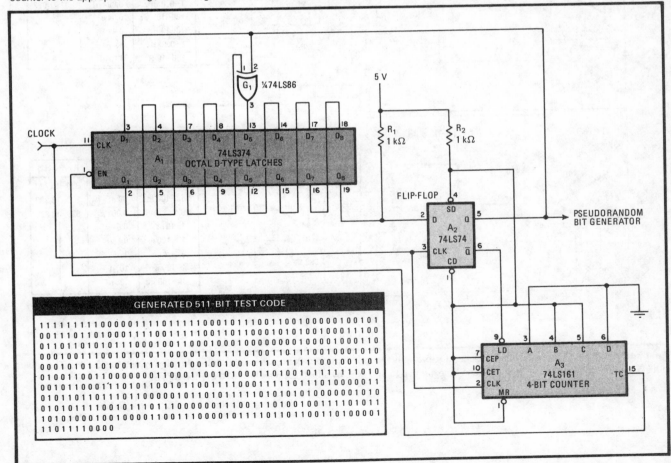

GENERATED 511-BIT TEST CODE

```
111111111000000111101111100010111001100100000100101
001110110110100011110011111100110110001010100100011100
011011010101011000100110001000100000000010000100110
000100111001010101011100001101111010011011110010001001010
000101011001001111111011100100010011011111100100001011
010011001100000001100010010010101001011111111010
001011000111101011001011100111100011111011101010000011
010011011011110000010110101111101010101000000001010
01101111100101110111100000001100111010110011111101011
10101001001000001000110001111101101011001101000001
11011110000
```

Two-chip pulse generator operates at 75 MHz

by M. U. Khan
Systronics, Naroda, Ahmedabad, India

Built from integrated circuits in the emitter-coupled-logic family, this pulse generator can provide independent control of delay and width (variable from 5 nanoseconds to 0.1 second) over the frequency range of 10 hertz to 75 megahertz. Only two chips are required—a quad line receiver and a dual D-type flip-flop.

The MC1692 line receiver, A_{1a}, configured as an astable multivibrator, provides a steady stream of pulses, at a frequency determined by R_1C_1, to the delay portion of the circuit. This section, which uses a second line receiver and one half of the MC10231 dual flip-flop, generates a corresponding pulse at the output of A_{2a} whose duration is proportional to R_2C_2. Its maximum duty cycle is greater than 80% at 10 MHz and decreases progressively to about 50% at 75 MHz. After inversion by A_{1c}, the signal is introduced to flip-flop A_{2b}.

A_{2b} is triggered on the positive-going edge of the signal, and so pin 15 of the flip-flop moves high after a time proportional to R_2C_2, thus effecting the delay time. The duration of the pulse emanating from A_{2b} (that is, its width) is set by the A_{2b}–A_{1d} combination, which is identical to the A_{2a}–A_{1b} configuration. Note that the polarity of the output appearing at Q_2 of A_{2b} matches that of the input signal, because the width-determining one-shot works on an inverted version of that signal.

If the flip-flops are replaced by two MC1670 types, the circuit will work beyond 100 MHz. In either case, the circuits used should be mounted on suitable heat sinks. □

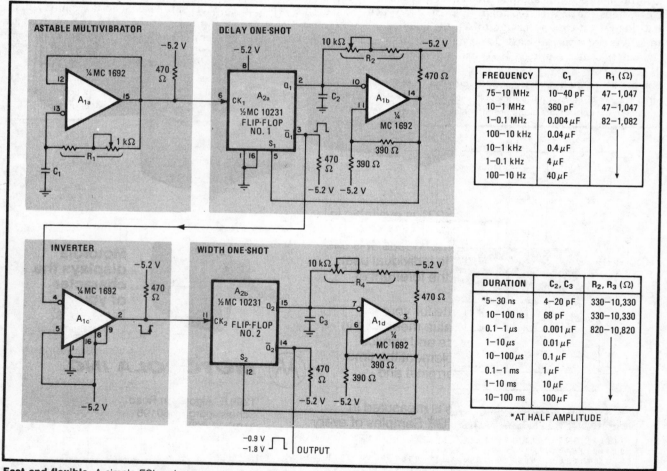

FREQUENCY	C_1	R_1 (Ω)
75–10 MHz	10–40 pF	47–1,047
10–1 MHz	360 pF	47–1,047
1–0.1 MHz	0.004 µF	82–1,082
100–10 kHz	0.04 µF	
10–1 kHz	0.4 µF	
1–0.1 kHz	4 µF	
100–10 Hz	40 µF	

DURATION	C_2, C_3	R_2, R_3 (Ω)
*5–30 ns	4–20 pF	330–10,330
10–100 ns	68 pF	330–10,330
0.1–1 µs	0.001 µF	820–10,820
1–10 µs	0.01 µF	
10–100 µs	0.1 µF	
0.1–1 ms	1 µF	
1–10 ms	10 µF	
10–100 ms	100 µF	

*AT HALF AMPLITUDE

Fast and flexible. A simple ECL pulse generator provides independent control of pulse width and delay and works to 75 MHz. The tables outline the component values. Operation can be extended to 100 MHz by substituting an MC1670 flip-flop for A_2.

Deglitcher–delay circuit serves also as pulse generator

by B. Seastrom and G. Goodwin
Sylvania Systems Group, GTE Products Corp., Needham Heights, Mass.

Sustaining its input pulse for a number of clock cycles before translating it into an output pulse, this circuit provides an effective means of discriminating between valid data and spurious pulses or glitches. The designer who uses the circuit has numerous options for adjusting the delay between the input and output transitions, as well as controlling the duration of the output pulse. Furthermore, it triggers on either a rising or a falling edge and generates complementary outputs.

Data entering serial shift register A_1 is sampled at the clock rate and shifted along from output Q_A to Q_H. Meanwhile, for the complement of the input at the output of A_2, the same process occurs at the shift register A_3. Since all 1s are required at gates A_4 or A_5 to toggle cross-coupled NAND gates A_6 and A_7, there is a delay in the leading edge of the output, as well as in the pulse duration. The delay and the pulse duration depend on how many and which taps are connected from the shift registers to the eight-input NAND gates.

It is apparent that noise—in fact, any changes in input level—will be subject to successive samples, whose number is equal to the tap count, before it results in a change in output. By employing different numbers of taps on registers A_1 and A_3, the criterion will be different for different polarity edges—A_1 controls the positive edges and A_3 controls the negative ones—and therefore the circuit is highly noise-resistant. Further, by starting with a tap other than Q_A, initial edge delays can be built in, again selectively for either positive or negative edges.

A version of the circuit allows it to modify the input pulse width. Feeding selected output taps of A_1 into A_5 (eliminating inverter A_2 and serial register A_3) controls the time at which the trailing edge of the output pulse occurs. By judiciously choosing which taps go to A_4 and which go to A_5, the designer can exercise control over the width of the output pulse.

The circuits' applications are enhanced by expanding on the basic concepts. Thus, smaller NAND gates may be used with fewer samples, and expanded gates may be used with more shift registers in tandem. Finally, additional timing signals may be generated by connecting additional sets of gates to the shift registers. ☐

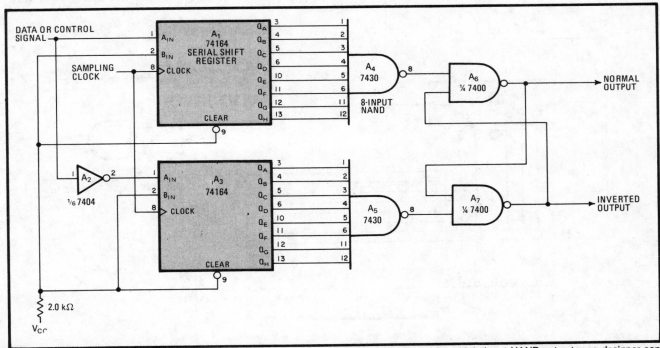

Tap dance. By changing the quantity and position of the shift register outputs into which the multiple-input NAND gates tap, a designer can mask unwanted spikes, as well as exercise a wide range of control over the output pulse width and rising and falling pulse edges.

Low-cost generator delivers all standard bit rates

by Robert E. Turner
Martian Technologies, Spring Valley, Calif.

Costing only $2, this generator can drive universal asynchronous receiver-transmitters and other RS-232 serial interface chips at any standard bit rate selected by the user. It is especially suitable for systems based on the Z80 microprocessor from which the generator can derive its 4-megahertz quartz-crystal time base.

As the figure shows, a 4-MHz input clock is divided by 13 by the 74LS393 counter (A_1) and a 74LS11 AND gate, thereby providing a 3.25-microsecond signal that is suitable for driving the CD4024 seven-stage counter, A_2. This signal is close to 16 times the maximum 19.2-kilobit/s output frequency. Smaller divisions are handled by the counter, which supplies 9,600-, 4,800-, 2,400-, 1,200-, 600-, 300-, 150-, and 110-b/s outputs.

The counter outputs are wired so that a bit rate may be selected for both channels of a Z80A serial input/output module or dual asynchronous receiver-transmitter serial interface chip. The output frequency of the generator is 16 times greater than the bit rate, so each serial data bit is sampled 16 times per bit period.

The bit-rate clock frequency is selected with either

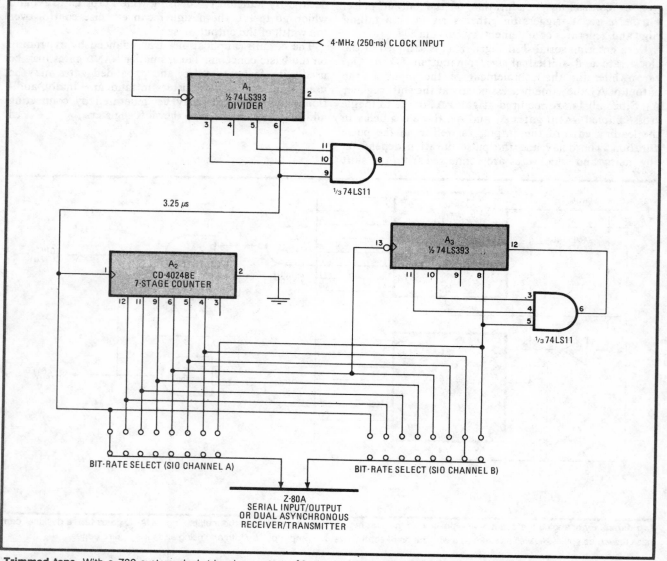

Trimmed taps. With a Z80 system clock trimming costs to $2, the four-chip generator delivers all standard bit rates for RS-232–based systems. The generated rate accuracy is high (see table). The system can be easily modified for older interfaces.

GENERATOR RESPONSE			
Period	Actual output (b/s)	Ideal output (b/s)	Error
52 μs	19,230.76	19,200	+0.16%
104 μs	9,615.38	9,600	+0.16%
208 μs	4,807.69	4,800	+0.16%
416 μs	2,403.84	2,400	+0.16%
832 μs	1,201.92	1,200	+0.16%
1.66 ms	600.96	600	+0.16%
3.33 ms	300.48	300	+0.16%
6.65 ms	150.24*	150	+0.16%
9.15 ms	109.26	110	−0.68%

*OUTPUT AVAILABLE, BUT NOT CONNECTED IN CIRCUIT SHOWN

printed-circuit–board jumpers or by small dual–in-line–packaged switches. The entire circuit is small enough to be mounted next to the Z80's DB-25 connectors that are mounted on its rear panel, making it easy for the end user of the RS-232 interface to select a bit rate. The dual-channel version of the circuit requires only five interface lines: the 4-MHz clock input, bit-rate clock A and B outputs, the 5-volt line, and logic ground.

As for the accuracy of the rates generated, they are well within the 1% timing variation standard required by the RS-232 interface (see table). The generator has been used with many different terminals and printers, and no operating difficulties have been encountered.

The circuit may also be used with most of the older serial interface chips like the 8251 and the 6850, if the user is willing to sacrifice the 19.2-kb/s output. In this case, the divide-by-11 counter would be driven by a 2-MHz clock, with the highest bit rate available becoming 9.6-kb/s. This signal drives the counter. The output of the counter that divides the 110-b/s signal by 11 (counter A$_3$) would then be connected to the new 1,200-b/s output of the seven-stage counter. □